Digital Signal Processing
A Student Guide

Other titles of related interest

W.A. Atherton, *From Compass to Computer*
B.W. Allen, *Analogue Electronics for Higher Studies*
M. Beasley, *Reliability for Engineers*
Paul V. Brennan, *Phase-Locked Loops - Principles and Practice*
C.W. Davidson, *Transmission Lines for Communications, second edition*
J.D. Edwards, *Electrical Machines and Drives*
M.E. Goodge, *Analog Electronics*
B.A. Gregory, *An Introduction to Electrical Instrumentation and Measurement Systems, second edition*
K. Jackson, *C Programming for Electronic Engineers*
Paul A. Lynn, *An Introduction to the Analysis and Processing of Signals, third edition*
R.J. Mitchell, *Microprocessor Systems - An Introduction*
Noel M. Morris, *Electrical Circuit Analysis and Design*
M.S. Nixon, *Introductory Digital Design - A Programmable Approach*
P. Silvester, *Electric Circuits*
L.A.A. Warnes, *Electronic and Electrical Engineering - Principles and Practice*
L.A.A. Warnes, *Electronic Materials*
B.W. Williams, *Power Electronics - Devices, Drivers, Applications and Passive Components*

New Electronics Series
Series Editor: Paul A. Lynn

G.J. Awcock and R. Thomas, *Applied Image Processing*
Rodney F.W. Coates, *Underwater Acoustic Systems*
M.D. Edwards, *Automatic Logic Synthesis Techniques for Digital Systems*
Peter J. Fish, *Electronic Noise and Low Noise Design*
W. Forsythe and R.M. Goodall, *Digital Control*
C.G. Guy, *Data Communications for Engineers*
Paul A. Lynn, *Digital Signals, Processors and Noise*
Paul A. Lynn, *Radar Systems*
R.C.V. Macario, *Cellular Radio - Principles and Design*
A.F. Murray and H.M. Reekie, *Integrated Circuit Design*
F.J. Owens, *Signal Processing of Speech*
Dennis N. Pim, *Television and Teletext*
M. Richharia, *Satellite Communications Systems*
P.R. Shepherd, *Integrated Circuits - Design, Fabrication and Test*
M.J.N. Sibley, *Optical Communications, second edition*
P.M. Taylor, *Robotic Control*
G.S. Virk, *Digital Computer Control Systems*
Allan Waters, *Active Filter Design*

Digital Signal Processing

A Student Guide

Trevor J. Terrell and Lik-Kwan Shark
Department of Electrical and Electronic Engineering
University of Central Lancashire
Preston, England

First published 1996 by
MACMILLAN PRESS LTD
Houndmills, Basingstoke, Hampshire RG21 6XS
and London
Companies and representatives
throughout the world

ISBN 0-333-63719-4

A catalogue record for this book is available from the British Library.

Printed in Great Britain by
Antony Rowe Ltd, Chippenham, Wiltshire

To

Jennifer* and *Hong

Pay attention to your teacher
and learn all you can.
Proverbs 23.12

Contents

Preface

Digital signal processing (DSP) systems have developed at a rapid pace over the past two decades, and in recent years they have made a very considerable impact in many areas of signal processing applications. There is no doubt that in the next ten to twenty years the application of DSP systems will grow extensively in response to the ever-growing market demand to provide and rapidly process more and more signal-data transmitted over various forms of communication channel. Clearly DSP techniques will be particularly significant for the development and effective operation of networked super information highways, and we may confidently expect DSP to have far-reaching effects in enabling the development and expansion of new/enhanced world-wide communication systems. To promote and sustain these advances there will be a continuing requirement for engineers, scientists and technologists to have a good working knowledge of DSP concepts, design methods, and practical implementation considerations. Consequently this implies that DSP should form a significant part of the core study material in relevant technician, undergraduate and postgraduate courses, particularly those associated with electronic engineering and computer systems disciplines.

The purpose of this book is to provide a basic students's guide to DSP and associated practical applications. The book differs from the general form of textbook by presenting theoretical and practical concepts in an introductory-summary format, underpinned and demonstrated by a significant number of worked examples. It is intended that this form of presentation will enable the reader to immediately concentrate on understanding the significance of the principles described; and therefore in trying to achieve this objective we have deliberately tried to avoid presenting verbose decriptions and cumbersome and difficult proofs. We have tried to demonstrate how practical DSP results may be obtained by straightforward application of the processes/algorithms presented. Worked examples (signified by ❖ **WE** prefix) and a number of detailed practical case studies are presented to show how the DSP principles may be applied to solve practical problems.

The first chapter introduces some of the main principles of digital signals and DSP systems which students need as basic foundation knowledge before progressing further with their DSP studies. In Chapter 2 the required mathematical concepts of the z-transform and the inverse z-transform are summarised and demonstrated. For students who find DSP mathematics difficult to understand and handle, it is recommended that they use the worked examples for tutorial study purposes and additionally use the end-of-chapter problems to test their understanding of the principles studied. By adopting this tutorial study approach for all of the DSP topics presented in this book, the reader should be able to work towards understanding the theoretical and practical principles described, and will be able to test their knowledge and understanding by solving the given problems. The discrete Fourier transform, the fast Fourier transform and other important allied topics are presented in Chapter 3. Some popular and useful design methods applicable to non-recursive (FIR) and recursive (IIR) digital filters are described in Chapter 4. Also in Chapter 4 we have included some basic considerations that must be given to quantisation effects in designing and implementing DSP processing operations. In Chapter 5 (the final chapter) hardware and software aspects of DSP system implementation are discussed in sufficient detail to enable the reader to build and test a simple low-cost hardware-based digital filter demonstrator. Two forms of implementation have been summarised: (i) a basic self-build M6802 microprocessor-based system, and (ii) a TMS320C26 based system (available off-the-shelf from Texas Instruments as the TMS320C2x DSP Starter Kit). Either is suitable for laboratory/project hands-on investigative signal processing activities, and considerable valuable experience can be gained by building/installing, programming and testing both forms of implementation. Thus by actually making the hardware process applied signals in real-time to satisfy the specified performance requirements, a student is able to learn about the various practical stages involved in producing a practical DSP system.

We believe that all students should be positively encouraged to extend their basic DSP knowledge and to develop research expertise by searching out several publications on a particular topic. We have therefore deliberately avoided directing the reader to specific references for additional information, instead we have provided a bibliography of DSP books which collectively contain a wealth of invaluable information, and which, as a starting point in seeking new/enhanced knowledge, the student could consult after the basic concepts presented in this book have been studied and understood.

This book is primarily intended for students wishing to gain an introduction to the basic principles of DSP and related topics. However, it is a fact of life that students and teachers share common interests in knowledge transfer, from one to the other, and we therefore sincerely hope that this book can serve the needs of student and teacher alike.

Trevor J. Terrell
Lik-Kwan Shark

1 Digital Signals and Systems

1.1 Introduction

Digital Signal Processing (DSP) is concerned with the use of programmable digital hardware and software (digital systems) to perform mathematical operations on a sequence of discrete numbers (a digital signal). Such processing is needed to facilitate the extraction of information embedded in the signal.

A digital signal may be obtained by sampling a continuously varying signal (analogue signal) at regular intervals and converting the samples to corresponding binary number representations. The main reason for digitising analogue signals is to enable signal processing to be carried out in the digital domain rather than directly in the analogue domain, thereby offering a number of significant advantages, namely:

(i) ***Control of data accuracy***: In DSP systems, processing accuracy can be simply increased by employing more binary bits to represent data values. Furthermore, with two voltage ranges rather than two exact voltage levels to distinguish two possible states of each binary bit, data accuracy is not affected by noise, component tolerances, and drift in device parameters due to temperature variation or ageing, unless the fluctuation in voltage caused by these effects exceeds the voltage range defined for each state.

(ii) ***Good performance characteristics***: DSP systems can be designed to have an approximately ideal frequency response, to have linear phase characteristics (the output signal being a delayed version of the input signal without distortion), to have no insertion loss, to handle very low frequency signals, and to implement sophisticated algorithms and non-linear mathematical functions.

(iii) ***Programmability***: The DSP system hardware can be programmed to perform different signal processing operations, and performance characteristics can be programmed to change adaptively.

(iv) ***Ease of design and implementation***: System design and implementation is generally straightforward due to the availability of software packages and the technological advance of very large scale integrated (VLSI) circuits. The replication of the prototype DSP system is guaranteed to have identical performance characteristics. Furthermore, DSP systems normally have high reliability and thus require little maintenance.

As a result of the above advantages, DSP has found application in a multitude of diverse fields of science and technology. Some typical examples of DSP applications are analysis of the electrocardiogram (ecg) to provide information about heart condition and analysis of the electroencephalogram (eeg) to provide information about brain activity in biomedical signal processing; speech synthesis in audio signal processing; pattern recognition in image processing; data compression and transmission in telecommunication systems; digital radio and television in broadcasting; analysis of seismic signals in oil and gas exploration; analysis of sonar and radar signals in object detection and location; the auto pilot as a digital control system; and the compact disc (CD) player.

The main disadvantage that limits DSP for some applications is processing speed. Current general-purpose DSP chips operate at clock frequencies up to about 80 MHz. To increase the processing speed, parallel processing systems and/or application-specific full-custom VLSI chips are used. The fastest VLSI technology is Gallium Arsenide (GaAs) which can achieve clock frequencies up to about 1 GHz, with up to about one thousand gates on a single chip.

1.1.1 DSP System Concept

A typical DSP system is shown schematically in Figure 1.1. To illustrate the basic operation of the DSP system, waveforms are shown at various stages. The analogue input signal, $v(t)$, is assumed to be the sum of three sinusoidal signals; one is a 1 kHz wanted sinusoidal signal with an amplitude of 5 mV, the other two are unwanted sinusoidal signals each with an amplitude of 3 mV, but with 3 kHz and 20 kHz frequencies respectively. The DSP system extracts the wanted signal embedded in the analogue input signal.

The first stage is an analogue amplifier, which needs to be included if the analogue input signal is weak (such as from a measurement transducer). This increases the input signal level to match the full-scale-voltage range of the A/D (analogue-to-digital) converter.

The amplified analogue signal is fed to an anti-aliasing filter which is an analogue lowpass or bandpass filter. The purpose of the anti-aliasing filter is to eliminate 'interference' caused by out-of-band unwanted signals. It therefore attempts to pass only signals in the desired frequency range to the A/D converter. In this example, the filtered analogue waveform, $x(t)$, is the sum of the wanted signal at 1 kHz and the in-band unwanted signal at 3 kHz, with the out-of-band unwanted signal at 20 kHz being removed by the lowpass anti-aliasing filter.

The signal $x(t)$ is then sampled at regular intervals by the A/D converter. The voltage level at each sampling instant is converted to a corresponding binary number representation, thereby forming the digital sequence, $x_d(t)$. Clearly these signal pre-processing and conversion stages are not required if the input signal is already in digital form.

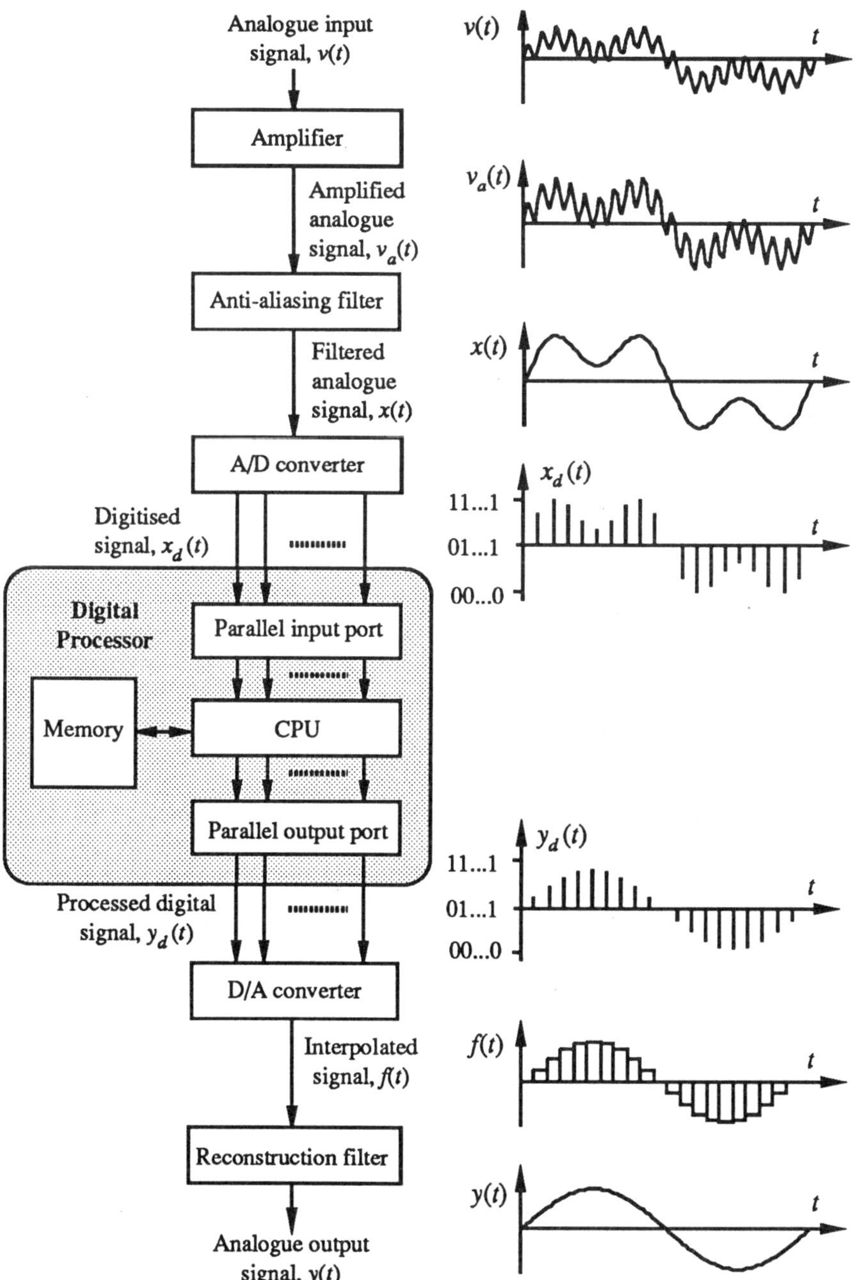

Figure 1.1 Block diagram of a typical DSP system

By executing a software program using the central processing unit (CPU), the digital processor, which could be a microprocessor-based system or a digital system based on a general-purpose DSP chip, operates on the sampled digital sequence received at the parallel input port, $x_d(t)$, to produce a digital output sequence, $y_d(t)$. In this example, the digital signal processing operation removes the in-band unwanted signal at 3 kHz to produce, at the parallel output port, the digital sequence corresponding to the wanted signal at 1 kHz.

If the final form of the processed signal is to be analogue, the D/A (digital-to-analogue) converter is included to convert the digital output sequence from the parallel output port to corresponding analogue voltage levels. This is followed by a reconstruction filter (e.g. an R-C analogue lowpass filter), which smoothes the staircase waveform of the zero-order hold interpolated signal, $f(t)$, from the D/A converter to produce the required analogue output signal, $y(t)$. In Figure 1.1, the final analogue output is shown to be the wanted 1 kHz sinusoidal waveform.

1.1.2 DSP System Design

A possible approach to the design of a DSP system is outlined in Figure 1.2. The first design phase is the analysis of the input signal to obtain the signal characteristics, such as maximum and minimum amplitude, bandwidth, spectral content, and signal-to-noise ratio (SNR).

The second design phase is concerned with the signal pre-processing and conversion, which is not required if the input signal is already in digital form. The signal amplitude determines the required gain of the amplifier to make use of the full-scale-voltage range of the A/D converter. The bandwidth of the input signal determines the passband of the anti-aliasing filter, the minimum sampling rate and the required operating speed of the A/D converter.

The third phase is concerned with the design of the DSP system. The spectral content and SNR of the input signal are used in conjunction with the output requirements, which may be the detection of a frequency component or the improvement of SNR, to determine the DSP system transfer function and the corresponding computation algorithms.

Computer simulation can be carried out to confirm the system performance by non-real-time processing of model input signals. Many DSP operations can be easily simulated by using a spreadsheet software package or by using a DSP design software package. The system signal flow graph is then derived from the successful simulated transfer function to form the basis for the hardware and software implementation of the required signal processing operation. In real-time signal processing, the signal bandwidth determines the processing speed and the partition of the processing work load between hardware and software.

The evaluation and verification of the speed performance may require a search for a more efficient form of implementation and/or computation saving algorithms.

The fourth design phase is system integration to form the final DSP system.

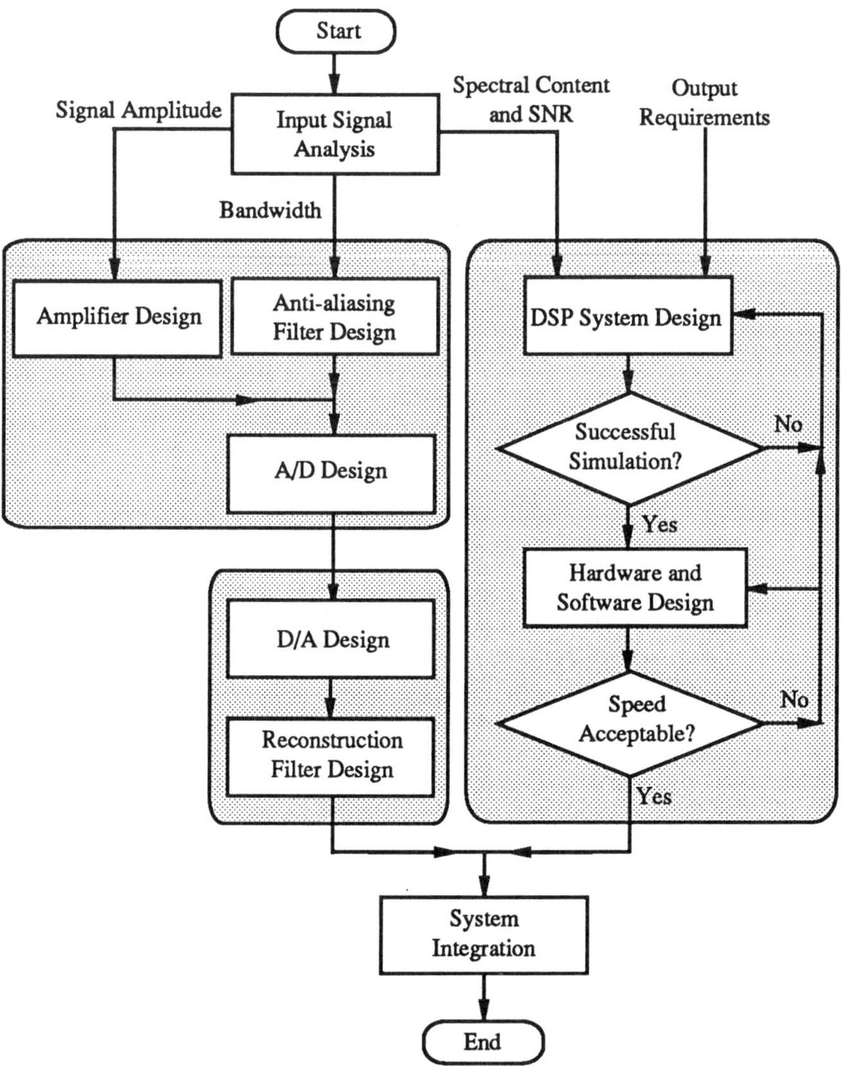

Figure 1.2 A possible approach to DSP system design

1.2 Digitisation of Analogue Signals

Figure 1.3 shows an expanded diagram of the A/D converter shown in Figure 1.1 with the same input and output signals. It is seen that the A/D converter consists of three internal stages, namely, (a) Sample-and-Hold circuit, which could be external for some A/D devices, (b) Quantiser, and (c) Coder.

In its simplest form the sample-and-hold circuit consists of a switch and a capacitor. In the sample mode the switch is closed for an interval of $(T - \tau)$ seconds, thereby allowing the capacitor to charge up to the voltage value of the analogue input. In the hold mode the switch is opened, and the capacitor holds the instantaneous voltage value acquired at the end of the sample mode for an interval of τ seconds, thereby allowing the A/D conversion to take place. Therefore the sample-and-hold circuit performs a time discretisation operation by converting the analogue input signal, $x(t)$, which is a ***continuous-time continuous-amplitude*** signal, to a ***discrete-time continuous-amplitude*** signal, $x^*(t)$, which is shown in Figure 1.3 to be a train of pulses with their heights equal to the instantaneous value of $x(t)$ at the end of the sample mode. The time interval between successive sample values, T, is called the ***sampling period***, and $f_s = 1/T$ is called the ***sampling frequency***. The waveforms in Figure 1.3 correspond to the sample-and-hold circuit operating at a sampling frequency of 10 kHz, and producing a repeated sequence of analogue samples of {0V, 5.79V, 2.99V, 2.99V, 5.79V, 0V, –5.79V, –2.99V, –2.99V, –5.79V}.

The quantiser performs an amplitude discretisation operation by converting the discrete-time continuous-amplitude signal, $x^*(t)$, to a ***discrete-time discrete-amplitude*** (digital) signal, $x_q(t)$, by representing the continuous amplitude range with a finite number of discrete levels (***quantisation levels***). As shown in Figure 1.3, the continuous amplitude range is quantised into seven discrete levels denoted by q_0 (corresponding to -6V) to q_6 (corresponding to 6V), with a ***quantisation interval*** (the difference between two consecutive quantisation levels), Q, of 2V. With each analogue sample value represented by the nearest quantisation level, the quantised signal is the repeated sequence {0V, 6V, 2V, 2V, 6V, 0V, –6V, –2V, –2V, –6V}. The inherent difference between $x^*(t)$ and $x_q(t)$ is called the ***quantisation error.***

The coder assigns binary numbers to $x_q(t)$ normalised with respect to the full-scale-voltage of the quantiser, where the full-scale-voltage is referred to as the maximum amplitude of the analogue input voltage. In Figure 1.3, the full-scale-voltage is 6V, therefore normalising $x_q(t)$ with respect to this full-scale-voltage of the quantiser produces the repeated sequence {0/6, 6/6, 2/6, 2/6, 6/6, 0/6, –6/6, –2/6, –2/6, –6/6} which reduces to {0/3, 3/3, 1/3, 1/3, 3/3, 0/3, –3/3, –1/3, –1/3, –3/3}. Using a 3-bit sign and magnitude binary code with the most significant bit acting as the sign bit and the two least significant bits acting as the magnitude bits, the digitised signal is the repeated sequence {000, 011, 001, 001, 011, 000, 111, 101, 101, 111}, where each binary code represents the numerator value of each corresponding fraction in the sequence.

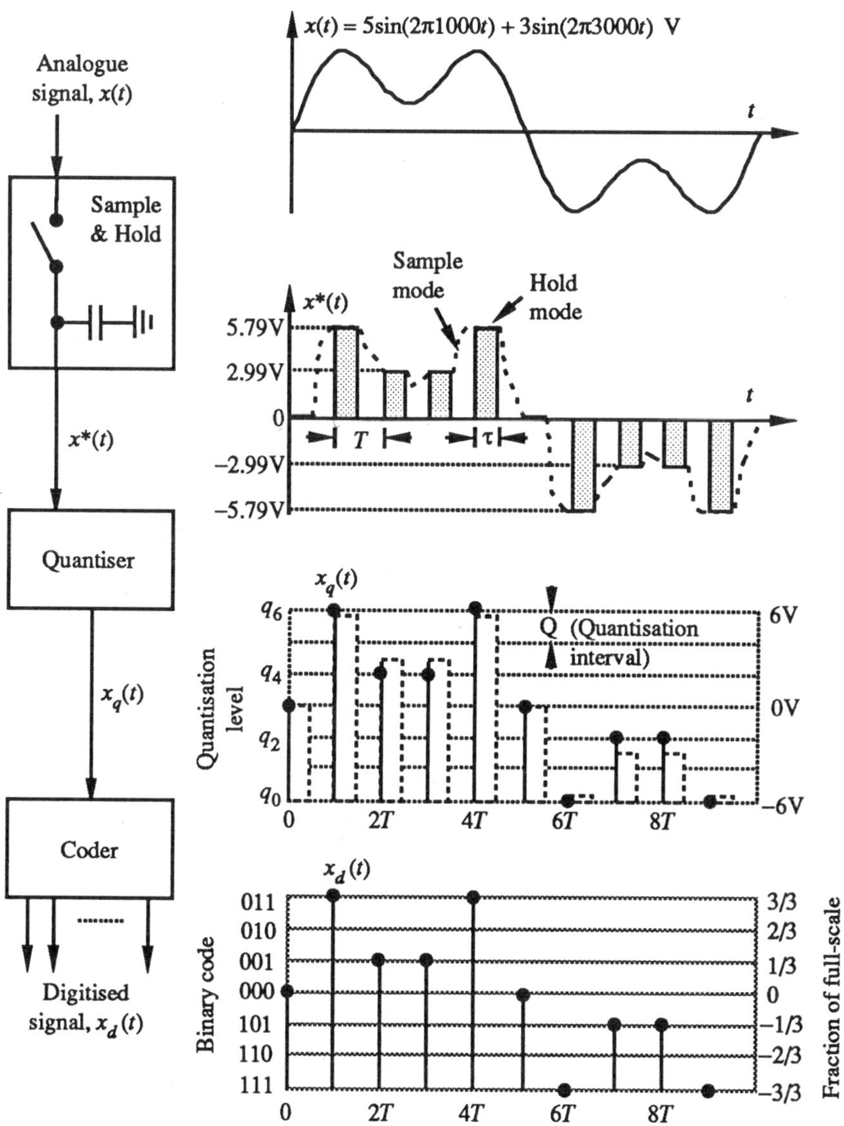

Figure 1.3 Expanded diagram of A/D converter with corresponding signal representations

1.2.1 Model of the Sampling Process

Referring to Figure 1.3, it is seen that the output of the sample-and-hold circuit is a train of finite width pulses with their heights equal to the instantaneous value of $x(t)$ at the end of the sample mode. If the hold time is negligible compared with the sampling period, i.e. $\tau << T$, the sampling process can be ideally modelled as a modulation process consisting of multiplying the analogue input signal by a train of ***unit-strength impulses***, as shown in Figure 1.4.

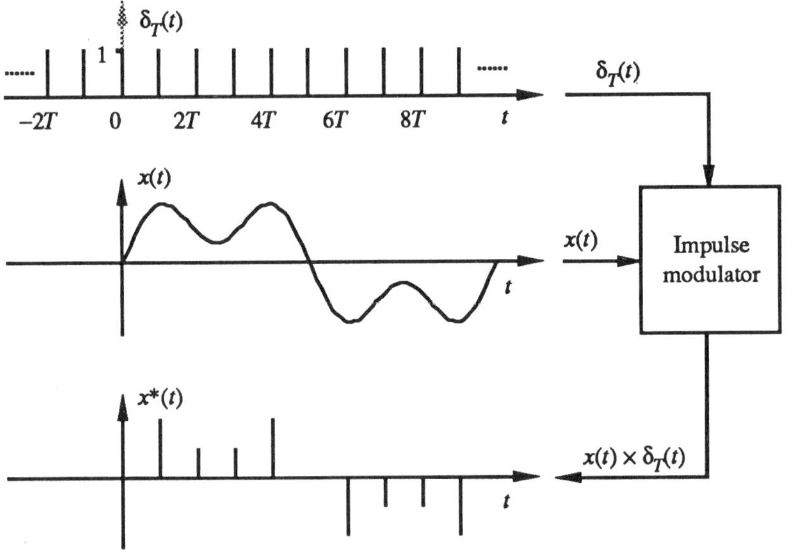

Figure 1.4 Impulse modulator model of the sampling process

The unit-strength impulse is defined as

$$\delta(t) = \begin{cases} 1 & \text{for} \quad t = 0 \\ 0 & \text{for} \quad t \neq 0 \end{cases} \tag{1.1}$$

The unit-strength impulse train, $\delta_T(t)$, can be viewed as the superposition of a set of shifted discrete-time unit-strength impulses and is expressed as

$$\delta_T(t) = \delta(t + \infty T) \ldots + \delta(t + 2T) + \delta(t + T) + \delta(t) + \delta(t - T) + \delta(t - 2T) + \ldots + \delta(t - \infty T)$$

$$= \sum_{n=-\infty}^{\infty} \delta(t - nT) \tag{1.2}$$

where $\delta(t - nT)$ denotes a delayed unit-strength impulse occurring at $t = nT$, and $\delta(t + nT)$ denotes an advanced unit-strength impulse occurring at $t = -nT$. Hence the ideal sampled signal is given by

$$x^*(t) = x(t) \times \delta_T(t) = x(t) \sum_{n=-\infty}^{\infty} \delta(t - nT) \tag{1.3}$$

Since the unit-strength impulse train is a periodic signal, it can be expanded as a weighted (scaled) sum of complex exponential (or sinusoidal) components (**Fourier series**) with frequencies that are multiples of the sampling frequency, that is

$$\delta_T(t) = \sum_{n=-\infty}^{\infty} C_n \, \mathrm{e}^{\mathrm{j} n \omega_s t}$$

where ω_s is the sampling frequency equal to $2\pi/T$ radians per second; C_n is the amplitude (**Fourier coefficient**) of the complex exponential component at frequency $n\omega_s$, and is given by

$$C_n = \frac{1}{T} \int_0^T \delta_T(t) \, \mathrm{e}^{-\mathrm{j} n \omega_s t} \, \mathrm{d}t$$

The Fourier series is described in more detail in Chapter 3, Sections 3.2 and 3.5.

Since the product of the unit-strength impulse train and the complex exponential function is unity at $t = 0$ and zero elsewhere over the integrating period, it is apparent that the result of the integration, which gives the area under the product curve, will be unity. Therefore

$$C_n = \frac{1}{T}$$

Hence

$$\delta_T(t) = \frac{1}{T} \sum_{n=-\infty}^{\infty} \mathrm{e}^{\mathrm{j} n \omega_s t}$$

and the ideal sampled signal produced by the impulse modulator becomes

$$x^*(t) = x(t) \times \delta_T(t) = \frac{1}{T} \sum_{n=-\infty}^{\infty} x(t) \, \mathrm{e}^{\mathrm{j} n \omega_s t} \tag{1.4}$$

The ideal sampled signal, $x^*(t)$, may be represented in the frequency domain by taking the Fourier transform of it, that is

$$X^*(j\,\omega) = \int_{-\infty}^{\infty} x^*(t)\, e^{-j\omega t}\, dt$$

$$= \int_{-\infty}^{\infty} \left(\frac{1}{T} \sum_{n=-\infty}^{\infty} x(t)\, e^{jn\omega_s t} \right) e^{-j\omega t}\, dt$$

$$= \frac{1}{T} \int_{-\infty}^{\infty} \sum_{n=-\infty}^{\infty} x(t)\, e^{-j(\omega - n\omega_s)t}\, dt$$

We can swap the order of summation and integration, thus giving

$$X^*(j\,\omega) = \frac{1}{T} \sum_{n=-\infty}^{\infty} \int_{-\infty}^{\infty} x(t)\, e^{-j(\omega - n\omega_s)t}\, dt$$

Note that $\int_{-\infty}^{\infty} x(t)\, e^{-j(\omega - n\omega_s)t}\, dt$ is the Fourier transform $X(j(\omega - n\omega_s))$,

thus

$$X^*(j\,\omega) = \frac{1}{T} \sum_{n=-\infty}^{\infty} X(j(\omega - n\omega_s)) \tag{1.5}$$

From equation (1.5), the frequency spectrum of the ideally sampled signal is seen to consist of the frequency spectrum of the analogue input signal as well as ***complementary spectra*** repeated ad-infinitum at intervals of ω_s. Assuming that the frequency spectrum of the analogue input signal is as shown in Figure 1.5(a), the significance of equation (1.5) is illustrated in Figure 1.5(b) and 1.5(c). If the sampling frequency $\omega_s > 2\omega_b$, where ω_b is the highest frequency component in the analogue input signal, the frequency spectrum of the sampled signal is as shown Figure 1.5(b) and is identical to the spectrum of the analogue input signal between $\pm\omega_s/2$ frequencies (except that the amplitude is scaled by a factor equal to $1/T$), consequently the original analogue input signal can be recovered from the sampled signal. In contrast, if $\omega_s < 2\omega_b$, the frequency spectrum of the sampled signal is as shown in Figure 1.5(c); folding of two consecutive frequency spectra occurs resulting in ***aliasing errors***, and consequently the original analogue input signal cannot be reclaimed from the sampled signal. This gives rise to the ***sampling theorem***, which states that the condition of $\omega_s \geq 2\omega_b$ must be obeyed to recover the original analogue signal from the sampled signal. This is why an analogue lowpass or bandpass filter is placed before the A/D converter to avoid aliasing by band limiting the frequency range of the analogue input signal to ensure that $\omega_b < \omega_s/2$.

(a)

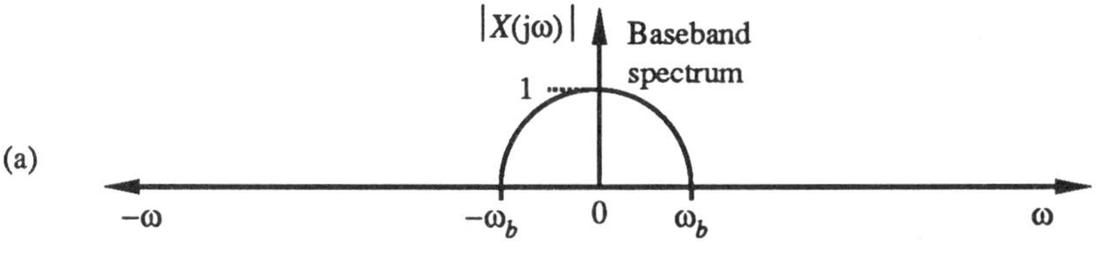

(b)

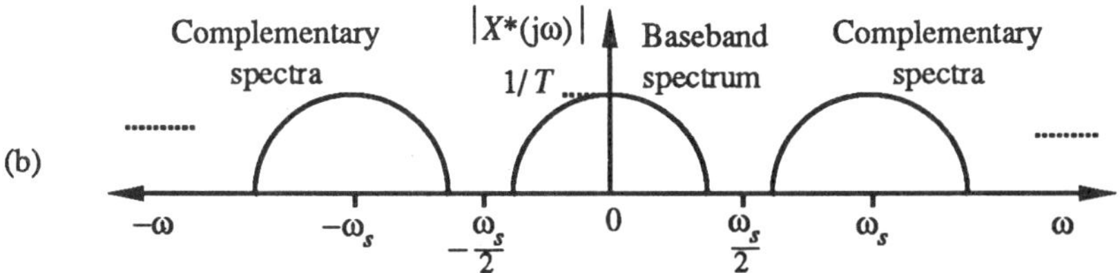

(c)

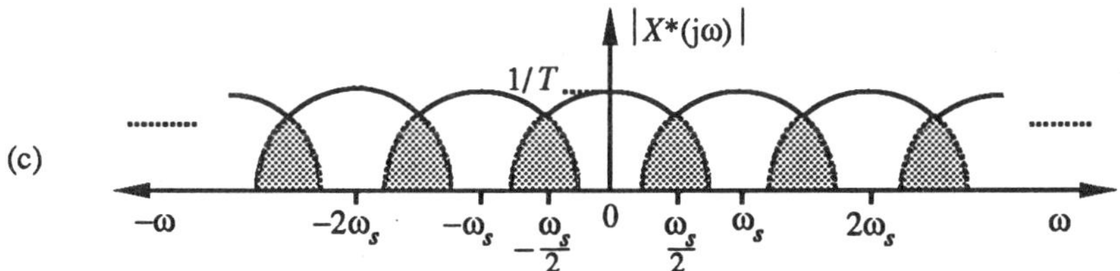

Figure 1.5 (a) Frequency spectrum of the analogue signal
(b) Frequency spectra of the sampled signal for $\omega_s > 2\omega_b$
(c) Frequency spectra of the sampled signal for $\omega_s < 2\omega_b$

Note: With reference to the sampling process, the nth sample, which is obtained when $t = nT$ (after n sampling periods), is sometimes denoted as $x(nT)$. However, in this book, in order to simplify the notation the nth sample is written as $x(n)$. Similarly, it follows that using this form of simplified notation, the nth sample delayed by k sampling periods is written as $x(n-k)$, and not as $x(nT - kT)$.

❖ WE 1.1

In a DSP system the A/D converter operates at a sampling frequency of 1 kHz and its preceding anti-aliasing filter has the magnitude/frequency response

$$|G(\mathrm{j}f)| = \frac{1}{\sqrt{1+\left(\frac{f}{800}\right)^4}}$$

(a) Using the impulse modulator model for the A/D sampling process, and ignoring quantisation, calculate the first six A/D output values when the filter input signal is $x(t) = 2\sin(2\pi\,200\,t) + 0.5\sin(2\pi\,400\,t)$ V.

(b) Sketch the magnitude/frequency spectrum of the A/D output signal, $x^*(t)$.

Solution:

(a) By considering each frequency component of the input signal, the output signal of the anti-aliasing filter, $x_f(t)$, is given by

$$x_f(t) = |G(j200)| \times 2\sin(2\pi 200\, t) + |G(j400)| \times 0.5\sin(2\pi 400\, t)$$

$$= 0.998 \times 2\sin(2\pi 200\, t) + 0.970 \times 0.5\sin(2\pi 400\, t)$$

$$= 1.996\sin(2\pi 200\, t) + 0.485\sin(2\pi 400\, t) \quad \text{V}$$

With the sampling period $T = 1/f_s = 1/10^3 = 10^{-3}$ sec, the output of the A/D converter, $x^*(t)$, equals $x_f(t)$ at $t = nT = 10^{-3}n$, i.e.

$$x^*(t) = 1.996\sin\left(2\pi 200 \times 10^{-3}n\right) + 0.485\sin\left(2\pi 400 \times 10^{-3}n\right) \quad \text{V}$$

Hence, the first six output values from the A/D converter, corresponding to $n = 0$ to 5, are {0V, 2.183V, 0.712V, −0.712V, −2.183V, 0V}.

(b) The output of the A/D converter, $x^*(t)$, can be rewritten as

$$x^*(t) = 1.996\sin\theta + 0.485\sin 2\theta \quad \text{V}$$

where $\theta = 2\pi 200 \times 10^{-3}n$

Applying Euler's identity yields

$$x^*(t) = 1.996\left(\frac{e^{j\theta} - e^{-j\theta}}{2j}\right) + 0.485\left(\frac{e^{j2\theta} - e^{-j2\theta}}{2j}\right)$$

$$= 0.998\left(\frac{e^{j\theta} - e^{-j\theta}}{j}\right) + 0.2425\left(\frac{e^{j2\theta} - e^{-j2\theta}}{j}\right) \quad \text{V}$$

θ is associated with a frequency value of 200 Hz, therefore the baseband magnitude/frequency spectrum of $x^*(t)$ consists of four components, namely, two located at ±200 Hz with a magnitude value of 0.998V and two located at ±400 Hz with a magnitude value of 0.2425V. This baseband magnitude/frequency spectrum is repeated ad-infinitum, centred about integer multiples of the sampling frequency, and is magnitude scaled by a factor $1/T = 10^3$, as shown in the following diagram.

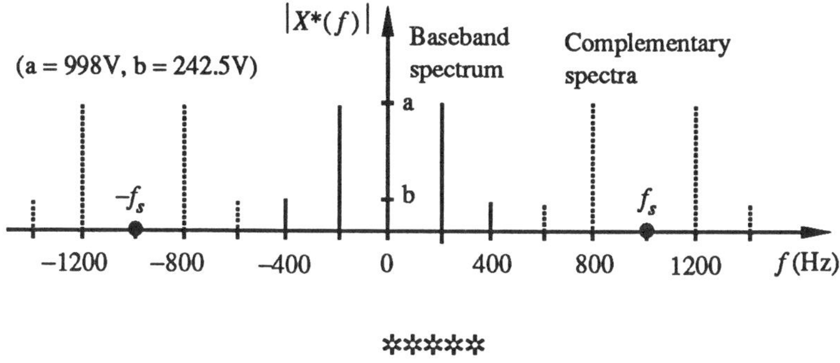

*****

1.2.2 Quantisation

It has been established that the quantisation process introduces an error between the continuous-amplitude signal $x^*(t)$ and the discrete-amplitude signal $x_q(t)$. With each analogue sample value represented by the nearest quantisation level, the quantisation error, $e(n)$, varies between $\pm Q/2$, where Q is the quantisation interval. That is

$$-\frac{Q}{2} < \left\{ e(n) = x_q(n) - x^*(n) \right\} \leq \frac{Q}{2} \tag{1.6}$$

In Figure 1.3, the full-scale-voltage range of the quantiser is shown to be ±6V and the number of quantisation levels is seven, which leads to $Q = 2$V; the corresponding quantisation error signal is shown in Figure 1.6. It is seen that quantisation error values do not exceed half of the quantisation interval.

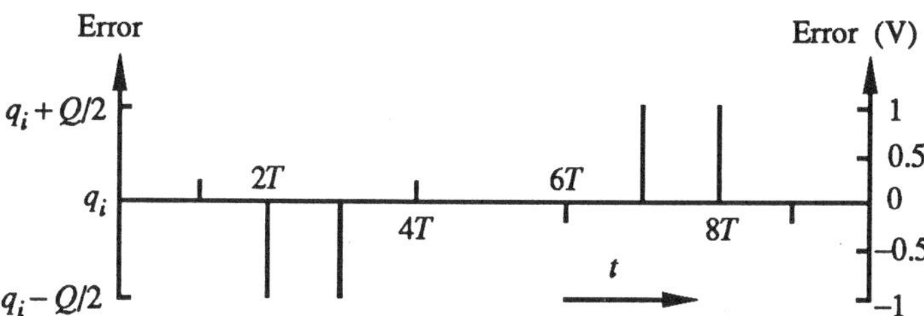

Figure 1.6 Quantisation error signal for the $x_q(t)$ signal shown in Figure 1.3

Figure 1.6 also shows that the average quantisation error value is zero, i.e. the sum of the positive errors equals the sum of the negative errors, and therefore cancel each other. If the distribution of all possible values of the quantisation error is assumed to be uniform between $\pm Q/2$, then the probability of the quantisation error having a particular value $e(n)$ is given by

$$p[e(n)] = \frac{\text{Area under probability distribution curve}}{\text{Error range}}$$

$$= \frac{1}{\frac{Q}{2} - \left(-\frac{Q}{2}\right)} = \frac{1}{Q}$$

Hence the mean-square error (variance or quantisation noise power) is given by

$$\sigma_q^2 = \int_{-\frac{Q}{2}}^{\frac{Q}{2}} e(n)^2 \; p[e(n)] \, de(n) = \frac{1}{Q} \int_{-\frac{Q}{2}}^{\frac{Q}{2}} e(n)^2 \, de(n) = \frac{1}{Q}\left[\frac{e(n)^3}{3}\right]_{-\frac{Q}{2}}^{\frac{Q}{2}} = \frac{Q^2}{12} \tag{1.7}$$

Now consider a full-scale sine wave applied to the input of an n-interval quantiser, the $x_q(t)$ signal amplitude of the sine wave is $nQ/2$, and the corresponding average signal power developed, assuming a 1Ω resistor load, is

$$P_{x_q(t)} = \frac{1}{2}\left(\frac{nQ}{2}\right)^2 = \frac{(nQ)^2}{8} \tag{1.8}$$

Hence the ***signal-to-quantisation noise ratio*** (SQNR) in decibels (dB) is given by

$$\text{SQNR} = 10 \log_{10}\left(\frac{P_{x_q(t)}}{\sigma_q^2}\right) = 10 \log_{10}\left(\frac{\frac{(nQ)^2}{8}}{\frac{Q^2}{12}}\right) = 10 \log_{10} \frac{3n^2}{2} \quad \text{dB} \tag{1.9}$$

Clearly the greater the number of quantisation intervals, the smaller the quantisation noise and the greater the signal-to-quantisation noise ratio.

❖ WE 1.2

If the dynamic range (the maximum to minimum amplitude ratio), DR, of an analogue signal to be digitised by an A/D converter is maintained at 60 dB by an automatic gain control amplifier preceding the A/D converter, determine (a) the minimum number of bits required in the A/D converter, and (b) the signal-to-quantisation noise ratio.

***Solution*:**
(a) The dynamic range of the A/D converter (the ratio of the full-scale-voltage range, V_{fsr}, to the quantisation interval, Q) should match the dynamic range of the input signal so that the maximum amplitude and the minimum amplitude of the input signal can be coded by the A/D converter. Hence

$$DR = 60 \text{ dB} = 20 \log_{10} \frac{V_{fsr}}{Q}$$

Since $V_{fsr} = nQ$, where n is the number of quantisation intervals, the above equation becomes

$$60 \text{ dB} = 20 \log_{10} \frac{nQ}{Q} = 20 \log_{10} n$$

Therefore the number of quantisation intervals required is

$$n = 10^{60/20} = 1000$$

and the minimum number of bits required in the A/D converter to code $(n + 1)$ quantisation levels to $(n + 1)$ different binary numbers is

$$b \geq \log_2 (n + 1) \geq \log_2 (1000 + 1)$$

Therefore the minimum number of bits is 10.

(b) The actual number of quantisation intervals $n = 2^b - 1 = 1023$, therefore applying equation (1.9) gives

$$\text{SQNR} = 10 \log_{10} \frac{3 \times 1023^2}{2} = 61.96 \text{ dB}$$

*****

1.2.3 Coding

The coding process is a mapping of quantisation levels to binary numbers. It has been mentioned that the coder assigns binary numbers to $x_q(t)$ expressed as a fraction of the full-scale-voltage. Some binary codes commonly used in A/D converters are presented below using the notation of C_{-i} as the bit value (1 or 0) of the ith bit, with C_0 as the most significant bit (MSB) and $C_{-(b-1)}$ as the least significant bit (LSB) in a b-bit binary code.

For ***unipolar analogue input signals*** (signals with positive values only) most A/D converters use the natural binary code. Decimal fractions of the full-scale-voltage are expressed as

$$\text{Decimal value} = \sum_{i=0}^{b-1} C_{-i}\, 2^{-i-1} \tag{1.10}$$

For example, a binary code of 1001 gives $2^{-1} + 2^{-4} = 0.5625$, which corresponds to 9/16 of the full-scale-voltage. Since this code uses all possible combinations of the binary number to represent different quantisation levels, the quantisation interval for a unipolar b-bit A/D coverter is

$$Q = \frac{V_{fsr}}{2^b - 1} \text{ V} \tag{1.11}$$

For ***bipolar analogue input signals*** (signals with positive and negative values) a variety of binary codes exist. Commonly used codes are:

(a) Offset binary code

This is a natural binary code offset by the full-scale-voltage, thereby resulting in the MSB set to 1 for positive fractional numbers. It is expressed as

$$\text{Decimal value} = 2\left(\sum_{i=0}^{b-1} C_{-i}\, 2^{-i-1}\right) - 1 \tag{1.12}$$

For example, if $b = 4$, the smallest binary number 0000 gives a value of -1, corresponding to the full-scale negative voltage; 1000 gives a value of 0, corresponding to zero input voltage; and the largest binary number 1111 gives a value of 0.875, which corresponds to 7/8 of the full-scale positive voltage. The quantisation interval is the same as the natural binary code.

(b) Sign and magnitude code

This code consists of a sign bit C_{-0} (0 for positive and 1 for negative) followed by magnitude bits in natural binary code, and it is expressed as

$$\text{Decimal value} = (-1)^{C_{-0}} \times \left(\sum_{i=1}^{b-1} C_{-i}\, 2^{-i}\right) \tag{1.13}$$

For example, if $b = 4$, the binary number 0111 gives the largest positive number of 0.875, which is 7/8 of the full-scale positive voltage, and 1111 gives the largest negative number of $-$ 0.875, which is 7/8 of the full-scale negative voltage. However, since zero input voltage is represented by either 0000 or

1000, the quantisation interval for a b-bit A/D converter using this code is

$$Q = \frac{V_{fsr}}{2^b - 2} \quad \text{V} \tag{1.14}$$

(c) One's complement code

The representation of positive fractional numbers is the same as for the sign and magnitude code, and the representation of negative fractional numbers is formed by complementing the corresponding bits of the magnitude code (changing 0s to 1s and 1s to 0s). It is expressed as

$$\text{Decimal valuc} = \begin{cases} \sum_{i=1}^{b-1} C_{-i}\, 2^{-i} & \text{for} \quad C_{-0} = 0 \\ -\sum_{i=1}^{b-1} (1 - C_{-i})\, 2^{-i} & \text{for} \quad C_{-0} = 1 \end{cases} \tag{1.15}$$

Let $b = 4$ again, the binary number 1000 gives the largest negative number of -0.875, which is $7/8$ of the full-scale negative voltage. Since zero input voltage is represented by either 0000 or 1111, the quantisation interval for this code is given by equation (1.14).

(d) Two's complement code

The representation of positive fractional numbers is the same as for the sign and magnitude code. The representation of negative fractional numbers is formed by adding 1 to the LSB of the one's complement representation, and is expressed as

$$\text{Negative decimal value} = -C_{-0} + \sum_{i=1}^{b-1} C_{-i}\, 2^{-i} \tag{1.16}$$

Let $b = 4$ again, the binary number 1000 gives the largest negative number of -1, which corresponds to full-scale negative voltage. Since this code uses all possible combinations of the binary number to represent different quantisation levels, the quantisation interval is given by equation (1.11).

❖ WE 1.3

The output of an 8-bit A/D converter with 20V full-scale-voltage range is the repeated sequence {00110001, 11000001}, determine the corresponding range of input voltage values if the output is coded using (a) offset binary, (b) sign and magnitude, (c) one's complement, and (d) two's complement.

Solution:
(a) For offset binary, applying equation (1.12) to the first number and the second number respectively and taking the possible quantisation error $\pm Q/2$ into account (with Q given by equation (1.11)) gives

(i) $$V_i = \frac{V_{fsr}}{2} \times \left\{ 2\left(\sum_{i=0}^{8-1} C_{-i}\, 2^{-i-1} \right) - 1 \right\} \pm \frac{V_{fsr}}{2\left(2^b - 1\right)}$$

$$= 10 \times \left\{ 2\left(1 \times 2^{-3} + 1 \times 2^{-4} + 1 \times 2^{-8}\right) - 1 \right\} \pm \frac{20}{2\left(2^8 - 1\right)}$$

$$= -\,6.171875\,\text{V} \;\pm 0.039216\,\text{V}$$

(ii) $$V_i = 10 \times \left\{ 2\left(1 \times 2^{-1} + 1 \times 2^{-2} + 1 \times 2^{-8}\right) - 1 \right\} \pm \frac{20}{2\left(2^8 - 1\right)}$$

$$-\,5.078125\,\text{V} \;\pm 0.039216\,\text{V}$$

(b) For sign and magnitude, applying equations (1.13) and (1.14) gives

(i) $$V_i = \frac{V_{fsr}}{2} \times \left\{ (-1)^{C_{-0}} \left(\sum_{i=1}^{8-1} C_{-i}\, 2^{-i} \right) \right\} \pm \frac{V_{fsr}}{2\left(2^b - 2\right)}$$

$$= 10 \times \left\{ (-1)^0 \left(1 \times 2^{-2} + 1 \times 2^{-3} + 1 \times 2^{-7}\right) \right\} \pm \frac{20}{2\left(2^8 - 2\right)}$$

$$= 3.828125\,\text{V} \;\pm 0.039370\,\text{V}$$

(ii) $$V_i = 10 \times \left\{ (-1)^1 \left(1 \times 2^{-1} + 1 \times 2^{-7}\right) \right\} + \frac{20}{2\left(2^8 - 2\right)}$$

$$= -\,5.078125\,\text{V} \;\pm 0.039370\,\text{V}$$

(c) For one's complement,, applying equations (1.15) and (1.14) gives

(i) Same as (b)(i).

(ii) $$V_i = \frac{V_{fsr}}{2} \times \left\{ - \sum_{i=1}^{8-1} (1 - C_{-i}) 2^{-i} \right\} \pm \frac{V_{fsr}}{2\left(2^b - 2\right)}$$

$$= 10 \times \left\{ - \left(1 \times 2^{-2} + 1 \times 2^{-3} + 1 \times 2^{-4} + 1 \times 2^{-5} + 1 \times 2^{-6} \right) \right\}$$

$$\pm \frac{20}{2\left(2^8 - 2\right)}$$

$$= -4.84375\,\mathrm{V} \ \pm 0.039370\,\mathrm{V}$$

(d) For two's complement, applying equations (1.13) and (1.11) to the first binary number and equations (1.16) and (1.11) to the second binary number, gives

(i) $$V_i = \frac{V_{fsr}}{2} \times \left\{ (-1)^{C_{-0}} \left(\sum_{i=1}^{8-1} C_{-i}\, 2^{-i} \right) \right\} \pm \frac{V_{fsr}}{2\left(2^b - 1\right)}$$

$$= 10 \times \left\{ (-1)^0 \left(1 \times 2^{-2} + 1 \times 2^{-3} + 1 \times 2^{-7} \right) \right\} \pm \frac{20}{2\left(2^8 - 1\right)}$$

$$= 3.828125\,\mathrm{V} \ \pm 0.039216\,\mathrm{V}$$

(ii) $$V_i = \frac{V_{fsr}}{2} \times \left\{ - C_{-0} + \sum_{i=1}^{8-1} C_{-i}\, 2^{-i} \right\} \pm \frac{V_{fsr}}{2\left(2^b - 1\right)}$$

$$= 10 \times \left\{ -1 + \left(1 \times 2^{-1} + 1 \times 2^{-7} \right) \right\} \pm \frac{20}{2\left(2^8 - 1\right)}$$

$$= -4.921875\,\mathrm{V} \ \pm 0.039216\,\mathrm{V}$$

*****

1.2.4 Practical A/D Converters

A wide range of practical A/D converter chips (integrated-circuits) are readily available to enable the DSP system design approach discussed in Section 1.1.2

to be accomplished. It is particularly useful to realise that the input and output signals of most forms of A/D converter can be functionally grouped (see Figure 1.7) as summarised below.

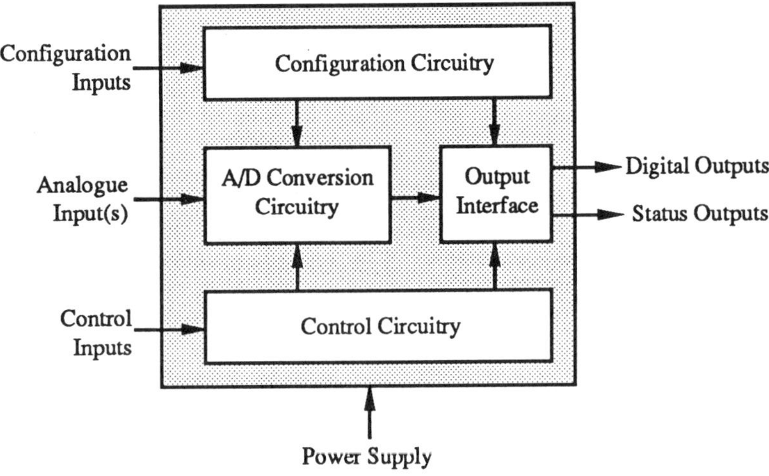

Figure 1.7 Grouping of input and output signals of practical A/D converters

Analogue input(s): While most A/D converter chips have only one analogue input pin to accept single-ended voltage signals, some A/D converter chips have extra analogue input pins to give options of handling different input ranges and accepting differential voltage signals.

Configuration inputs: Configuration inputs are used to select modes of A/D conversion, such as bipolar or unipolar input, output codes, serial or parallel output, and number of output bits.

Control inputs: For A/D converter chips without a microprocessor bus interface, the basic control input is the ***start of conversion*** command, which is a pulse to initiate an A/D conversion. An external clock is also required in some A/D converter chips as a control input to time the A/D operation. For A/D converter chips with a microprocessor bus interface, generally $\overline{CS}$ (Chip Select) and $R/\overline{W}$ (read / $\overline{\text{write}}$) control signals are provided. The outputs of the A/D converter are only connected to the data bus when the $\overline{CS}$ control signals are ***active low*** and $R/\overline{W}$ is ***active high,*** and are disconnected from the data bus (high impedance state) otherwise.

Status outputs: The basic status output is ***end of conversion*** to indicate that data are available as digital outputs from the A/D converter. Some A/D converter chips provide an extra status output to indicate an out-of-range error.

Digital outputs: These can be serial or parallel connections, with tri-state or transparent interfaces, and these can be in natural binary code form or have some other selected format.

Power supply: The power supply will be a single supply or a dual supply. Some A/D converter chips also require a reference voltage input.

To select an appropriate A/D converter chip for a given application, the specifications of the above input and output signals need to be taken into consideration. In addition, other prime factors, such as conversion speed (which can be as high as 500 million samples per second), resolution (number of output bits, which can be as high as 24 bits), accuracy (the difference between the theoretical and the actual analogue input voltages required to produce the given output code) and cost should be taken into account when selecting an A/D converter.

1.3 Recovery of Analogue Signals

It was shown in Figure 1.1 that the recovery of an analogue signal from its corresponding digital sequence is achieved by a D/A converter followed by a lowpass reconstruction filter. The output waveform from the D/A converter was shown as a staircase waveform – the D/A converter holds the voltage level generated for each digital number for T seconds, i.e. the D/A converter acts basically as a zero-order hold linear filter.

If we consider the input to the D/A converter to be the unit-impulse signal occurring at time $t = 0$, the corresponding zero-order hold output (***unit-impulse response***) will be as illustrated in Figure 1.8.

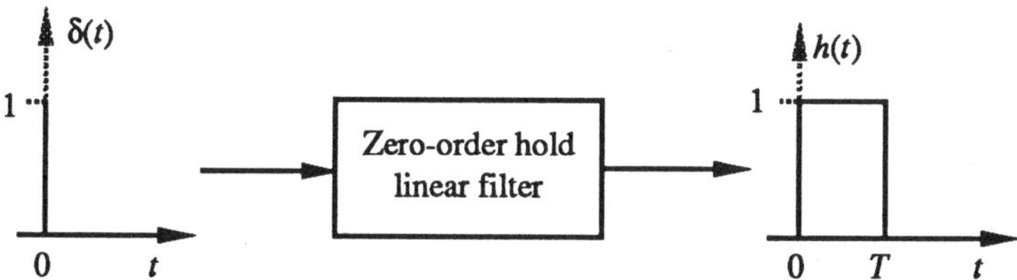

Figure 1.8 Unit-impulse response of the zero-order hold linear filter

The unit-impulse response of the zero-order hold linear filter is

$$h(t) = \begin{cases} 1 & \text{for} \quad 0 \le t \le T \\ 0 & \text{otherwise} \end{cases} \tag{1.17}$$

The corresponding frequency response of the zero-order hold linear filter (D/A converter) can be obtained by taking the Fourier transform of the unit-impulse response, that is

$$H(\mathrm{j}\,\omega) = \int_{-\infty}^{\infty} h(t)\,\mathrm{e}^{-\mathrm{j}\,\omega\,t}\,\mathrm{d}t$$

$$= \int_{0}^{T} 1 \times \mathrm{e}^{-\mathrm{j}\,\omega\,t}\,\mathrm{d}t$$

$$= \left[\frac{\mathrm{e}^{-\mathrm{j}\,\omega\,t}}{-\mathrm{j}\,\omega}\right]_0^T$$

$$= -\frac{1}{\mathrm{j}\,\omega}\left[\mathrm{e}^{-\mathrm{j}\,\omega\,T} - 1\right]$$

$$= -\frac{\mathrm{e}^{-\frac{\mathrm{j}\,\omega\,T}{2}}}{\mathrm{j}\,\omega}\left[\mathrm{e}^{-\frac{\mathrm{j}\,\omega\,T}{2}} - \mathrm{e}^{\frac{\mathrm{j}\,\omega\,T}{2}}\right]$$

$$= \frac{2\,\mathrm{e}^{-\frac{\mathrm{j}\,\omega\,T}{2}}}{\omega}\left[\frac{\mathrm{e}^{\frac{\mathrm{j}\,\omega\,T}{2}} - \mathrm{e}^{-\frac{\mathrm{j}\,\omega\,T}{2}}}{2\,\mathrm{j}}\right]$$

$$= \frac{\sin\left(\frac{\omega\,T}{2}\right)}{\frac{\omega\,T}{2}} \times T\,\mathrm{e}^{-\frac{\mathrm{j}\,\omega\,T}{2}} \tag{1.18}$$

Figure 1.9 compares the magnitude/frequency response of the zero-order hold linear filter (D/A converter) with the magnitude/frequency response of an ideal lowpass filter having a cut-off frequency of $\omega_s/2$ (used to recover the analogue signal from the digital signal). Two differences are apparent, namely, (a) the output of the zero-order hold linear filter contains undesirable frequency components above $\omega_s/2$, this justifies the need for a lowpass filter after the D/A converter, and (b) the attenuation effect on the desired frequency components in the range $-\omega_s/2 \leq \omega \leq \omega_s/2$, due to the $(\sin\,x)/x$ term in equation (1.18), where $x = \omega\,T/2$. Attenuation of these frequency components results in the D/A converter introducing amplitude distortion in the recovered analogue signal, however, this can be reduced by using a $(\sin x)/x$ digital correction filter (see Chapter 4) placed before the D/A converter.

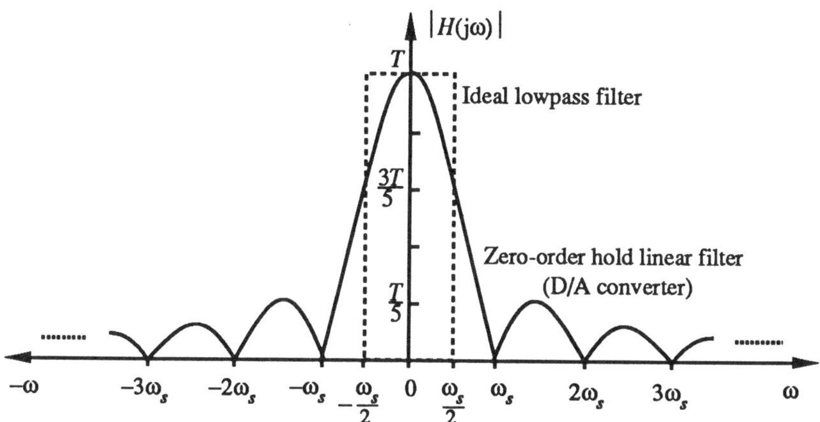

Figure 1.9 Magnitude/frequency response of D/A converter and ideal lowpass filter

❖ WE 1.4

Compute the attenuation at 20 kHz for a digital audio system due to the sin$x$/x effect introduced by the D/A converter, if the sampling frequency is (a) 44.1 kHz, and (b) 176.4 kHz.

Solution:

(a) For $f_s = 44.1$ kHz, $T = 1/44.1 \times 10^3 \approx 22.68$ μsec, $|H(j\omega)|$ when $f = 20$ kHz is given by

$$\left|H\left(j\,4\pi \times 10^4\right)\right| = \frac{\sin\left(4\pi \times 10^4 \times 22.68 \times 10^{-6}/2\right)}{4\pi \times 10^4 \times 22.68 \times 10^{-6}/2} T = 0.694\,T$$

From Figure 1.9, we deduce that $|H(j\omega)| = T$ corresponds to zero attenuation, therefore the attenuation at 20 kHz is

$$20 \log_{10} 0.694 \cong -3.2 \text{ dB}$$

(b) For $f_s = 176.4$ kHz, $T = 1/176.4 \times 10^3 \approx 5.669$ μsec, $|H(j\omega)|$ when $f = 20$ kHz is given by

$$\left|H\left(j\,4\pi \times 10^4\right)\right| = \frac{\sin\left(4\pi \times 10^4 \times 5.669 \times 10^{-6}/2\right)}{4\pi \times 10^4 \times 5.669 \times 10^{-6}/2} T = 0.979T$$

Therefore the attenuation at 20 kHz is

$$20 \log_{10} 0.979 \cong -0.2 \text{ dB}$$

1.3.1 Practical D/A Converters

A wide range of practical D/A converter chips (integrated-circuits) are readily available to enable the DSP system design approach discussed in Section 1.1.2 to be accomplished. It is particularly useful to realise that the input and output signals of most forms of D/A converter can be functionally grouped (see Figure 1.10) as summarised below.

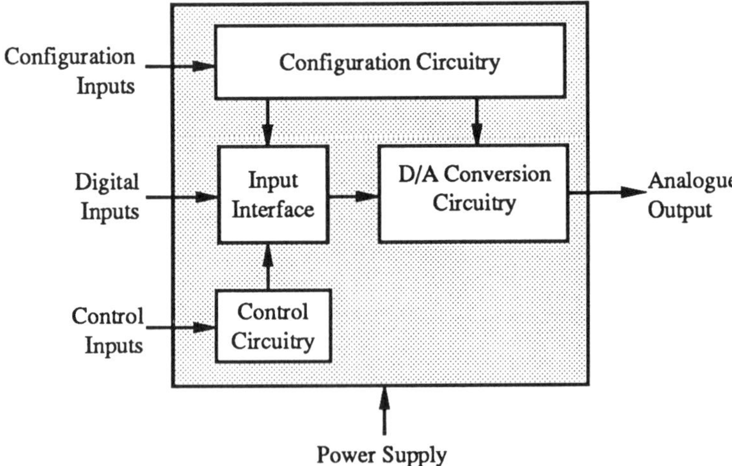

Figure 1.10 Grouping of input and output signals of practical D/A converters

Digital inputs: These can be serial or parallel connections.

Configuration inputs: Configuration inputs are used to select modes of D/A conversion, such as the digital input code format, bipolar or unipolar analogue output, and the analogue output range.

Control inputs: For D/A converter chips without a microprocessor bus interface there are no control inputs because the conversion speed is relatively fast (the analogue output is capable of following the digital input change with a delay time typically between 5 ns to 10 μs). For D/A converter chips with a microprocessor bus interface, generally $\overline{CS}$ (Chip Select) and $\overline{WR}$ ($\overline{\text{write}}$) control signals are provided, which must be active low to enable the digital inputs to be converted to an analogue output.

Analogue output: The analogue output can be unipolar or bipolar, with a current drive output or a voltage output.

Power supply: The power supply will be a single supply or a dual supply. Some D/A converter chips also require a reference voltage input.

The prime factors used in selecting an appropriate D/A converter chip for a given application are conversion speed (which can be as high as 5 ns), resolution (number of input bits which can be as high as 20 bits), accuracy (the difference between the actual analogue output and the expected output for a given binary input code) and cost.

1.4 Digital Signals

As shown in Section 1.2, sampling an analogue signal produces a discrete-time continuous-amplitude signal with its amplitude only known at the sampling instants $t = nT$. Also it was shown that quantising a discrete-time continuous-amplitude signal produces a digital signal, with its amplitude only able to take on a finite number of possible values. As the number of possible values increase, the distinction between discrete-time continuous-amplitude signals and digital signals becomes insignificant. It is therefore convenient to treat all discrete-time signals as digital signals denoted by $x(n)$. If a digital signal exists in the range $-\infty < n \leq 0$ or $0 \leq n < \infty$, it is referred to as a ***left-sided sequence*** or a ***right-sided sequence*** respectively. However, if it exists in both ranges, it is referred to as a ***two-sided sequence***.

A digital signal can be either a ***deterministic signal*** that can be predicted with certainty, or a ***random signal*** that is unpredictable. Due to ease in signal generation and the need for predictability, deterministic signals are used as stimuli for system simulation studies and testing system performance. Standard forms of some deterministic digital signals frequently used in DSP are presented below.

(a) Unit-sample sequence

The unit-sample sequence (a unit-strength impulse), shown graphically in Figure 1.11, is defined as

$$\delta(n) = \begin{cases} 1 & \text{for} \quad n = 0 \\ 0 & \text{for} \quad n \neq 0 \end{cases} \tag{1.19}$$

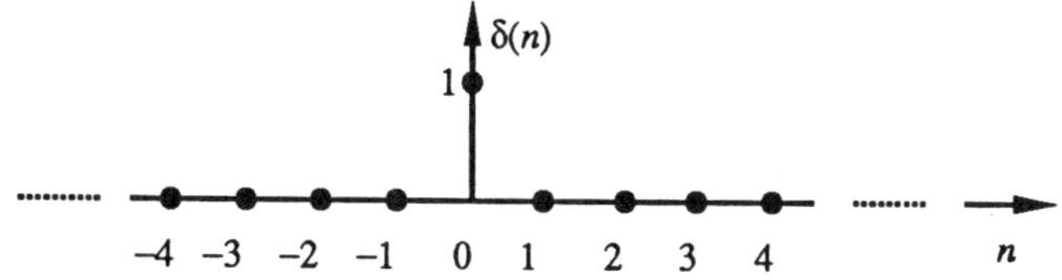

Figure 1.11 Unit-sample sequence

Note that in Section 1.2.1 the unit-strength impulse was defined in the continuous-time domain (equation (1.1)) to enable modelling of the sampling process, whereas the above definition is for the discrete-time domain.

(b) Unit-step sequence

The unit-step sequence, shown graphically in Figure 1.12, is defined as

$$u(n) = \begin{cases} 1 & \text{for} \quad n \geq 0 \\ 0 & \text{for} \quad n < 0 \end{cases} \tag{1.20}$$

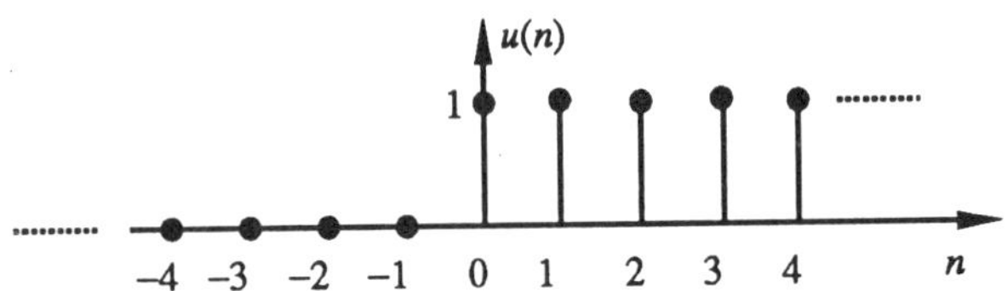

Figure 1.12 Unit-step sequence

(c) Sinusoidal sequence

The sinusoidal sequence is defined as

$$x(n) = \begin{cases} A\cos\left(2\pi f_d\, n + \theta\right) \\ \text{or} \\ A\sin\left(2\pi f_d\, n + \theta\right) \end{cases} \tag{1.21}$$

where A is the amplitude of the sinusoidal sequence, θ is the phase, and f_d is given by

$$f_d = \frac{f}{f_s} \tag{1.22}$$

where f is the frequency of the original analogue sinusoidal signal and f_s is the sampling frequency.

Figure 1.13 shows a sinusoidal sequence with f_d equal to 1/12 (i.e. 12 samples per cycle of the original analogue sinusoidal signal).

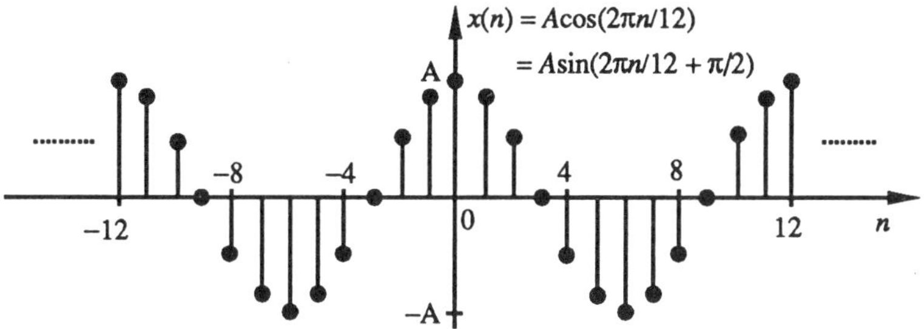

Figure 1.13 A sinusoidal sequence

(d) Complex exponential sequence
The complex exponential sequence is defined as

$$x(n) = \left(r\, e^{j2\pi f_d}\right)^n = r^n\left(\cos\ 2\pi f_d\ n + j\sin\ 2\pi f_d\ n\right) \tag{1.23}$$

It is seen that the magnitude part of the complex exponential sequence is a real exponential sequence. If $|r| < 1$, the real and imaginary parts of the complex exponential sequence are exponentially decreasing sinusoids; if $|r| > 1$, the real and imaginary parts of the complex exponential sequence are exponentially increasing sinusoids; and if $r = \pm 1$, the real and imaginary parts of the sequence are undamped sinusoids with their magnitude equal to unity. Figure 1.14 shows graphically the magnitude part of a complex exponential sequence with $r = 0.8$.

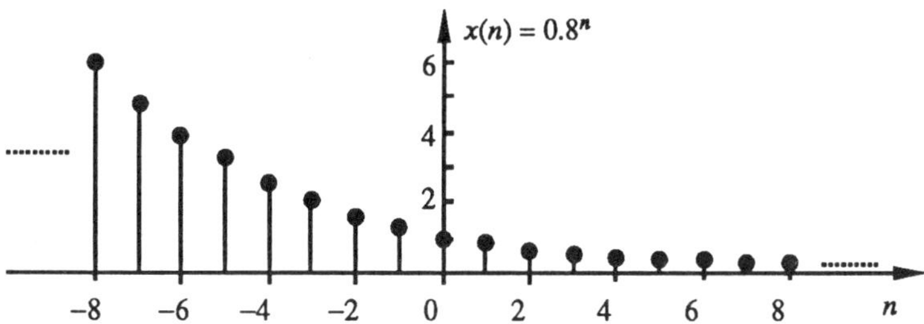

Figure 1.14 An exponential sequence

1.4.1 Basic Signal Classification

Power and energy are two fundamental measures used in the classification of signals. Since data values are represented by voltage levels in the DSP circuitry, each number can be viewed as carrying an instantaneous power of $x^2(n)$.

Therefore, for a physical digital signal with $x(n) = 0$ for $n < 0$, the average power is given by

$$P = \frac{1}{N} \sum_{n=0}^{N-1} x^2(n) \tag{1.24}$$

If $x(n)$ is a complex sequence, then the average power is given by

$$P = \frac{1}{N} \sum_{n=0}^{N-1} |x(n)|^2 \tag{1.25}$$

In the above average power equations, N is the number of samples in one period of a periodic signal, such as sinusoidal waves satisfying the periodicity condition of $x(n+N) = x(n)$. It is convenient to consider that N extends to infinity for aperiodic signals such as a single short pulse with no value of N to be found to satisfy the periodicity condition. Consequently, for periodic signals, the average power is equal to a finite value, i.e. equal to the average power over a single period. For aperiodic pulse-like signals, the average power tends to zero as N tends to infinity. Periodic signals are therefore called ***power signals***.

Since power is the rate of expending energy, it follows that the energy of a digital signal is given by

$$E = \sum_{n} |x(n)|^2 \tag{1.26}$$

As n tends to infinity, the energy of periodic signals tends to infinity, whereas the energy of aperiodic pulse-like signals tends a finite value. Consequently, these aperiodic pulse-like signals are called ***energy signals***.

❖ WE 1.5

Given that the analogue signal $x(t) = 2\sin(2\pi 200t) + 0.5\cos(2\pi 200t)$ is sampled at a rate of 800 samples per second, determine the average power and energy per period of the digital signal.

Solution:

With the sampling period given as $T = 1/f_s = 1/800 = 1.25$ ms, the digital signal, $x^*(t)$, equals $x(t)$ at $t = nT = 1.25\times10^{-3}n$ seconds, i.e.

$$x^*(t) = 2\sin\left(2\pi 200 \times 1.25 \times 10^{-3} n\right) + 0.5\cos\left(2\pi 200 \times 1.25 \times 10^{-3} n\right) \text{ V}$$

This equation generates a periodic sequence of {0.5V, 2V, −0.5V, −2V}. Applying equation (1.24) with 4 samples in one period, the average power is given by

$$P = \frac{1}{4}\sum_{n=0}^{3} x(n)^2$$

$$= \frac{1}{4}\left[0.5^2 + 2^2 + (-0.5)^2 + (-2)^2\right] = 2.125 \text{ watts}$$

Using equation (1.26), E will tend to an infinite value as n tends to infinity. Each cycle produces 8.5 Joules of energy, and since the signal is periodic having an infinite number of cycles, the energy of a periodic signal is therefore infinite.

*****

Another measure used in the classification of signals is their symmetrical characteristic. A digital signal is a ***symmetric sequence*** (even function), if it satisfies the relation

$$x(n) = x(-n) \tag{1.27}$$

Equation (1.27) implies that the sequence is symmetric with respect to $n = 0$ as shown in Figure 1.15(a).

Similarly a digital signal is an ***anti-symmetric sequence*** (odd function) if it satisfies the relation

$$x(n) = -x(-n) \tag{1.28}$$

An example of an anti-symmetric sequence is shown in Figure 1.15(b).

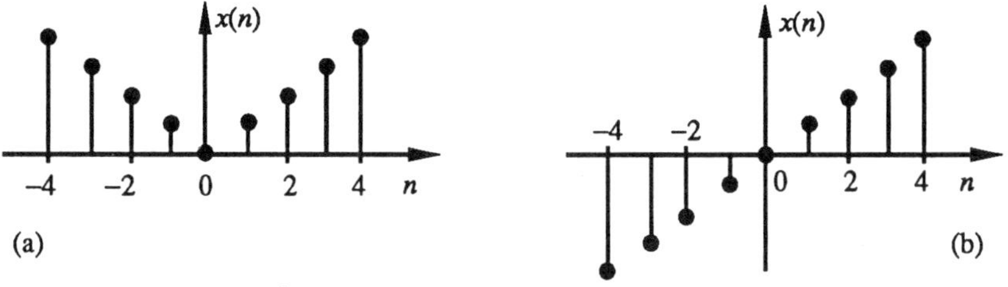

Figure 1.15 (a) A symmetric sequence; (b) An anti-symmetric sequence

It is possible that signal $x(n)$ is neither even nor odd, however, such a signal can always be decomposed into an even sequence, $x_e(n)$, plus an odd sequence, $x_o(n)$. That is

$$x(n) = x_e(n) + x_o(n) \tag{1.29}$$

where

$$x_e(n) = \frac{1}{2}[x(n) + x(-n)] \tag{1.30}$$

and

$$x_o(n) = \frac{1}{2}[x(n) - x(-n)] \tag{1.31}$$

❖ **WE 1.6**
Determine the even and odd digital signal sequences that make up the discrete-time unit-step signal.

Solution:
Figure 1.12 shows the discrete-time unit-step signal. Using equation (1.30) we obtain the discrete-time signal $x_e(n)$ shown below:

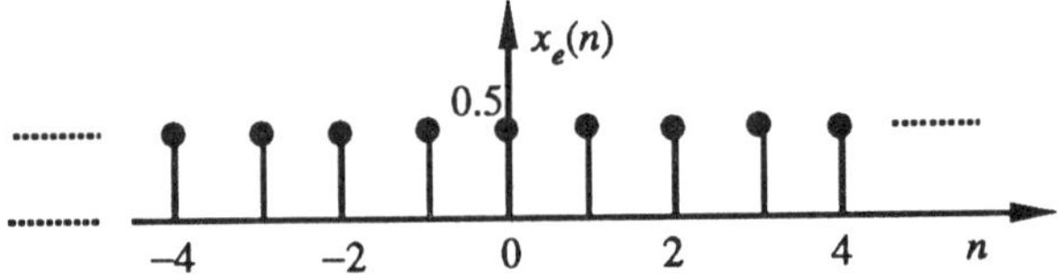

Using equation (1.31) we obtain the discrete-time signal $x_o(n)$ shown below:

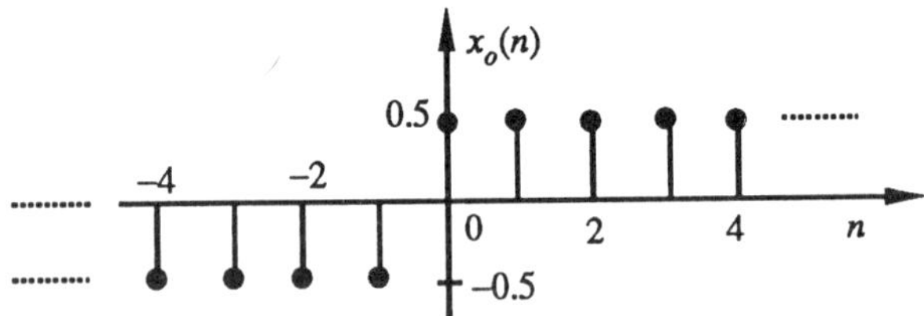

Clearly adding the discrete-time signals $x_e(n)$ and $x_o(n)$, on a sample-by-sample basis, produces the discrete-time unit-step signal.

*****

1.4.2 Signal Manipulations

DSP is essentially concerned with the manipulation of digital sequences, and implementation is generally based on a combination of some of the basic mathematical operations presented in this section.

(a) Addition/Subtraction

Addition/subtraction of two sequences was used in Section 1.4.1 to decompose a digital signal into an even sequence (equation (1.30)) and an odd sequence (equation (1.31)). Addition/subtraction of two digital signals, $x_1(n)$ and $x_2(n)$, is defined as

$$y(n) = x_1(n) \pm x_2(n) \tag{1.32}$$

where $y(n)$ is the sum or difference of the two digital signals computed on a sample-by-sample basis.

❖ WE 1.7

Plot the periodic discrete-time signal $y(n) = 2\cos(2\pi f_1 n/f_s) - \cos(2\pi f_2 n/f_s)$, where $f_1 = 200$ Hz, $f_2 = 400$ Hz, and $f_s = 1$ kHz.

Solution:

$$y(n) = 2\cos\left(\frac{2\pi 200\, n}{1000}\right) - \cos\left(\frac{2\pi 400\, n}{1000}\right)$$

$$= 2\cos\left(\frac{2\pi n}{5}\right) - \cos\left(\frac{4\pi n}{5}\right)$$

$$= x_1(n) - x_2(n)$$

n	$x_1(n)$	$x_2(n)$	$y(n)$	
0	2	1	1	1st period
1	0.618	– 0.809	1.427	
2	–1.618	0.309	–1.927	
3	–1.618	0.309	–1.927	
4	0.618	– 0.809	1.427	
5	2	1	1	2nd period
6	0.618	– 0.809	1.427	
:	:	:	:	:

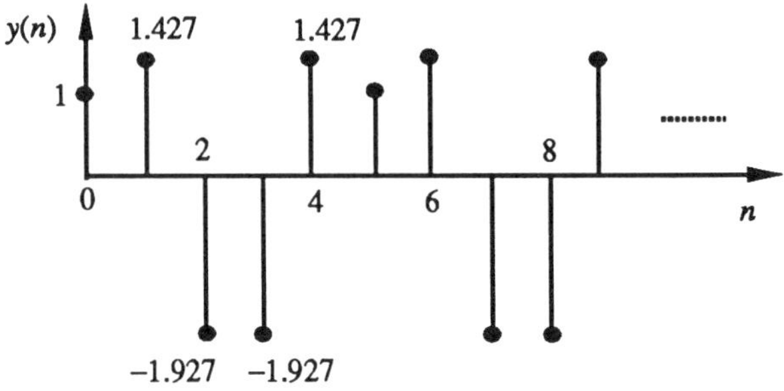

*****

(b) Multiplication

Multiplication of two digital signals, $x_1(n)$ and $x_2(n)$, is defined as

$$y(n) = x_1(n) \times x_2(n) \tag{1.33}$$

where $y(n)$ is the product of the two signals computed on a sample-by-sample basis.

❖ WE 1.8

Plot the periodic discrete-time signal $y(n) = 2\cos(2\pi n/5)\cos(4\pi n/5)$.

Solution:

$$y(n) = 2\cos\left(\frac{2\pi n}{5}\right)\cos\left(\frac{4\pi n}{5}\right)$$

$$= x_1(n) \times x_2(n)$$

n	$x_1(n)$	$x_2(n)$	$y(n)$	
0	2	1	2	1st period
1	0.618	− 0.809	− 0.5	
2	−1.618	0.309	− 0.5	
3	−1.618	0.309	− 0.5	
4	0.618	− 0.809	− 0.5	
5	2	1	2	2nd period
6	0.618	− 0.809	− 0.5	
:	:	:	:	:

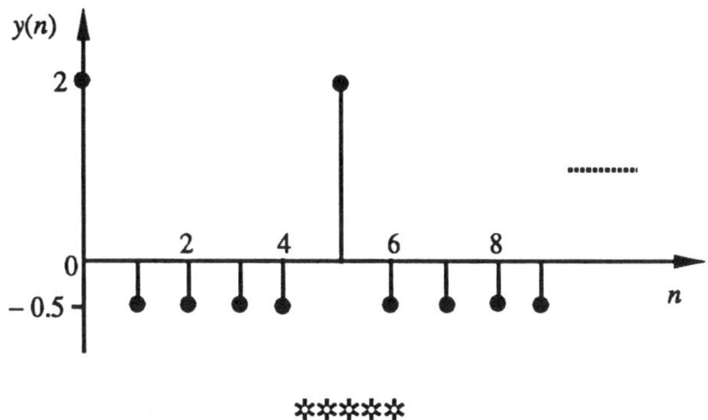

*****

(c) Scaling
Scaling of a digital signal $x(n)$ is defined as

$$y(n) = ax(n) \tag{1.34}$$

where a is a positive or negative constant.

❖ **WE 1.9**
Plot the discrete-time signal $y(n) = 0.5u(n)$.

***Solution*:**
Each sample amplitude shown in Figure 1.12 is scaled by a factor of 0.5 to produce the discrete-time signal $y(n) = 0.5u(n)$ shown below:

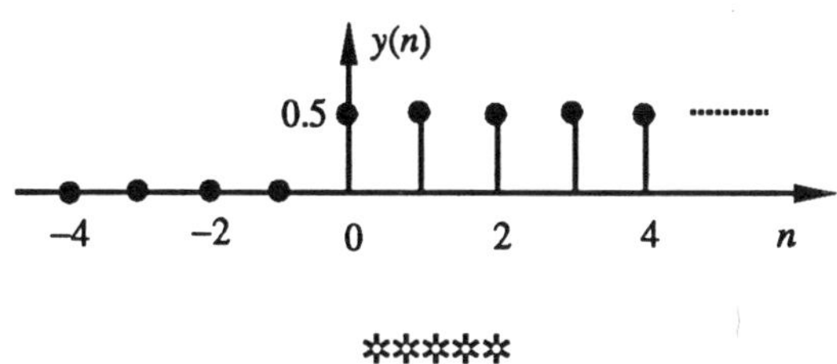

*****

(d) Time shifting by $\pm kT$
Time shifts (delays or advances in time) of a digital signal sequence $x(n)$ are defined as

$$y(n) = x(n \pm k) \tag{1.35}$$

where k denotes the shift interval (multiples of the sampling period). The shifted digital sequence corresponding to $x(n-k)$ signifies that $y(n)$ is a time delayed version of $x(n)$, whereas $x(n+k)$ signifies that $y(n)$ is a time advanced version of $x(n)$.

The time shifting operation and the principle of superposition were applied to the unit-impulse to obtain the unit-impulse train $\delta_T(t)$ shown in Figure 1.4.

Clearly in practice it is not possible to advance the sequence in real-time because knowledge of future sample values does not exist. However, the advance of a sequence in non-real-time may be implemented by shifting the previously acquired sequence stored in the memory of the DSP system.

❖ **WE 1.10**

Express the discrete-time signal sequence $\{1, 0, 2, 0, 3\}$ as (a) a sum of weighted unit-sample sequences appropriately shifted in time, and (b) a sum of weighted unit-step sequences appropriately shifted in time.

Solution:

(a) The non-zero sample values in the given discrete-time signal sequence can be considered to be weighted unit-samples appropriately shifted in time, as shown below:

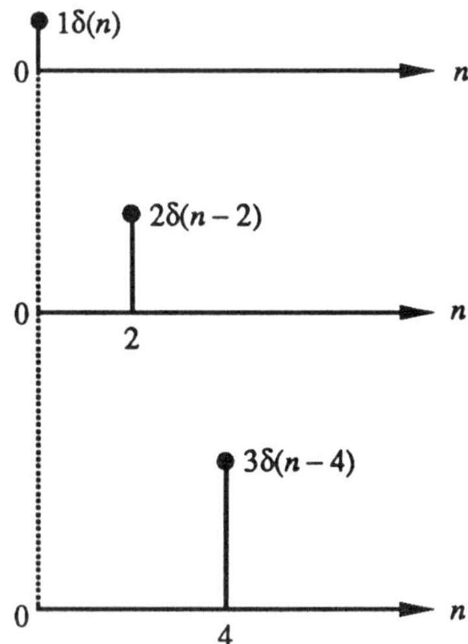

The sum of the above three signals on a sample-by-sample basis produces the discrete-time signal $y(n) = \delta(n) + 2\delta(n-2) + 3\delta(n-4)$, which is shown in the following diagram.

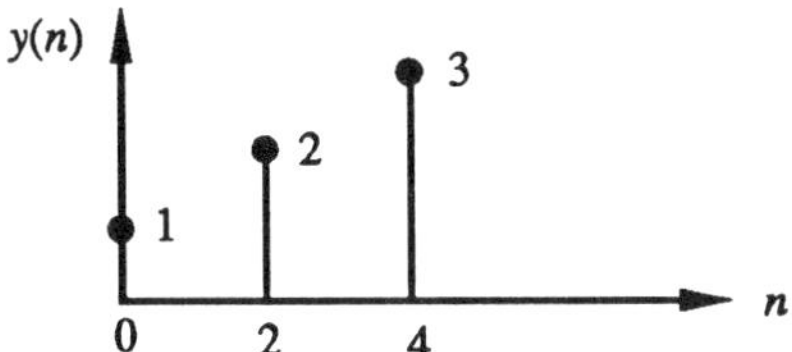

(b) A weighted unit-sample shifted in time by k sampling periods can be expressed as the sum of two equally weighted unit-step sequences appropriately shifted in time, i.e.

$$A\delta(n-k) = A[u(n-k) - u(n-k-1)]$$

It follows that

$$\delta(n) = u(n) - u(n-1)$$

$$2\delta(n-2) = 2[u(n-2) - u(n-3)]$$

$$3\delta(n-4) = 3[u(n-4) - u(n-5)]$$

Hence

$$y(n) = u(n) - u(n-1) + 2u(n-2) - 2u(n-3) + 3u(n-4) - 3u(n-5)$$

*****

(e) Folding

The operation of folding a digital signal sequence $x(n)$ is defined as

$$y(n) = x(-n) \tag{1.36}$$

where $y(n)$ is the reflection (rotation through 180°) of $x(n)$ about the sample at $n = 0$ (the pivotal axis).

❖ WE 1.11

Given that the digital signal sequence $x(n) = n[u(n+3) - u(n-3)]$, plot $x(n)$ and $x(-n)$.

Solution:

The given digital signal sequence can be built up in stages as shown in the following diagram.

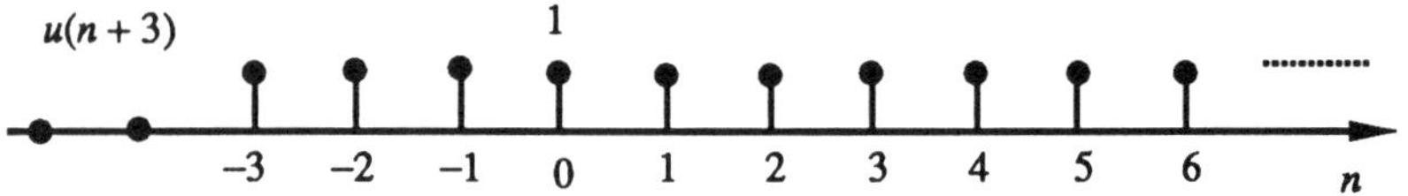

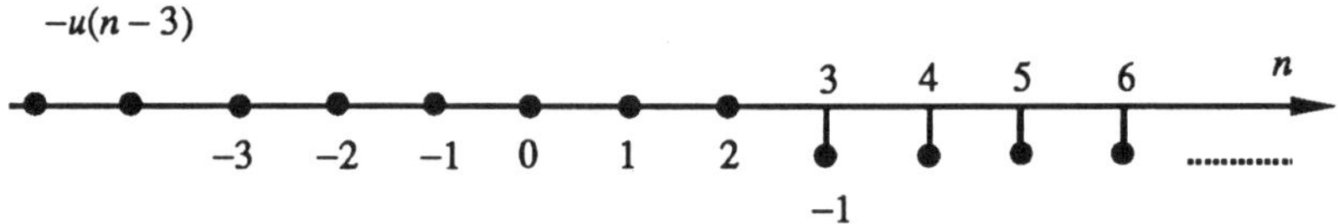

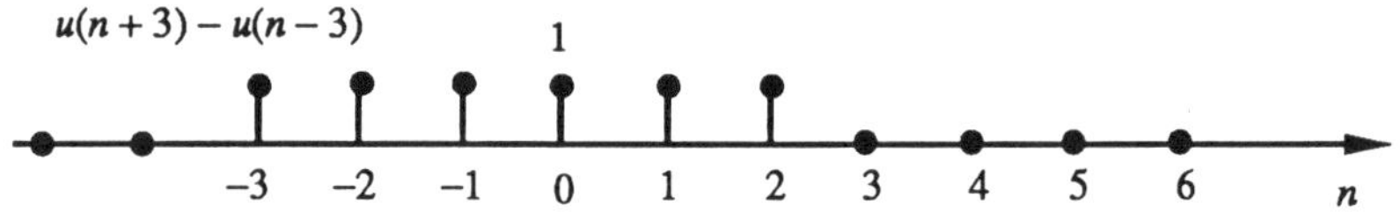

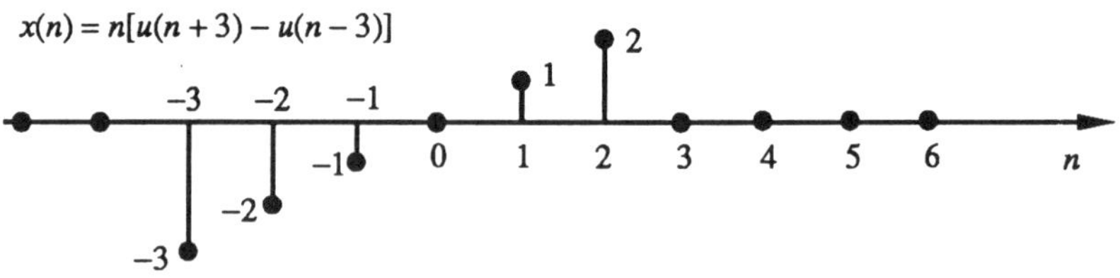

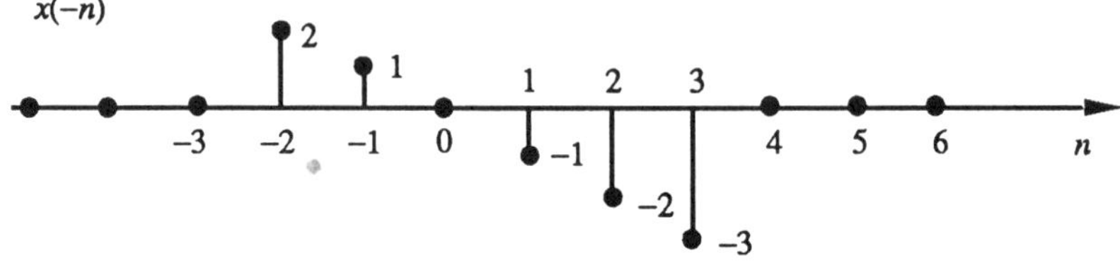

*****

(f) Down-sampling

Down-sampling (decimation) of a digital signal $x(n)$ by a factor D is the operation of discarding $D - 1$ samples for every D samples of $x(n)$ and is defined as

$$y(n) = x(nD) \tag{1.37}$$

❖ **WE 1.12**

The input to a 3-to-1 down-sampler is $x(n) = n/4$, plot the input and output waveforms, and determine the effective sampling frequency.

***Solution*:**

$D = 3$, therefore we discard 2 samples in every 3 samples.

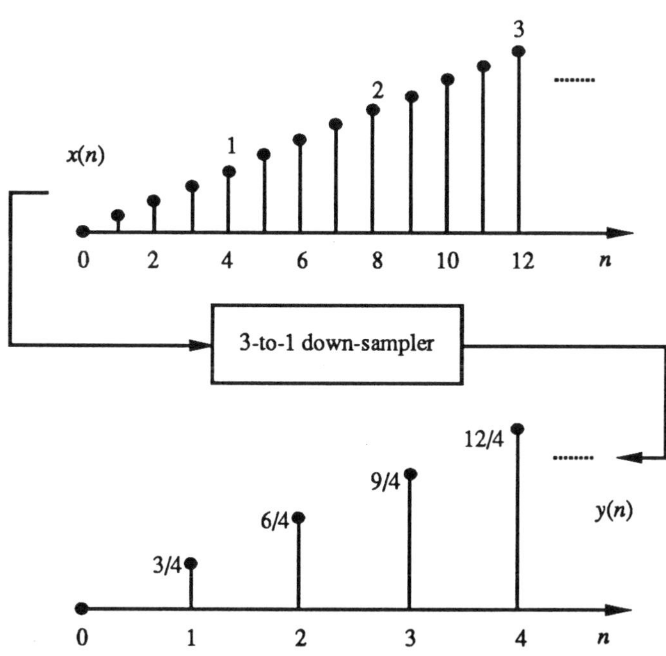

The effective sampling frequency is one-third of the sampling frequency for sequence $x(n)$.

*****

(g) Up-sampling

Up-sampling (interpolation) of a digital signal $x(n)$ by a factor I is the operation of inserting $I-1$ equally spaced samples between successive samples of $x(n)$. A convenient sample value to insert is zero, and in this case the output of the up-sampler is defined as

$$y(n) = \begin{cases} x\left(\dfrac{n}{I}\right) & \text{for} \quad n = 0, \pm I, \pm 2I, \pm 3I, \ldots \\ 0 & \text{otherwise} \end{cases} \tag{1.38}$$

❖ **WE 1.13**

If the output waveform of WE 1.12 is applied to a 1-to-3 up-sampler, plot the output waveform and determine the effective sampling frequency.

***Solution*:**

$I = 3$, therefore we may insert 2 equally spaced zero-value samples between the samples of the $y(n)$ signal of WE1.12.

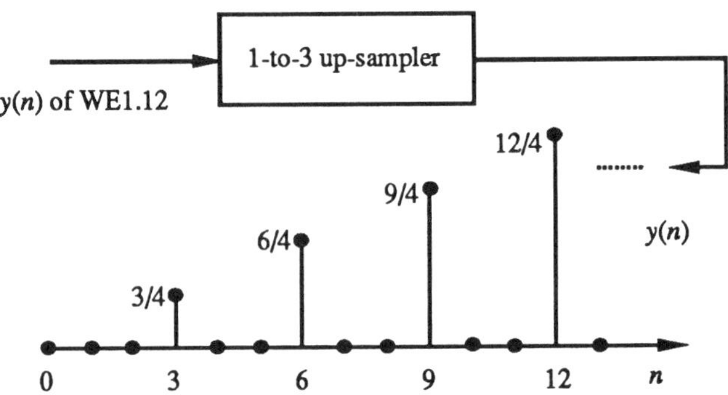

The effective sampling frequency is three times the sampling frequency for the sequence $y(n)$ of WE1.12.

*****

1.5 DSP Systems

A DSP system can, in a broad sense, be considered as any hardware and/or software system capable of executing an algorithm on a digital input sequence $x(n)$ to produce a digital output sequence $y(n)$. The general structure of a DSP system is shown in Figure 1.16, where the present output value at any sampling instant is not only a function of the present input sample value and previous input sample values, but also a function of previous output sample values due to the presence of the feedback. Although the processing algorithm can be either linear or non-linear, most DSP applications involve linear processing algorithms as they are much easier to design and implement.

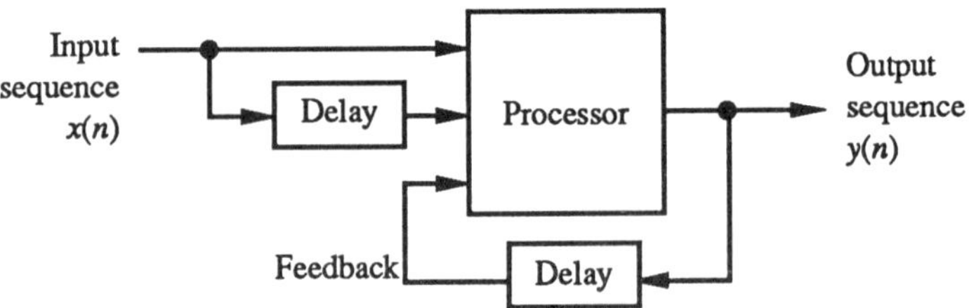

Figure 1.16 General structure of a DSP system

For linear digital signal processing, the relationship between the input and output of a DSP system is described by the ***general difference equation***

$$y(n) = \sum_{k=0}^{p} a_k\, x(n-k) - \sum_{k=1}^{q} b_k\, y(n-k) \qquad (1.39)$$

where a_k and b_k are the feedforward and feedback constant coefficients. This general difference equation states that the present output value $y(n)$ is a linear combination of scaled versions of the present and previous input values, $\{x(n), x(n-1), ..., x(n-p)\}$, and scaled versions of previous output values $\{y(n-1), y(n-2), ..., y(n-q)\}$. The dependency on the previous output values due to the presence of the feedback results in a ***recursive DSP system***. The structure shown in Figure 1.17 is often referred to as the ***direct form*** of implementation.

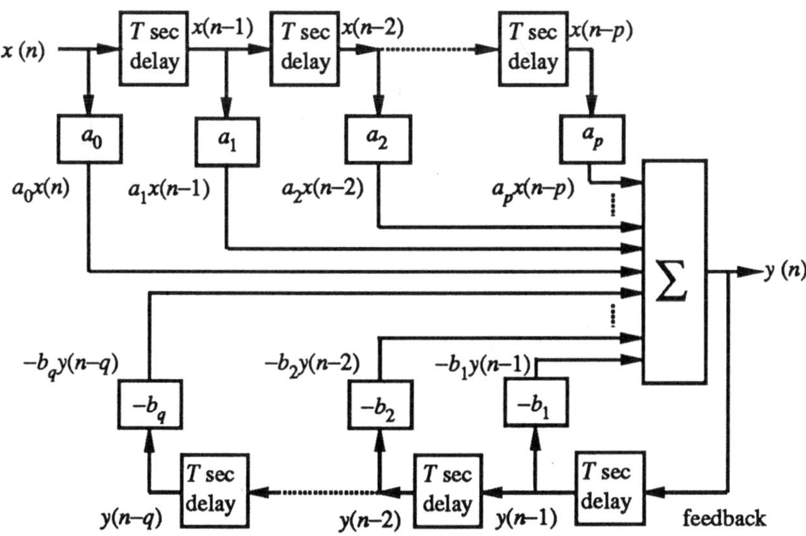

Figure 1.17 Block diagram of recursive DSP system

If the effect of the feedback in Figure 1.17 is removed by making all feedback constant coefficients b_k in the general difference equation equal to zero, then a ***non-recursive DSP system*** is formed with the present output value $y(n)$ depending only on the present and previous input values. The top half of Figure 1.17, which is the non-recursive DSP system in block diagram form, can be redrawn as shown in Figure 1.18 using an alternative form of representation known as the ***signal flow graph***.

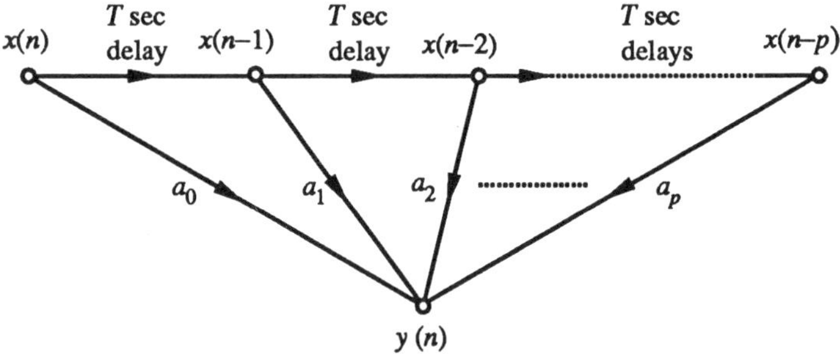

Figure 1.18 Signal flow graph of non-recursive DSP system

Clearly, using branches and nodes the signal flow graph presents the same structural information as the block diagram. In the signal flow graph, a branch is directed from one node to another to represent the signal processing operation performed on the signal flowing along the branch, such as multiplication by a constant, a delay by one sampling period, or some other signal processing operations; a node is used to represent a signal value equal to the sum of the processed signals flowing along all of the branches connected to the node.

❖ WE 1.14

For the signal flow graph of a DSP system shown below, determine:

(a) The difference equation of the system.
(b) The response to a unit-impulse input for $0 \le n \le 6$.
(c) The difference equation if the feedback link is removed.
(d) The response to a unit-impulse input with the feedback link removed.

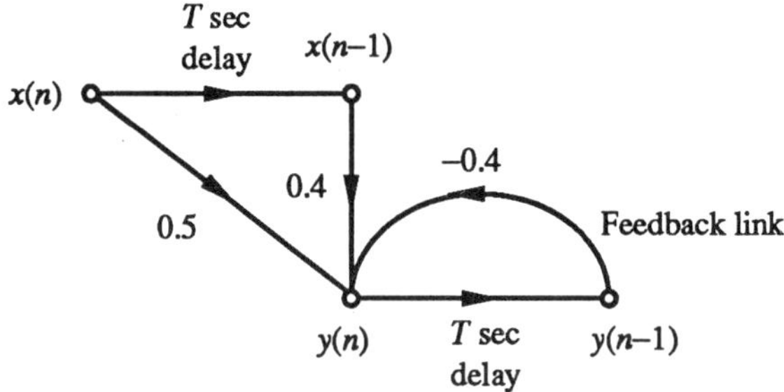

Solution:

(a) $y(n) = 0.5\,x(n) + 0.4\,x(n-1) - 0.4\,y(n-1)$

(b)

n	$0.5x(n)$	$0.4x(n-1)$	$-0.4y(n-1)$	$y(n)$
0	0.5	0	0	0.5
1	0	0.4	−0.2	0.2
2	0	0	−0.08	−0.08
3	0	0	0.032	0.032
4	0	0	−0.0128	−0.00128
5	0	0	0.00512	0.00512
6	0	0	−0.002048	−0.002048
⋮	⋮	⋮	⋮	⋮

(c) $y(n) = 0.5\,x(n) + 0.4\,x(n-1)$

(d) The unit-impulse response of the system with no feedback corresponds to the coefficient values of the difference equation, i.e. for this example, the response is

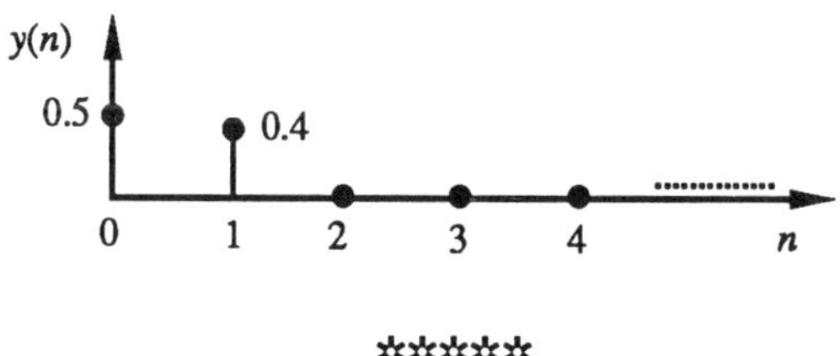

*****

From WE 1.14, it is seen that the unit-impulse response of a recursive system is infinite in duration due to the output being continuously fed back to generate new outputs (even after the input source becomes zero-valued), but in contrast the unit-impulse response of a non-recursive system is finite in duration and the output values equal the feedforward constant coefficients a_k. Hence recursive systems are referred to as ***Infinite Impulse Response*** (**IIR**) systems, and non-recursive systems are referred to as ***Finite Impulse Response*** (**FIR**) systems.

1.5.1 Properties of a DSP System

The applicability of the difference equation as the description of a DSP system depends on the properties of linearity and time-invariance. Furthermore, the properties of stability and causality are required for the system to be practically realisable. These properties are summarised in this section.

(a) Linearity
A DSP system is said to be linear if the response of the system to an input consisting of a number of weighted signals is a linear superposition of the

responses obtained by applying the weighted signals individually. Hence if $x_1(n)$ and $x_2(n)$ are two arbitrary input sequences, a_1 and a_2 are two arbitrary constants, and $y_1(n)$ and $y_2(n)$ are the output sequences in response to the two input sequences applied individually, the condition for the DSP system to be linear is then given by

$$F\left[a_1 x_1(n) + a_2 x_2(n)\right] = a_1 F\left[x_1(n)\right] + a_2 F\left[x_1(n)\right]$$

$$= a_1 y_1(n) + a_2 y_2(n) \qquad (1.40)$$

where $F[\,]$ denotes a signal processing function performed by the DSP system.

❖ **WE 1.15**

Determine whether the DSP systems described by the following equations are linear:

(a) $y(n) = \frac{1}{N} \sum_{k=0}^{N-1} x(n-k)$

(b) $y(n) = [x(n)]^2$

Solution:

(a) Let $y_1(n) = \frac{1}{N} \sum_{k=0}^{N-1} x_1(n-k)$, and $y_2(n) = \frac{1}{N} \sum_{k=0}^{N-1} x_2(n-k)$

then

$$y(n) = y_1(n) + y_2(n) = \frac{1}{N} \sum_{k=0}^{N-1} x_1(n-k) + \frac{1}{N} \sum_{k=0}^{N-1} x_2(n-k)$$

$$= \frac{1}{N} \sum_{k=0}^{N-1} \left[x_1(n-k) + x_2(n-k)\right]$$

$$= \frac{1}{N} \sum_{k=0}^{N-1} x(n-k)$$

i.e. this DSP system is linear.

(b) $y(n) = \left[x_1(n) + x_2(n)\right]^2$

$$= \left[x_1(n)\right]^2 + 2x_1(n)\,x_2(n) + \left[x_2(n)\right]^2$$

$$\neq \left[x_1(n)\right]^2 + \left[x_2(n)\right]^2$$

i.e. this DSP system is non-linear.

(b) Time-invariance
A DSP system is said to be time-invariant if the relationship between the input and output does not change with time. Hence in this case

$$\text{if } y(n) = F[x(n)] \qquad \text{then } y(n-k) = F[x(n-k)] \tag{1.41}$$

❖ WE 1.16
Determine whether the DSP systems described by the following equations are time-invariant:
(a) $y(n) = x(n) - ax(n-1)$
(b) $y(n) = x(-n)$

Solution:
(a) Let $x(n) = \{A_1, A_2, A_3, A_4, A_5, A_6, \ldots\}$, then

$$-ax(n-1) = \left\{0, -aA_1, -aA_2, -aA_3, -aA_4, \ldots\right\}$$

$$y(n) = \left\{A_1, -aA_1 + A_2, -aA_2 + A_3, -aA_3 + A_4, \ldots\right\}$$

Let a delay of 2 sampling periods be introduced:

$$y(n-2) = \left\{0,\ 0,\ A_1, -aA_1 + A_2, -aA_2 + A_3, \ldots\right\}$$

$$x(n-2) = \left\{0,\ 0,\ A_1,\ A_2,\ A_3,\ A_4,\ A_5, \ldots\right\}$$

$$x(n-2-1) = \left\{0, 0, 0,\ A_1,\ A_2,\ A_3,\ A_4,\ A_5, \ldots\right\}$$

$$-ax(n-3) = \left\{0,\ 0,\ 0, -aA_1, -aA_2, -aA_3, -aA_4, -aA_5, \ldots\right\}$$

$$x(n-2) - ax(n-3) = \{0,\ 0,\ A_1,\ -aA_1 + A_2,\ -aA_2 + A_3, \ldots\}$$

$$= y(n-2)$$

Therefore this DSP system is time-invariant.

(b) Let $x(n) = \{A_1, A_2, A_3, A_4, A_5, A_6, \ldots\}$, then

$$y(n) = x(-n) = \{\ldots,\ A_6,\ A_5,\ A_4,\ A_3,\ A_2,\ A_1\}$$

Let a delay of 2 sampling periods be introduced:

$$y(n-2) = \{0,\ 0, \ldots,\ A_6,\ A_5,\ A_4,\ A_3,\ A_2,\ A_1\}$$

$$x(n-2) = \{0, 0, A_1, A_2, A_3, A_4, A_5, A_6, \ldots\}$$

$$x(-(n-2)) = \{\ldots\ A_6,\ A_5,\ A_4,\ A_3,\ A_2,\ A_1, 0, 0,\}$$

$$\neq y(n-2)$$

Therefore this DSP system is not time-invariant.

*****

(c) Stability

A DSP system is said to be stable if any input of finite amplitude produces a corresponding output of finite amplitude. In practice, unstable DSP systems generally result in numerical overflow in the computation of the $y(n)$ output values, which is clearly a condition that must be avoided. Stability considerations are described in Chapter 2, Section 2.4.1.

❖ WE 1.17

Determine the stability condition for the DSP systems described by the following equations:

(a) $y(n) = a^n u(n)$

(b) $y(n) = x(n) + by(n-1)$

Solution:

(a) For stability, $|a|$ must be less than or equal to 1, because when $|a|$ is greater than 1, $y(n)$ tends to an infinite value as n approaches infinity.

(b) For stability the range of b must be $(-1 < b < 1)$ to ensure that $y(n)$ takes on a finite value for any finite input signal $x(n)$. Effectively b is a feedback fraction used to ensure that a stable output signal is obtained.

*****

(d) Causality
A DSP system is said to be causal if the present output value at any instant of time is dependent only on present and previous input and/or previous output values, and is not dependent on future input values.

In real-time signal processing applications, a non-causal system is practically unrealisable, as it is not possible to know future input values. However, in non-real-time processing with all signal values available in memory, a non-causal system is realisable as an off-line process.

❖ **WE 1.18**
Determine whether the DSP systems described by the following equations are causal:
(a) $y(n) = x(n) - ax(n-1)$
(b) $y(n) = x(-n)$

***Solution*:**
(a) $y(n)$ is computed using only the present input sample value, $x(n)$, and a scaled previous input sample value, $ax(n-1)$, therefore this DSP system is causal.

(b) $y(n)$ is determined using the corresponding sample value located on the negative time axis, and this DSP system is therefore non-causal, since sample values can not be obtained before $t = 0$.

*****

1.5.2 Convolution-Summation

It was shown in Section 1.2.1 that a sampled signal in the continuous-time domain can be modelled by the product of the analogue input signal and a unit-strength impulse train, that is

$$x^*(t) = x(t) \times \delta_T(t) = x(t) \sum_{n=-\infty}^{\infty} \delta(t - nT)$$

Expressing the above equation in the discrete-time domain for a physical signal with $x(t) = 0$ for $t < 0$ yields

$$x(n) = \sum_{k=0}^{\infty} x(k)\,\delta(n-k) \tag{1.42}$$

where $x(k)$ is the amplitude of a digital sequence $x(n)$ at $n = k$, $\delta(n - k)$ is the unit-sample sequence delayed in time by k sampling periods. With $\delta(n - k)$ equal to unity at $n = k$ and equal to zero elsewhere in equation (1.42), a digital signal can be viewed as consisting of a set of weighted unit-sample sequences appropriately delayed in time.

Let the unit-sample response of a system be $h(n)$; if the system is linear and time-invariant, then each individual weighted unit-sample sequence $x(k)\delta(n - k)$ will produce a weighted unit-sample response correspondingly delayed in time, $x(k)h(n - k)$, and the output of the system $y(n)$ at a particular sampling instant of time can be viewed as the superposition of the amplitudes of all the weighted and delayed unit-sample responses at that time. Hence

$$y(n) = \sum_{k=0}^{\infty} x(k)\;h(n-k) \tag{1.43}$$

This equation is known as the convolution-summation operation, and is denoted by the $*$ symbol, that is

$$y(n) = x(n) * h(n) \tag{1.44}$$

The convolution-summation operation therefore allows the output of a linear time-invariant system, described by its unit-sample response, to be determined for any given input signal.

❖ WE 1.19

For a DSP system described by a unit-sample response of {3, 1, 0.5}, determine the output sequence of the system in response to the digital input sequence {2, 1, 0, −1, −2}

***Solution*:**

Table 1.1 illustrates the calculation of the convolution-summation operation using the following steps:

Step 1: Shifting the unit-sample response to the right by k sampling periods to obtain the delayed unit-sample responses $h(n - k)$.

Step 2: Multiplying $h(n - k)$ by $x(k)$ to obtain the weighted and delayed unit-sample responses $x(k)h(n - k)$.

Step 3: Adding the amplitudes of the weighted and delayed unit-sample responses at each sampling instant.

Table 1.1

n	0	1	2	3	4	5	6	≥7
$x(n)$	2	1	0	−1	−2	0	0	0
$x(0)h(n-0)$	6	2	1	0	0	0	0	0
$x(1)h(n-1)$	0	3	1	0.5	0	0	0	0
$x(2)h(n-2)$	0	0	0	0	0	0	0	0
$x(3)h(n-3)$	0	0	0	−3	−1	−0.5	0	0
$x(4)h(n-4)$	0	0	0	0	−6	−2	−1	0
$y(n)$	6	5	2	−2.5	−7	−2.5	−1	0

Another way to calculate the convolution values is to view the delayed unit-sample response $h(n-k)$ as equivalent to $h(-(k-n))$, thereby implementing the process as a folded unit-sample response delayed in time by n sampling periods. Table 1.2 illustrates this method; it uses the following steps:

Step 1: Folding the unit-sample response delayed in time by n sampling periods to obtain $h(-(k-n))$.
Step 2: Multiplying $h(-(k-n))$ by $x(n)$ to obtain $x(n)h(-(k-n))$.
Step 3: Adding the product values obtained in step 2.

Table 1.2

n	−2	−1	0	1	2	3	4	5	6	≥7	$y(n)$
$x(n)$	0	0	2	1	0	−1	−2	0	0	0	
$h(-(k))$	0.5	1	3	0	0	0	0	0	0	0	$y(0) = (2\times3) + (0\times1) + (0\times0.5) = 6$
$h(-(k-1))$	0	0.5	1	3	0	0	0	0	0	0	$y(1) = (1\times3) + (2\times1) + (0\times0.5) = 5$
$h(-(k-2))$	0	0	0.5	1	3	0	0	0	0	0	$y(2) = (0\times3) + (1\times1) + (2\times0.5) = 2$
$h(-(k-3))$	0	0	0	0.5	1	3	0	0	0	0	$y(3) = (-1\times3) + (0\times1) + (1\times0.5) = -2.5$
$h(-(k-4))$	0	0	0	0	0.5	1	3	0	0	0	$y(4) = (-2\times3) + (-1\times1) + (0\times0.5) = -7$
$h(-(k-5))$	0	0	0	0	0	0.5	1	3	0	0	$y(5) = (0\times3) + (-2\times1) + (-1\times0.5) = -2.5$
$h(-(k-6))$	0	0	0	0	0	0	0.5	1	3	0	$y(6) = (0\times3) + (0\times1) + (-2\times0.5) = -1$
$h(-(k-7))$	0	0	0	0	0	0	0	0.5	1	3	$y(7) = (0\times3) + (0\times1) + (0\times0.5) = 0$

Note: It is observed that the duration of the output sequence produced by the convolution-summation operation is equal to the sum of the lengths of the unit-sample sequence and the input sequence, minus one.

*****

1.5.3 Interconnection of DSP Systems

The convolution-summation operation possesses a number of useful properties that can be applied to enable the interconnection of small DSP systems to form a larger DSP system or to decompose a large DSP system into smaller subsystems.

(a) Commutative property
Assuming that the unit-sample sequence, $h(n)$, is equal to 0 for n less than zero, and that the input signal sequence, $x(n)$, is also equal to 0 for n less than zero, then the commutative property can be expressed as

$$y(n) = \sum_{k=0}^{\infty} x(k)\, h(n-k) = \sum_{k=0}^{\infty} h(k)\, x(n-k)$$

or $\quad x(n) * h(n) = h(n) * x(n)$ (1.45)

As shown in Figure 1.19, the commutative property implies that connecting an input sequence $x(n)$ to a system with a unit-sample sequence $h(n)$ is equivalent to connecting an input sequence $h(n)$ to a system with a unit-sample response of $x(n)$.

$x(n) \rightarrow$ [$h(n)$] $\rightarrow y(n)$ ⟷ $h(n) \rightarrow$ [$x(n)$] $\rightarrow y(n)$

Figure 1.19 Commutation of input sequence and unit-sample response

❖ **WE 1.20**
Repeat WE 1.19 using $y(n) = h(n) * x(n)$.

***Solution*:**
$y(n) = h(n) * x(n)$ is computed as shown in the following table.

n	0	1	2	3	4	5	6	≥7
$h(n)$	3	1	0.5	0	0	0	0	0
$h(0)x(n-0)$	6	3	0	− 3	− 6	0	0	0
$h(1)x(n-1)$	0	2	1	0	−1	− 2	0	0
$h(2)x(n-2)$	0	0	1	0.5	0	− 0.5	− 1	0
$y(n)$	6	5	2	− 2.5	− 7	− 2.5	− 1	0

*****

(b) Associative property and serial interconnection of DSP systems
The associative property can be expressed as

$$y(n) = \left[\ldots \left[\left[x(n) * h_1(n) \right] * h_2(n) \right] \ldots * h_m(n) \right]$$

$$= x(n) * h_s(n) \qquad (1.46)$$

where

$$h_s(n) = h_1(n) * h_2(n) * \ldots h_m(n) \qquad (1.47)$$

As shown in Figure 1.20, the associative property implies that the interconnection of DSP systems in series results in a unit-impulse response of the combined system equal to the convolution-summation of the unit-impulse responses of the systems in series. Furthermore, due to the commutative property of the convolution-summation operation, the order of the systems in series can be interchanged without affecting the output.

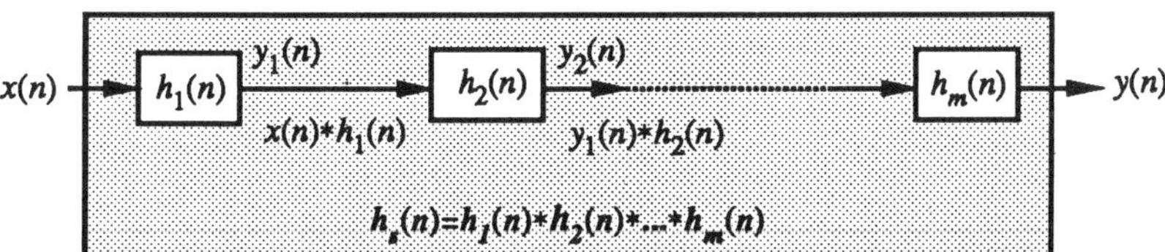

Figure 1.20 Serial interconnection of DSP systems

❖ **WE 1.21**
Two DSP systems having unit-sample responses of {2, 1, 0.5} and {2, 2, 1, 1} are connected in series. Determine the output sequence for the digital input sequence {– 2, 1}.

Solution:
(i) $h_s(n) = h_1(n) * h_2(n)$ is computed as shown in the following table.

n	0	1	2	3	4	5	≥6
$h_1(n)$	2	1	0.5	0	0	0	0
$h_1(0)h_2(n-0)$	4	4	2	2	0	0	0
$h_1(1)h_2(n-1)$	0	2	2	1	1	0	0
$h_1(2)h_2(n-2)$	0	0	1	1	0.5	0.5	0
$h_s(n)$	4	6	5	4	1.5	0.5	0

(ii) $y(n) = x(n) * h_s(n)$ is computed as shown in the following table.

n	0	1	2	3	4	5	6	≥7
$h_s(n)$	4	6	5	4	1.5	0.5	0	0
$x(0)h_s(n-0)$	−8	−12	−10	−8	−3	−1	0	0
$x(1)h_s(n-1)$	0	4	6	5	4	1.5	0.5	0
$y(n)$	−8	−8	−4	−3	1	0.5	0.5	0

*****

(c) Distributive property and parallel interconnection of DSP systems
The distributive property can be expressed as

$$y(n) = x(n) * h_1(n) + x(n) * h_2(n) + \ldots + x(n) * h_m(n)$$

$$= x(n) * h_p(n) \quad (1.48)$$

where

$$h_p(n) = \sum_{k=1}^{m} h_k(n) \quad (1.49)$$

As shown in Figure 1.21, the distributive property implies that interconnection of DSP systems in parallel results in a unit-sample response of the combined system equal to the sum of unit-sample responses of the systems operating in parallel.

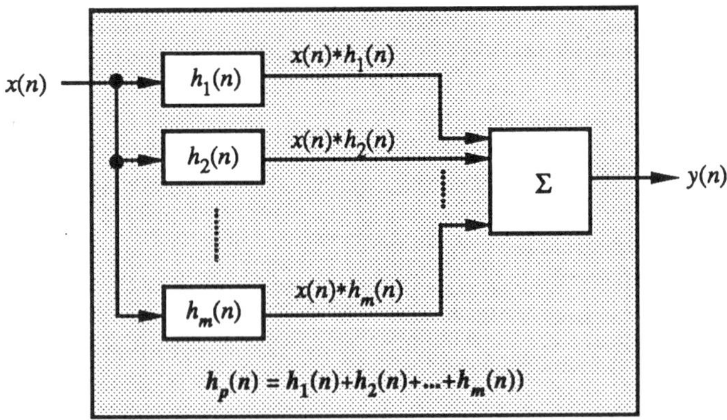

Figure 1.21 Parallel interconnection of DSP systems

❖ **WE 1.22**
Repeat WE 1.21 with the two DSP systems connected in parallel.

***Solution*:**
Applying equation (1.49) gives

$$h_p(n) = h_1(n) + h_2(n)$$

$$= \{2,\ 1, 0.5\} + \{2, 2, 1, 1\}$$

$$= \{4, 3, 1.5,\ 1\}$$

$y(n) = x(n) * h_p(n)$ is computed as shown in the following table.

n	0	1	2	3	4	≥5
$h_p(n)$	4	3	1.5	1	0	0
$x(0)h_p(n-0)$	−8	−6	−3	−2	0	0
$x(1)h_p(n-1)$	0	4	3	1.5	1	0
$y(n)$	−8	−2	0	−0.5	1	0

*****

1.6 Case Study: Realisation of an Analogue Second-order Differentiator

***Aim*:**

The aim of this case study is to demonstrate how an analogue system can be approximated by a DSP system using a design method known as the **first-difference approximation**, and how a number of the principles presented in this chapter may be used to determine the performance of the derived DSP system.

***Problem*:**

The analogue circuit shown in Figure 1.22(a) is a second-order differentiator. Design an equivalent DSP system in the form of a signal flow graph.

Using the triangular input waveform shown in Figure 1.22(b), determine the output of the equivalent DSP system, and evaluate the accuracy of the digital approximation for a sampling frequency set to (i) 2 kHz and (ii) 10 kHz.

Using the unit-impulse response and the convolution-summation process as an alternative method, confirm the triangular signal response of the equivalent DSP system operating with the 2 kHz sampling frequency. Express all computation results to three decimal places.

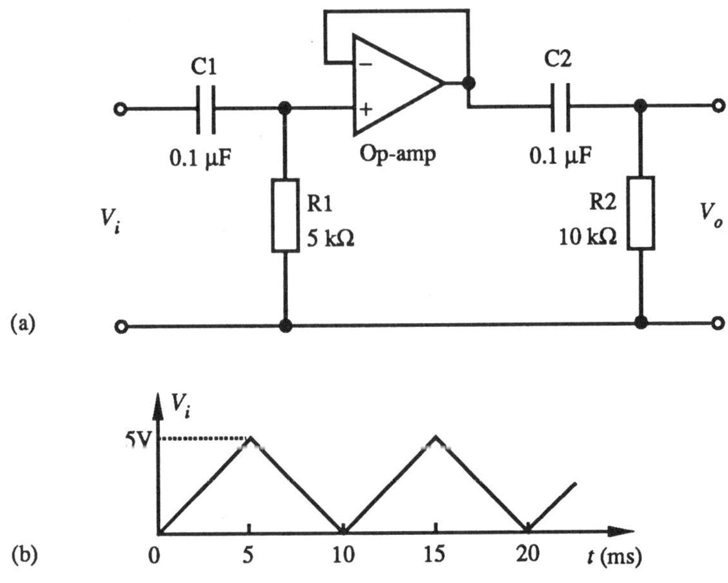

Figure 1.22 (a) Second-order analogue differentiator
(b) Triangular input waveform

Method:

(a) Analogue Circuit Analysis
Unless the analogue system to be approximated digitally is a simple circuit, it is always a good idea to start with circuit analysis of the analogue system with the objective of decomposing it into as many simple functional blocks as possible, such that each block performs only a basic signal processing operation and can therefore be easily approximated by a simple DSP unit.

(b) DSP System Design
The next step is to design a DSP unit to approximate each analogue functional block, and to form the final equivalent DSP system by interconnecting the DSP units in the same topology as that of the analogue system. This step can be carried out by a simple design method known as the first-difference approximation. Essentially, this method converts the differential equation, which characterises the performance of an analogue functional block in the continuous-time domain, to a difference equation in the discrete-time domain.

(c) Design Confirmation and Evaluation
The final step is to confirm and evaluate the design by comparing the output sequence of the DSP system with the output signal that would be produced by the analogue system. The computation of the digital output sequence can be carried out by using the difference equation of the DSP system or using the convolution-summation operation, i.e. discrete-time convolution of the unit-impulse response of the DSP system with the input signal sequence.

Execution of the Method:

(a) Analogue Circuit Analysis
From Figure 1.22(a), the analogue circuit is seen to consist of two simple R-C circuits separated by an op-amp (operational amplifier) configured as a unity-gain non-inverting amplifier. Each R-C circuit functions as a first-order differentiator. As this op-amp circuit is characterised by its extremely high input impedance and extremely low output impedance, the loading effect of the second R-C circuit on the first R-C circuit is negligible, and the output of the op-amp can be viewed as an ideal controlled voltage source with zero internal resistance connected to the input of the second R-C circuit. Consequently, the approximation task of the second-order analogue differentiator is decomposed into a much simpler approximation task as two first-order differentiators connected in series, as shown in Figure 1.23.

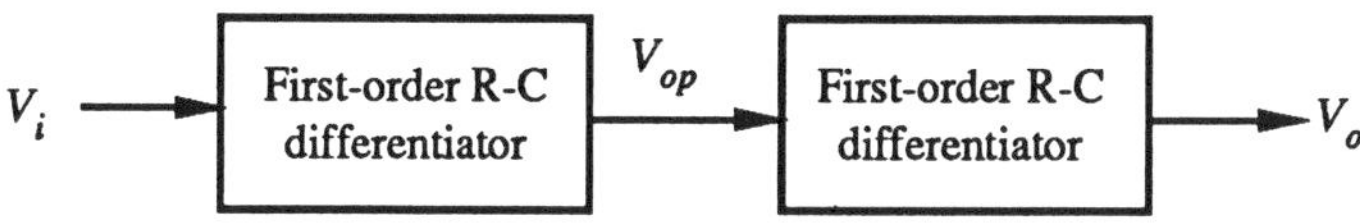

Figure 1.23 Decomposed second-order analogue differentiator

(b) DSP System Design
Consider the s-domain representation of the decomposed first-order R-C differentiator shown in Figure 1.24.

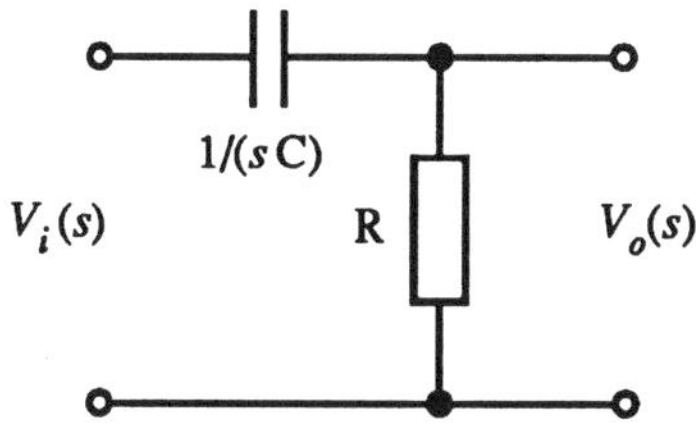

Figure 1.24 First-order R-C differentiator

The relationship between the input and the output voltages is

$$V_o(s) = \frac{R}{R + X_c(s)} V_i(s) \tag{1.50}$$

where

$$X_c(s) = \frac{1}{sC} \tag{1.51}$$

Substituting equation (1.51) into equation (1.50) and rearranging yields

$$V_o(s)\, sCR + V_o(s) = V_i(s)\, s\, CR \tag{1.52}$$

For zero initial conditions, the inverse Laplace transform of $F(s)$ and $sF(s)$ are given by

$$L^{-1}[F[s]] = f(t) \tag{1.53}$$

$$L^{-1}[sF(s)] = \frac{\mathrm{d} f(t)}{\mathrm{d} t} \tag{1.54}$$

Hence, applying equations (1.53) and (1.54), assuming the capacitor is initially uncharged, equation (1.52) becomes

$$CR\frac{\mathrm{d}\, v_o(t)}{\mathrm{d} t} + v_o(t) = CR\frac{\mathrm{d}\, v_i(t)}{\mathrm{d} t} \tag{1.55}$$

The differential equation (1.55) which characterises the performance of the first-order R-C differentiator in the continuous-time domain can be approximated by a difference equation in the discrete-time domain using the first-difference approximation method illustrated in Figure 1.25, whereby a first-order derivative is approximated by the difference between consecutive samples, i.e.

$$\frac{\mathrm{d}[f(t)]}{\mathrm{d} t} \cong \left.\frac{f(n) - f(n-1)}{T}\right|_{T \neq 0} \tag{1.56}$$

From Figure 1.25, it is seen that the accuracy of the approximation increases as T approaches zero, thereby implying that the sampling frequency in a practical implementation should be high enough to ensure the validity of the approximation.

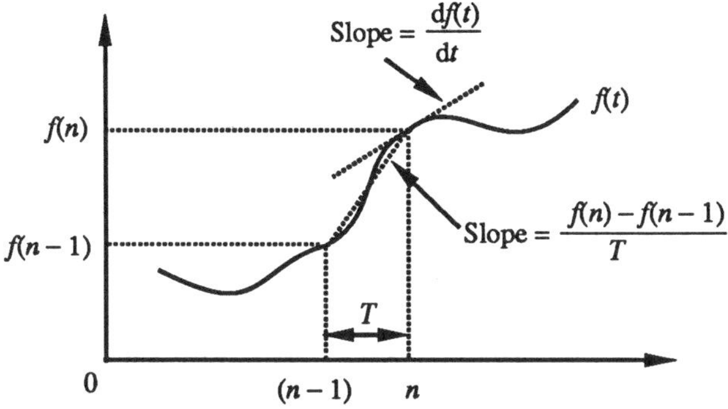

Figure 1.25 First-difference approximation

Applying equation (1.56), equation (1.55) becomes

$$\frac{CR}{T}\left[v_o(n) - v_o(n-1) \right] + v_o(n) = \frac{CR}{T}\left[v_i(n) - v_i(n-1) \right]$$

and rearranging yields

$$v_o(n) = \frac{CR}{T + CR}\left[v_i(n) - v_i(n-1) + v_o(n-1) \right] \qquad (1.57)$$

The signal flow graph representation of this difference equation is shown in Figure 1.26.

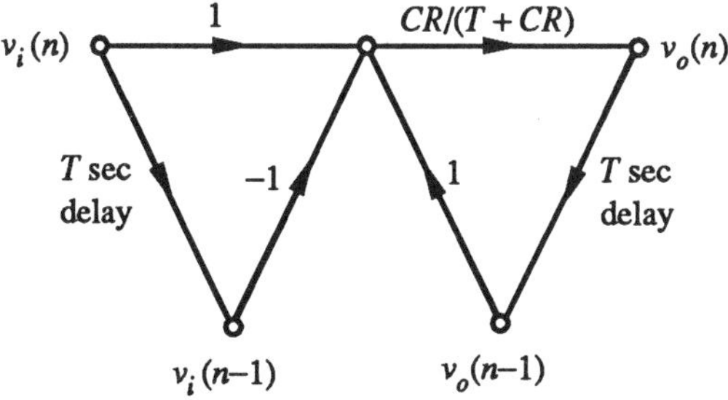

Figure 1.26 Signal flow graph of the DSP system for the decomposed first-order R-C differentiator

By cascading two signal flow graphs of the form shown in Figure 1.26, the complete signal flow graph of the DSP system equivalent to the analogue circuit shown in Figure 1.22(a) is formed. This is shown in Figure 1.27.

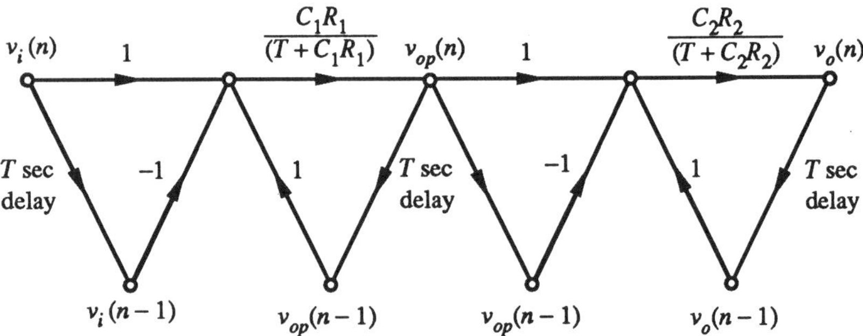

Figure 1.27 Signal flow graph of the complete DSP system as the discrete-time representation of the second-order analogue differentiator

(c) Design Confirmation and Evaluation

This design confirmation and evaluation section is divided into two parts. In part 1, the difference equation of the DSP system, equation (1.57), is used to determine the DSP system output and to evaluate the accuracy of the digital approximation using the two specified sampling frequencies. In part 2, the convolution-summation of the impulse response of the DSP system and the input sequence is used as an alternative method to confirm the validity of the DSP system output for a 2 kHz sampling frequency.

Part 1

(i) Computation of analogue output for the first R-C differentiator:

The triangular input waveform has a slope of ±5V per 5 ms (±1000V/s) and can be described by the infinite time series

$$v_i(t) = 1000\ t\ u(t) - 2000\ (t - 0.005)\ u(t - 0.005)$$
$$+ 2000\ (t - 0.01)\ u(t - 0.01) - 2000\ (t - 0.015)\ u(t - 0.015) + \dots \quad (1.58)$$

where $u(t-c)$ is the delayed unit-step function, with c indicating the instant of time at which the unit-step function changes from 0 to 1. Taking the Laplace transform of equation (1.58) gives

$$V_i(s) = \frac{1000}{s^2} - \frac{2000\ e^{-0.005s}}{s^2} + \frac{2000\ e^{-0.01s}}{s^2} - \frac{2000\ e^{-0.015s}}{s^2} + \dots \quad (1.59)$$

Substituting equation (1.59), as well as 0.1 μF for C and 5 kΩ for R, in equation (1.50), and rearranging gives the output from the first R-C differentiator as

$$V_{op}(s) = 0.5\left\{\left(\frac{1}{s} - \frac{1}{s+2000}\right) - 2\,e^{-0.005s}\left(\frac{1}{s} - \frac{1}{s+2000}\right)\right.$$

$$\left. + 2\,e^{-0.01s}\left(\frac{1}{s} - \frac{1}{s+2000}\right) - \ldots\right\} \tag{1.60}$$

Taking the inverse Laplace transform of equation (1.60), the output from the first R-C differentiator in the continuous-time domain is

$$v_{op}(t) = 0.5\left\{\left(1 - e^{-2000t}\right)u(t) - 2\left(1 - e^{-2000(t-0.005)}\right)u(t-0.005)\right.$$

$$+ 2\left(1 - e^{-2000(t-0.01)}\right)u(t-0.01)$$

$$\left. - 2\left(1 - e^{-2000(t-0.015)}\right)u(t-0.015) + \ldots\right\} \tag{1.61}$$

(ii) Computation of digital output sequence for the first-order digital differentiator:

In the computation of the digital output sequence from the first-order digital differentiator, the digital input sequence, $v_i(n)$, computed using equation (1.58) at multiple intervals of the sampling period, is assumed to be a discrete-time continuous-amplitude signal (with no amplitude quantisation).

By substituting in equation (1.57) 0.1 μF for C and 5 kΩ for R and the sampling period corresponding to sampling frequencies of 2 kHz and 10 kHz respectively, the digital output sequence from the approximated digital differentiator, $v_{op}(n)$, can be computed iteratively in terms of the current input sample, $v_i(n)$, the previous input sample, $v_i(n-1)$, and the previous output sample, $v_{op}(n-1)$. To compute the first digital output sample at $n = 0$, the previous input and output samples are taken as zero (zero initial conditions since the capacitor is assumed to be initially uncharged).

(iii) Triangular signal response for the first-order differentiator:

Figure 1.28 shows the resulting triangular signal response computed in (i) and (ii) for the first-order analogue differentiator and the corresponding digital differentiator operating at two different sampling frequencies. With the triangular input signal having a constant slope of ±5V per 5 ms, the response of an ideal first-order differentiator should be a ±0.5V square wave having a 10 ms period. However, due to the finite time required to charge and discharge the capacitor, the shape of the triangular signal response approximates roughly to a scaled down version of the ideal square wave. Nevertheless, the most important observation is that the DSP system is able to approximate the time-domain characteristics of the analogue system and that the smaller the sampling period (i.e. the higher the sampling frequency) the more accurate the digital approximation of the analogue system.

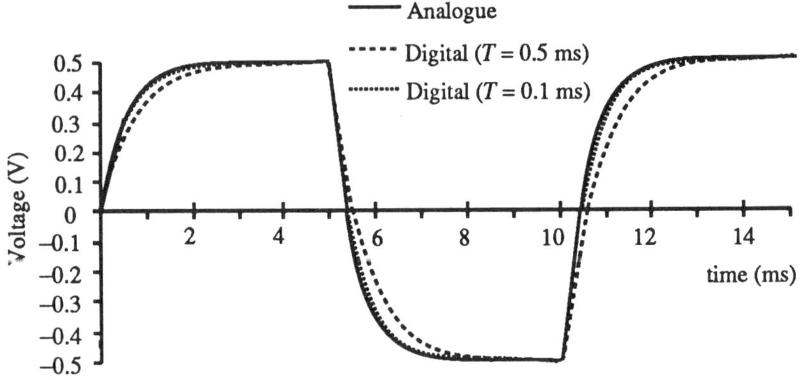

Figure 1.28 Triangular signal response for the first-order differentiator

(iv) Computation of analogue output for the second R-C differentiator:

Substituting equation (1.60) for $V_i(s)$, as well as 0.1 μF for C and 10 kΩ for R, in equation (1.50), and rearranging gives the output from the second R-C differentiator as

$$V_o(s) = 0.5\left\{\left(\frac{1}{s+1000} - \frac{s}{(s+2000)(s+1000)}\right)\right.$$

$$-2\,e^{-0.005s}\left(\frac{1}{s+1000} - \frac{s}{(s+2000)(s+1000)}\right)$$

$$\left. +2\,e^{-0.01s}\left(\frac{1}{s+1000} - \frac{s}{(s+2000)(s+1000)}\right) + \ldots\right\} \qquad (1.62)$$

Taking the inverse Laplace transform of equation (1.62), the output from the second R-C differentiator in the continuous-time domain is

$$v_o(t) = 0.5\left\{ u(t)\left(e^{-1000t} - \frac{2000\ e^{-2000t} - 1000\ e^{-1000t}}{1000}\right)\right.$$

$$-2u(t-0.005)\left(e^{-1000(t-0.005)}\right.$$

$$\left.-\frac{2000\ e^{-2000(t-0.005)} - 1000\ e^{-1000(t-0.005)}}{1000}\right)$$

$$+2u(t-0.01)\left(e^{-1000(t-0.01)}\right.$$

$$\left.\left.-\frac{2000\ e^{-2000(t-0.01)} - 1000\ e^{-1000(t-0.01)}}{1000}\right) + \ldots\right\}$$

(1.63)

(v) Computation of digital output sequence for the second-order digital differentiator:

By substituting in equation (1.57) 0.1 μF for C and 10 kΩ for R and the sampling period corresponding to sampling frequency of 2 kHz and 10 kHz respectively, the digital output sequence for the approximated second-order digital differentiator, $v_o(n)$, can be computed iteratively in terms of the current input sample, $v_{op}(n)$, and the previous input sample, $v_{op}(n-1)$ computed in (ii) plus the previous output sample, $v_o(n-1)$. Again, all input and output samples are taken as zero for $n < 0$.

(vi) Triangular signal response for the second-order differentiator:

Figure 1.29 shows the resulting triangular signal responses computed in (iv) and (v) for the second-order analogue differentiator and the approximated digital differentiator operating at two different sampling frequencies. The triangular signal response of an ideal second-order differentiator can be considered as the square wave response of an ideal first-order differentiator and should therefore be an impulse of ±0.5V in this case. Again, due to the finite time required to charge and discharge the capacitor, the shape of the second-order triangular signal response approximates roughly to a scaled down version of the ideal impulse output. Furthermore, with the zero initial condition applied, the first peak is of a comparatively lower amplitude than all subsequent peaks of the output signal. Nevertheless, the second-order DSP system is seen to approximate the time-domain characteristics of the second-order analogue system.

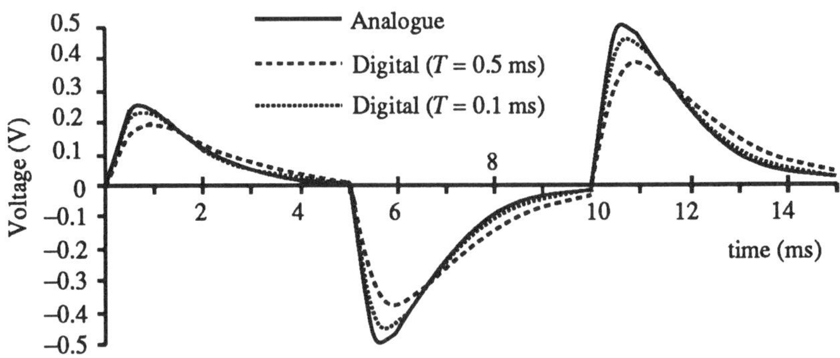

Figure 1.29 Triangular signal response for the second-order differentiator

It is seen in Figure 1.29 that the maximum error of approximation occurs when the triangular input signal changes from a positive slope to a negative slope, and vice versa. Note that the error of approximation is reduced as the sampling frequency is increased from 2 kHz to 10 kHz.

Part 2

(i) Unit-impulse response for the second-order digital differentiator:

The unit-impulse response of the approximated second-order digital differentiator can be obtained in the same way as that used for computing the triangular signal response as described in Part 1 (ii) and (v). A different, but equivalent way, is to apply the associative property described in Section 1.5.3 by treating the second-order digital differentiator as two first-order digital differentiators connected in series. The results are shown in Table 1.3.

In Table 1.3, $h_1(n)$ and $h_2(n)$ are the unit-impulse responses of the two first-order digital differentiators corresponding to the first and the second R-C circuits respectively. These unit-impulse responses were computed iteratively using equation (1.57) with the unit-sample sequence as the input, the sampling period was set to 5 msec, corresponding to a 2 kHz sampling frequency, C was set to 0.1 μF, and R was set to 5 kΩ and 10 kΩ for the first and the second differentiator respectively. The actual unit-impulse response sequences of both digital differentiators are infinitely long due to the presence of the feedback. However, expressing the results to three decimal places causes the infinite impulse response sequence to be truncated and become a finite impulse response sequence. Furthermore, with the RC time constant of the second R-C circuit being larger than that of the first R-C circuit, $h_2(n)$ is correspondingly longer than $h_1(n)$.

$h(n)$ in Table 1.3 is the unit-impulse response of the second-order digital differentiator and is obtained by convolution of the unit-impulse responses of the two first-order digital differentiators. With the lengths of $h_1(n)$ and $h_2(n)$ equal to 10 and 14 respectively, the length of $h(n)$ should be 23. However, expressing the results to three decimal places makes $h(n) = 0$ after n exceeds 12.

Table 1.3

n	$h_1(n)$	$h_2(n)$	$h(n)=h_1(n) * h_2(n)$
0	0.500	0.667	0.334
1	− 0.250	− 0.222	− 0.278
2	− 0.125	− 0.099	− 0.102
3	− 0.063	− 0.066	− 0.027
4	− 0.031	− 0.044	0.004
5	− 0.016	− 0.029	0.012
6	− 0.008	− 0.020	0.043
7	− 0.004	− 0.013	− 0.003
8	− 0.002	− 0.009	0.002
9	− 0.001	− 0.006	0.003
10	0	− 0.004	0.006
11	0	− 0.003	0.003
12	0	− 0.002	0.001
13	0	− 0.001	0

(ii) Triangular signal response for the second-order differentiator:

The unit-impulse response of the approximated second-order digital differentiator obtained in (i) above can be used in the convolution-summation operation with the triangular input sequence to produce the digital output sequence. Figure 1.30 shows the resulting digital output sequence for a 2 kHz sampling frequency as well as the corresponding analogue and the DSP system outputs obtained in Part 1 at the same sampling frequency. It is seen that the digital output computed using the convolution method is similar to that computed using the difference equation in Part 1.

It is seen in Figure 1.30 that the error produced by the convolution method (Part 2) differs from that of the difference equation method (Part 1), except during the initial period, this is due to the effect of the infinite impulse response sequence being truncated into a finite one. Furthermore, because of this sequence truncation the error produced by the convolution method is higher.

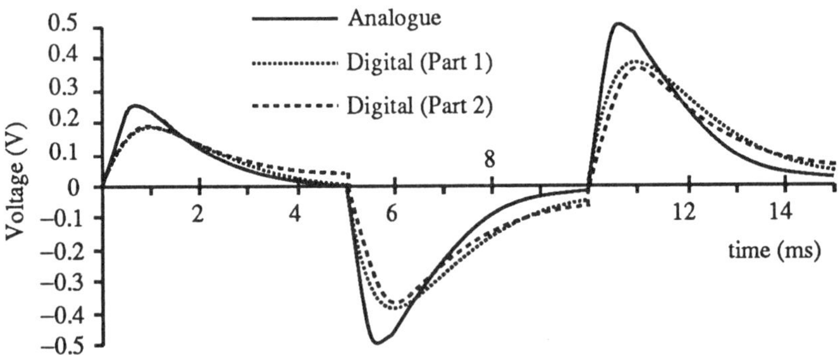

Figure 1.30 Second-order triangular signal response (2 kHz sampling frequency for both digital approximations)

Note:
If the op-amp circuit was removed from the analogue circuit shown in Figure 1.22(a), then the implication is that the overall circuit can not be decomposed, as described previously, into two first-order circuits in series due to the loading effect of the second R-C circuit on the first R-C circuit, and the resulting differential equation of the circuit will contain second-order derivatives. Equation (1.56) can be applied twice to approximate the second-order derivatives, that is

$$\frac{\mathrm{d}^2 f(t)}{\mathrm{d}t^2} = \frac{\mathrm{d}}{\mathrm{d}t}\left[\frac{\mathrm{d}f(t)}{\mathrm{d}t}\right]$$

$$\cong \frac{\mathrm{d}}{\mathrm{d}t}\left[\frac{f(n)-f(n-1)}{T}\right]$$

$$\cong \frac{\left[\frac{f(n)-f(n-1)}{T}\right]-\left[\frac{f(n-1)-f(n-2)}{T}\right]}{T}$$

$$= \frac{f(n)-2f(n-1)+f(n-2)}{T^2} \qquad (1.64)$$

By applying equation (1.56) repeatedly, a kth-order derivative is approximated by

$$\frac{\mathrm{d}^k f(t)}{\mathrm{d}t^k} = \frac{1}{T^k} \sum_{m=0}^{k} (-1)^m C_m^k f(n-m) \tag{1.65}$$

where

$$C_m^k = \frac{k!}{m!(k-m)!}$$

Problems

P1.1
A transducer signal is filtered so that it has no significant frequency components above 100 Hz. The signal is recorded for 20 seconds using a tape recorder with a wide bandwidth and with a sufficiently fast response. Equally spaced samples are taken over the duration of the data record to enable signal analysis of the transducer output. What is the minimum number of samples required to ensure that aliasing is avoided?

P1.2
An analogue signal $s(t) = 0.5A(\sin 70\pi t + 0.1\sin 160\pi t)$ is sampled at a frequency of (i) 80 Hz, (ii) 160 Hz and (iii) 250 Hz. For each sampling case, draw the resulting magnitude/frequency spectra and comment on the choice of sampling frequency.

P1.3
An analogue-to-digital converter has a signal-to-quantisation noise ratio of 23.3 dB. Calculate the full-scale-voltage range of this A/D converter when the quantisation interval is specified as 250 mV.

P1.4
The output of a 12-bit A/D converter with 6V full-scale-voltage range is the repeated sequence {010001000100, 101010101010}, determine the corresponding input voltage values if the output is coded using (a) offset binary, (b) sign and magnitude, (c) one's complement, and (d) two's complement.

P1.5
Determine the attenuation (expressed in dBs) at 2 kHz for a speech signal processing system exhibiting a $\sin x/x$ effect introduced by the digital-to-analogue converter. The system sampling frequency is 8 kHz.

P1.6

For the signal flow graph of the DSP system shown in Figure P1.6, determine:

(a) The difference equation of the system when contacts C1 and C2 are closed.
(b) The response to a unit-sample input for $0 \le n \le 8$ when contacts C1 and C2 are closed.
(c) The difference equation when contact C1 is open and contact C2 is closed.
(d) The response to a unit-sample input when contact C1 is closed and contact C2 is open.

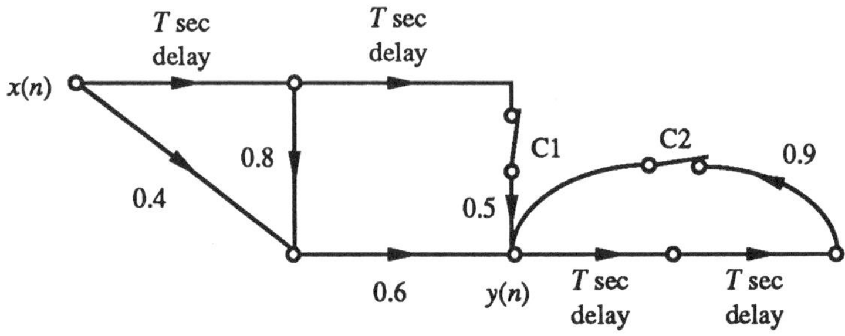

Figure P1.6

P1.7

An FIR DSP system is characterised by the linear difference equation:

$$y(n) = 0.2\,x(n) - 0.5\,x(n-2) + 0.4\,x(n-3)$$

Given that the digital input sequence $\{-1, 1, 0, -1\}$ is applied to this DSP system, determine the corresponding digital output sequence.

P1.8

Two DSP systems are connected either (i) in series, or (ii) in parallel. The unit-sample response of the first DSP system corresponds to the case defined in P1.6(d), and the unit-sample response of the second DSP system is that produced by the linear difference equation given in P1.7. Determine the output sequence of the overall series connected DSP system and the overall parallel connected DSP system when the digital input sequence is $\{2, 1, -1, -2\}$.

P1.9

The analogue cicuit shown in Figure P1.9 is a simple first-order R-C integrater. Use the first-difference approximation design method to derive an equivalent DSP system in the form of a signal flow graph.

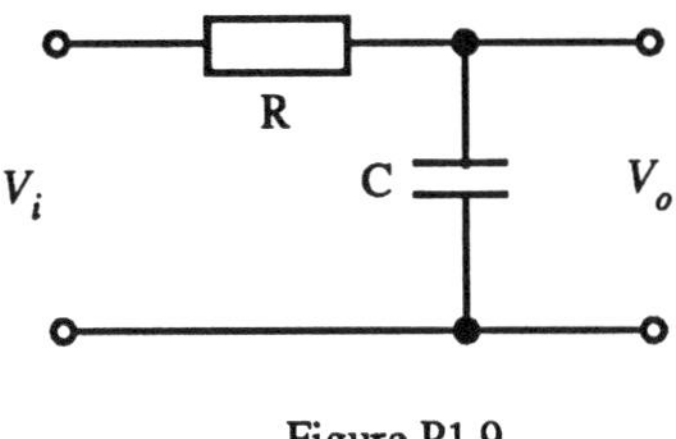

Figure P1.9

P1.10

The standard form for a second-order differential equation is

$$\frac{d^2y}{dt^2} + 2\zeta\omega_n \frac{dy}{dt} + \omega_n^2\, y = kx$$

Use the first-difference approximation design method to derive an equivalent DSP system in the form of a signal flow graph.

2 z-Transforms

2.1 z-Transform (standard form)

The Laplace transform plays an important role in the analysis of analogue signals or systems, since it uses a generalised complex frequency variable $s = \pm\sigma \pm j\omega$, with σ describing amplitude growth and decay of the sinusoidal signal having a radian frequency of ω. However, complications arise in using the s-plane representation to analyse a sampled signal or sampled-data system due to their characteristic infinite number of complementary frequency spectra. Let us consider a sinusoidal signal $\cos\omega_b t$ which, using Euler's identity ($e^{\pm j\theta} = \cos\theta \pm j\sin\theta$), can be expressed as

$$\cos\omega_b t = \frac{1}{2}\left(e^{j\omega_b t} + e^{-j\omega_b t}\right)$$

This signal may be represented by two frequency components at $\pm\omega_b$, each having a magnitude value of 0.5. The frequency component at $-\omega_b$ does not correspond to a physical quantity, but it enables mathematical modelling of the signal in the frequency domain.

The Laplace transform of $\cos\omega_b t$ (see Table 2.2, page 71) is

$$\boldsymbol{L}\left[\cos\omega_b t\right] = \frac{s}{s^2 + \omega_b^2} = \frac{s}{\left(s + j\omega_b\right)\left(s - j\omega_b\right)}$$

Consequently we see that the s-plane representation of this signal is described by a pair of complex conjugate poles (corresponding to the value of s for which $\boldsymbol{L}[\cos\omega_b t] = \infty$) at $s = \pm j\omega_b$ and a zero (the values of s for which $\boldsymbol{L}[\cos\omega_b t] = 0$) at $s = 0$ in the s-plane representation. It was shown in Section 1.2.1 that sampling of the $\cos\omega_b t$ signal will result in an infinite number of complementary frequency components at $\pm n\omega_s \pm \omega_b$ for $n = 1$ to ∞. There must therefore be an infinite number of poles and zeros associated with the s-plane representation of the sampled signal. Thus the analysis of any sampled signal or sampled-data system in the frequency domain is extremely difficult using the s-plane representation, because signal and system equations will contain infinitely long polynomials created by the characteristic infinite number of poles and zeros. Fortunately, this problem may be overcome by using the z-transform, which reduces poles and zeros to a finite number in the z-plane, thereby yielding a mathematical description that is simple to analyse.

The purpose of the z-transform is to **map** (transform) any point $s(\pm\sigma, \pm j\omega)$ in the s-plane to a corresponding point $z(r\angle\theta)$ in the z-plane by the relationship

$$z = e^{sT} \tag{2.1}$$

where T is the sampling period (seconds) and $s = \pm\sigma \pm j\omega$.

Let us consider the case when the real part of s is zero-valued, i.e. $\sigma = 0$, and therefore $z = e^{\pm j\omega T} = 1\angle\pm\omega T$, which gives the values of z (in polar form) shown in Table 2.1:

Table 2.1

$\sigma = 0,\ \omega_s = 2\pi/T$									
$j\omega$	0	$\omega_s/8$	$\omega_s/4$	$3\omega_s/8$	$\omega_s/2$	$5\omega_s/8$	$3\omega_s/4$	$7\omega_s/8$	ω_s
$z=1\angle\omega T$	$1\angle 0°$	$1\angle 45°$	$1\angle 90°$	$1\angle 135°$	$1\angle 180°$	$1\angle 225°$	$1\angle 270°$	$1\angle 315°$	$1\angle 360°$

From Table 2.1 it may be deduced that the imaginary axis (frequency axis) in the s-plane maps to the circumference of the unit-circle in the z-plane. This mapping process is illustrated in Figure 2.1.

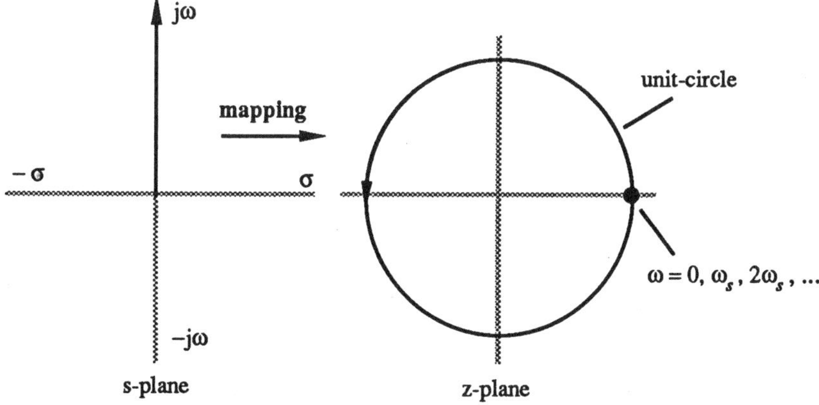

Figure 2.1 s-plane to z-plane mapping for $z = e^{j\omega T}$

Let us now consider the case where $z = e^{(-\sigma \pm j\omega)T}$, which is the mapping of a point in the left-hand half of the s-plane to the z-plane.

We may write the complex variable, z, as

$$z = e^{-\sigma T} \times e^{\pm j\omega T} = e^{-\sigma T}\ \angle \pm \omega T$$

Since σ is negative then $|z| < 1$. In contrast when σ is positive (right-hand half of the s-plane) $|z| > 1$. This means that points located in the left-hand half of the s-plane map inside the unit-circle in the z-plane, and points located in the right-hand half of the s-plane map outside the unit-circle in the z-plane.

It is interesting to consider two points in the left-hand half of the s-plane which are separated along the frequency axis by ω_s. The corresponding two points in the z-plane are

$$z_1 = e^{(-\sigma + j\omega)T} \quad \text{and} \quad z_2 = e^{(-\sigma + j(\omega + \omega_s))T}$$

i.e.

$$z_1 = e^{-\sigma T} \angle \omega T \quad \text{and} \quad z_2 = e^{-\sigma T} \times e^{j(\omega + \omega_s)T}$$

but

$$(\omega + \omega_s)T = \omega T + \omega_s T = \omega T + \left\{\left(\frac{2\pi}{T}\right) \times T\right\}$$
$$= \omega T + 2\pi$$

using this relationship we may write

$$e^{j(\omega + \omega_s)T} = e^{j\omega T}$$

therefore $\quad z_2 = e^{-\sigma T} \angle \omega T \quad$ consequently $\quad z_1 = z_2$

Thus it is seen that points (for example, poles and zeros) separated by ω_s along the frequency axis in the s-plane map (transform) to **coincident** points in the z-plane. This means that all sets of poles and zeros separated by ω_s along the frequency axis in the s-plane (which is the case for sampled-data signals or systems) effectively transform to a corresponding single set of poles and zeros in the z-plane.

In Chapter 1 (equation (1.3)) it was shown that

$$x^*(t) = x(t) \times \delta_T(t) = x(t) \times \sum_{n=-\infty}^{\infty} \delta(t - nT)$$

However, in using a sampling process the value of $x(t)$ is only known for $t = nT$ and furthermore, for a physical system $x(t) = 0$ for $t < 0$, therefore

$$x^*(t) = \sum_{n=0}^{\infty} x(nT) \times \delta(t - nT)$$

Obtaining the Laplace transform of $x^*(t)$ using Table 2.2 (page 71) gives

$$\mathbf{L}[x^*(t)] = \sum_{n=0}^{\infty} x(nT)\, e^{-nsT}$$

but for the z-transform we have $z = e^{sT}$, therefore $z^{-n} = e^{-nsT}$ (which corresponds to a delay of n sampling periods). The z-transform of $x^*(t)$ is therefore

$$\mathbf{Z}[x^*(t)] = X(z) = \sum_{n=0}^{\infty} x(nT)\, z^{-n} \tag{2.2}$$

Equation (2.2) simply implies that the z-transform is a method of converting a sequence of numbers (sample values, $x(nT)$) into a function of the complex variable z.

However, referring to the note on page 11, the nth sample is written as $x(n)$, hence equation (2.2) becomes

$$X(z) = \sum_{n=0}^{\infty} x(n)\, z^{-n} \tag{2.3}$$

❖ **WE 2.1**

An input sequence corresponding to a sampled signal is {2, 0.5, 0, −0.8, −3}, determine the z-transform of this sequence.

Solution:

By inspection and applying equation (2.3) the z-transform is

$$X(z) = 2 + 0.5\,z^{-1} - 0.8\,z^{-3} - 3\,z^{-4} \tag{2.4}$$

Note: In deriving this solution we have assumed that the sampled signal produces a right-sided sequence, that is, $x(n) = 0$ for negative n. The coefficients of z in equation (2.4) are the sample amplitudes, and the exponents of z indicate the position of each sample in the sequence (the first exponent is zero and since $z^0 = 1$, it has been omitted).

*****

❖ **WE 2.2**

Given that the analogue input signal applied to a digital filter is $x(t) = e^{-\alpha t}$, determine the z-transform of $x^*(t)$.

Solution:

For $t = nT$ the sampled signal sequence is

$$x^*(t) = \left\{e^0,\ e^{-\alpha T},\ e^{-2\alpha T},\ e^{-3\alpha T}, \ldots\right\}$$

By inspection and applying equation (2.3) the z-transform is

$$X(z) = 1 + e^{-\alpha T} z^{-1} + e^{-2\alpha T} z^{-2} + e^{-3\alpha T} z^{-3} + \ldots$$

Applying the geometric series summation formula

$$\sum_{n=0}^{\infty} x^n = \frac{1}{1-x} \qquad \text{for} \quad x \leq 1$$

yields $$X(z) = \sum_{n=0}^{\infty} e^{-\alpha nT} z^{-n} = \sum_{n=0}^{\infty} \left(e^{-\alpha T} z^{-1}\right)^n = \frac{1}{1 - e^{-\alpha T} z^{-1}}$$

Multiplying top and bottom by z gives

$$X(z) = \frac{z}{z - e^{-\alpha T}}$$

This ***closed form*** result may be confirmed by referring to Table 2.2 (Selected z-transforms) on page 71.

*****

The concept of using a standard deterministic test signal was introduced in Chapter 1. In order to analyse a digital signal processing system in the z-domain it is necessary to represent this test signal by its equivalent z-transform. For example, the weighted unit-impulse, $A\delta(t)$, and the weighted unit-step, $Au(t)$, may be deduced from Table 2.2, as shown in WE 2.3 and WE 2.4 respectively.

❖ WE 2.3

Determine the z-transform of the weighted unit-impulse, $A\delta(t)$.

Solution:

$A\delta(t)$ is $A\delta(t - nT)$ for $n = 0$, and therefore from Table 2.2 the corresponding z-transform is Az^{-n} for $n = 0$ which is equal to A since $z^0 = 1$.

*****

❖ WE 2.4

Determine the z-transform of the weighted unit-step, $Au(t)$.

Solution:

$$\mathbf{Z}[Au(t)] = A\mathbf{Z}[u(t)]$$

Substituting into the above expression the corresponding z-transform of $u(t)$ given in Table 2.2 yields

$$\mathbf{Z}[Au(t)] = \frac{Az}{z-1}$$

*****

Table 2.2 Selected z-Transforms

$x(t)$	$X(s)$	$X(z)$
$\delta(t-nT)$	e^{-nTs}	z^{-n}
$u(t)$	$\frac{1}{s}$	$\frac{z}{z-1}$
$e^{-\alpha t}$	$\frac{1}{s+\alpha}$	$\frac{z}{z-e^{-\alpha T}}$
t	$\frac{1}{s^2}$	$\frac{zT}{(z-1)^2}$
$\sin\beta t$	$\frac{\beta}{s^2+\beta^2}$	$\frac{z\sin\beta T}{z^2-2z\cos\beta T+1}$
$\cos\beta t$	$\frac{s}{s^2+\beta^2}$	$\frac{z(z-\cos\beta T)}{z^2-2z\cos\beta T+1}$
$\cosh\alpha t$	$\frac{s}{s^2-\alpha^2}$	$\frac{z(z-\cosh\alpha T)}{z^2-2z\cosh\alpha T+1}$
$\sinh\alpha t$	$\frac{\alpha}{s^2-\alpha^2}$	$\frac{z\sinh\alpha T}{z^2-2z\cosh\alpha T+1}$
$e^{-\alpha t}\sin\beta t$	$\frac{\beta}{(s+\alpha)^2+\beta^2}$	$\frac{ze^{-\alpha T}\sin\beta T}{z^2-2ze^{-\alpha T}\cos\beta T+e^{-2\alpha T}}$
$e^{-\alpha t}\cos\beta t$	$\frac{s+\alpha}{(s+\alpha)^2+\beta^2}$	$\frac{z(z-e^{-\alpha T}\cos\beta T)}{z^2-2ze^{-\alpha T}\cos\beta T+e^{-2\alpha T}}$
t^2	$\frac{2}{s^3}$	$\frac{zT^2(z+1)}{(z-1)^3}$
$te^{-\alpha t}$	$\frac{1}{(s+\alpha)^2}$	$\frac{zTe^{-\alpha T}}{(z-e^{-\alpha T})^2}$

2.1.1 *z-Transformation via Partial Fraction Expansion*

The technique of partial fraction expansion is used to decompose a signal or system transfer function, expressed as a ratio of two polynomials in s, into a sum of standard functions that can be z-transformed using Table 2.2. Let us consider the transfer function $G(s)$ expressed in the form

$$G(s) = \frac{k}{s^n + a_1 s^{n-1} + \cdots + a_n s^0} \tag{2.5}$$

which may be expanded and expressed as

$$G(s) = \frac{A_1}{s - p_1} + \frac{A_2}{s - p_2} + \cdots + \frac{A_n}{s - p_n} \tag{2.6}$$

Each term $\dfrac{A_k}{s - p_k}$, where $1 \leq k \leq n$, may be transformed to its z-plane representation using Table 2.2, i.e.

$$G(z) = \frac{A_1 z}{z - e^{p_1 T}} + \frac{A_2 z}{z - e^{p_2 T}} + \cdots + \frac{A_n z}{z - e^{p_n T}} \tag{2.7}$$

The steps of z-transformation via partial fraction expansion are:

(i) Factorise the denominator polynomial of the function into prime factors.

(ii) Decompose the function into a sum of partial fractions:

(a) A linear factor $(s + a)$ gives a partial fraction $\dfrac{A}{s + a}$

(b) A repeated linear factor $(s + a)^n$ gives

$$\frac{A_1}{s + a} + \frac{A_2}{(s + a)^2} + \ldots + \frac{A_n}{(s + a)^n}$$

(c) A quadratic factor $(s^2 + a_1 s + a_2)$ gives $\dfrac{A_1 s + A_2}{s^2 + a_1 s + a_2}$

(iii) Multiply both sides of the equation by the factorised denominator.

(iv) Determine each constant by substituting the appropriate value for s to make the associated prime factor zero, or by equating coefficients of s that have equal exponents.

(v) Obtain the z-transform from Table 2.2.

❖ **WE 2.5**

Given that an analogue system has the transfer function

$$G(s) = \frac{1}{\left(s^2 + 3s + 2\right)}$$

derive the z-transform of $G(s)$.

Solution:

Factorising the denominator and expanding into partial fractions gives

$$G(s) = \frac{1}{s^2 + 3s + 2} = \frac{1}{(s+1)(s+2)} = \frac{A_1}{(s+1)} + \frac{A_2}{(s+2)}$$

Multiplying both sides by the factorised denominator gives

$$1 = A_1(s+2) + A_2(s+1)$$

Substituting $s = -2$ and $s = -1$ respectively to make one of the bracketed terms zero gives

$$s = -2: \qquad 1 = A_2(-2+1), \qquad \therefore A_2 = -1$$

$$s = -1: \qquad 1 = A_1(-1+2), \qquad \therefore A_1 = 1$$

$$\therefore \qquad G(s) = \frac{1}{s+1} - \frac{1}{s+2}$$

From Table 2.2, the corresponding z-transform is

$$G(z) = \frac{z}{z - e^{-T}} - \frac{z}{z - e^{-2T}}$$

✲✲✲✲✲

❖ **WE 2.6**

Given that $G(s) = \dfrac{s}{(s+1)^2}$ derive its z-transform.

***Solution*:**

Expanding into partial fractions by applying the rule for repeated linear factors gives

$$G(s) = \frac{s}{(s+1)^2} = \frac{A_1}{s+1} + \frac{A_2}{(s+1)^2}$$

$$\therefore \qquad s = A_1(s+1) + A_2$$

$$s = -1: \qquad -1 = A_2$$

$$s = 0: \qquad 0 = A_1 + A_2, \qquad \therefore A_1 = 1$$

$$\therefore \qquad G(s) = \frac{1}{s+1} - \frac{1}{(s+1)^2}$$

$$\therefore \qquad G(z) = \frac{z}{z - e^{-T}} - \frac{zT\,e^{-T}}{\left(z - e^{-T}\right)^2}$$

*****

❖ **WE 2.7**

Given that $G(s) = \dfrac{(s+1)}{s\left(s^2 + s + 1\right)}$ derive its z-transform.

***Solution*:**

Expanding into partial fractions by applying rules for a linear factor and a quadratic factor respectively gives

$$G(s) = \frac{s+1}{s\left(s^2+s+1\right)} = \frac{A_1}{s} + \frac{A_2 s + A_3}{s^2 + s + 1}$$

$$\therefore \qquad s + 1 = A_1\left(s^2 + s + 1\right) + \left(A_2 s + A_3\right) s$$

Equating coefficients of s that have equal exponents gives

$$s^0: \quad 1 = A_1$$

$$s^1: \quad 1 = A_1 + A_3 \qquad \therefore A_3 = 0$$

$$s^2: \quad 0 = A_1 + A_2 \qquad \therefore A_2 = -1$$

$$\therefore \quad G(s) = \frac{1}{s} - \frac{s}{s^2 + s + 1}$$

$$= \frac{1}{s} - \frac{s}{(s + 0.5)^2 + 0.75}$$

$$= \frac{1}{s} - \frac{s + 0.5 - 0.5}{(s + 0.5)^2 + 0.75}$$

$$= \frac{1}{s} - \frac{s + 0.5}{(s + 0.5)^2 + 0.75} - \frac{\frac{\sqrt{3}}{2} \times \frac{1}{\sqrt{3}}}{(s + 0.5)^2 + 0.75}$$

$$\therefore \quad G(z) = \left\{ \frac{z}{z - 1} - \frac{z\left(z - e^{-\frac{T}{2}} \cos \frac{\sqrt{3}T}{2}\right)}{z^2 - 2ze^{-\frac{T}{2}} \cos \frac{\sqrt{3}T}{2} + e^{-T}} - \frac{\frac{z}{\sqrt{3}} e^{-\frac{T}{2}} \sin \frac{\sqrt{3}T}{2}}{z^2 - 2ze^{-\frac{T}{2}} \cos \frac{\sqrt{3}T}{2} + e^{-T}} \right\}$$

*****

❖ **WE2.8**

Given that $G(s) = \dfrac{s + 1}{s^2(s^2 + 2s + 1)}$ derive its z-transform.

***Solution*:**
Expanding into partial fractions by applying rules for a repeated linear factor and a quadratic factor respectively gives

$$G(s) = \frac{s+1}{s^2\left(s^2+2s+1\right)} = \frac{A_1}{s} + \frac{A_2}{s^2} + \frac{A_3 s + A_4}{s^2+2s+1}$$

$$\therefore \quad s+1 = A_1 s\left(s^2+2s+1\right) + A_2\left(s^2+2s+1\right) + \left(A_3 s + A_4\right)s^2$$

Equating coefficients of s that have equal exponents gives

$$\begin{array}{lll} s^0: & 1 = A_2 & \\ s^1: & 1 = A_1 + 2A_2, & \therefore A_1 = -1 \\ s^2: & 0 = 2A_1 + A_2 + A_4, & \therefore A_4 = 1 \\ s^3: & 0 = A_1 + A_3, & \therefore A_3 = 1 \end{array}$$

$$\therefore \quad G(s) = -\frac{1}{s} + \frac{1}{s^2} + \frac{s+1}{s^2+2s+1}$$

$$= -\frac{1}{s} + \frac{1}{s^2} + \frac{s+1}{(s+1)^2}$$

$$= -\frac{1}{s} + \frac{1}{s^2} + \frac{1}{s+1}$$

$$\therefore \quad G(z) = \frac{-z}{z-1} + \frac{zT}{(z-1)^2} + \frac{z}{z-e^{-T}}$$

*****

2.1.2 *z-Transformation via the Residue Method*

The residue method, derived from complex variable theory, can be expressed mathematically as

$$G(z) = \sum_{\substack{\text{all poles} \\ \text{of } G(s)}} \text{Residues of} \left[\frac{G(s)}{1-e^{sT}z^{-1}}\right] \tag{2.8}$$

For a pole of order m at $s = x$, the corresponding residue used in equation (2.8) is given by

$$Residue = \frac{1}{(m-1)!} \lim_{s \to x} \left\{ \frac{d^{m-1}}{ds^{m-1}} \left[(s-x)^m \, G(s) \frac{z}{z - e^{sT}} \right] \right\} \qquad (2.9)$$

❖ WE2.9

Using the residue method determine the z-transform of

(i) $X(s) = \dfrac{k}{s(s+1)}$, and

(ii) $X(s) = \dfrac{s}{(s+1)^2}$.

Solutions:

(i) $X(s)$ has two poles of order $m = 1$ at $s = 0$ and $s = -1$. By applying equation (2.9), the corresponding residues are:

For pole at $s = 0$:

$$Residue = \frac{1}{0!} \lim_{s \to 0} \left\{ \frac{d^0}{ds^0} \left[(s-0)^1 \frac{k}{s(s+1)} \frac{z}{z - e^{sT}} \right] \right\} = \frac{kz}{z-1}$$

For pole at $s = -1$:

$$Residue = \frac{1}{0!} \lim_{s \to -1} \left\{ \frac{d^0}{ds^0} \left[(s-(-1))^1 \frac{k}{s(s+1)} \frac{z}{z - e^{sT}} \right] \right\}$$

$$= \frac{-kz}{z - e^{-T}}$$

Applying equation (2.8) gives

$$X(z) = kz \left[\frac{1}{z-1} - \frac{1}{z - e^{-T}} \right]$$

(ii) $X(s)$ has a double pole (order, m, is therefore equal to 2) at $s = -1$. The corresponding residue is

$$Residue = \frac{1}{(2-1)!} \lim_{s \to -1} \left\{ \frac{d^1}{ds^1} \left[(s-(-1))^2 \frac{s}{(s+1)^2} \frac{z}{z - e^{sT}} \right] \right\}$$

$$= \lim_{s \to -1} \left\{ \frac{d}{ds} \left[\frac{s \times z}{z - e^{sT}} \right] \right\}$$

Differentiating the quotient using

$$\frac{d\left(\frac{u}{v}\right)}{ds} = \frac{v\frac{du}{ds} - u\frac{dv}{ds}}{v^2}$$

enables the residue to be determined as

$$Residue = \lim_{s \to -1} \left\{ \frac{\left(z - e^{sT}\right) z - s z\left(-T e^{sT}\right)}{\left(z - e^{sT}\right)^2} \right\}$$

$$= \left\{ \frac{\left(z - e^{-T}\right) z - z T e^{-T}}{\left(z - e^{-T}\right)^2} \right\}$$

$$\therefore \quad X(z) = \frac{z}{z - e^{-T}} - \frac{z T e^{-T}}{\left(z - e^{-T}\right)^2}$$

*****

2.2 Useful z-Transform Properties

A number of z-transform properties relate a signal processing operation in the time-domain to a corresponding one in the z-domain. They provide a powerful tool not only for obtaining the z-transform of a signal processing operation performed on a sequence, but also they reduce the computation complexity of some signal processing operations in the time-domain. Some useful z-transform properties are presented in this section and demonstrated using worked examples.

(a) *Linearity*

If $\quad y(n) = ax(n) + bv(n)$,

then $\quad Y(z) = aX(z) + bV(z) \qquad (2.10)$

❖ **WE2.10**

Two sampled-data sequences $x(n)$ and $v(n)$ are $\{1, 2\}$ and $\{0.5, 1\}$. If $y(n) = 0.5x(n) + 2v(n)$, prove that $Y(z) = 0.5X(z) + 2V(z)$.

Solution:

Substituting $x(n)$ and $v(n)$ sequences into the given $y(n)$ equation yields

$$y(n) = 0.5\{1, 2\} + 2\{0.5, 1\} = \{0.5, 1\} + \{1, 2\} = \{1.5, 3\}$$

Applying equation (2.3) the z-transform of $y(n)$ is

$$Y(z) = 1.5 + 3z^{-1}$$

Also the z-transform of $x(n)$ and $v(n)$ are

$$X(z) = 1 + 2z^{-1} \qquad \text{and} \qquad V(z) = 0.5 + 1z^{-1},$$

Substituting $X(z)$ and $V(z)$ into the given $Y(z)$ equation yields

$$\begin{aligned} Y(z) &= 0.5\left(1 + 2z^{-1}\right) + 2\left(0.5 + 1z^{-1}\right) \\ &= 0.5 + z^{-1} + 1 + 2z^{-1} \\ &= 1.5 + 3z^{-1} \end{aligned}$$

The result is the same as that obtained previously.

*****

Hence the linearity property implies that the z-transform of a complex signal can be obtained as a sum of standard signals whose z-transforms are known.

(b) ***Right Shifting***

If $\quad \mathbf{Z}[x(n)] = X(z)$, where $x(n) = 0$ for $n < 0$,

then $\quad \mathbf{Z}[x(n-k)] = X(z)\, z^{-k}$ (2.11)

❖ **WE2.11**

The sampled-data sequence $\{1.5, -0.5, 2\}$ is delayed by two sampling periods, derive the corresponding z-transform of the delayed sequence.

Solution:

Applying the right shifting property gives

$$\mathbf{Z}[x(n-2)] = \left(1.5 - 0.5z^{-1} + 2z^{-2}\right)z^{-2}$$
$$= 1.5z^{-2} - 0.5z^{-3} + 2z^{-4}$$

✲✲✲✲✲

(c) ***Left Shifting***

If $\mathbf{Z}[x(n)] = X(z)$, where $x(n) = 0$ for $n < 0$,

then $\mathbf{Z}[x(n+k)] = X(z)z^{k} - \sum_{n=0}^{k-1} x(n)\, z^{-(n-k)}$, if $x(n+k) = 0$ for $n < 0$ (2.12)

❖ **WE2.12**
The sampled-data sequence {3, 2, 1, 2} is advanced by two sampling periods, derive the corresponding z-transform of the advanced sequence.

Solution:
An advance by two sampling periods corresponds to $k = 2$. Applying the left shifting property gives

$$\mathbf{Z}[x(n+2)] = \left(3 + 2z^{-1} + z^{-2} + 2z^{-3}\right)z^{2} - \sum_{n=0}^{1} x(n)\, z^{-(n-2)}$$
$$= 3z^{2} + 2z + 1 + 2z^{-1} - \left(3z^{2} + 2z\right)$$
$$= 1 + 2z^{-1}$$

Note: The advance of a sequence in time may be implemented in practice by shifting the sequence stored in the digital signal processor's memory.

✲✲✲✲✲

(d) ***Convolution-Summation***

If $y(n) = \sum_{i=0}^{\infty} g(i) \times x(n-i)$,

then $Y(z) = G(z) \times X(z)$ (2.13)

❖ **WE2.13**

Suppose that the two sampled-data sequences in WE2.10 are convolved to produce the sequence $y(n)$, show that $Y(z) = X(z) \times V(z)$.

***Solution*:**

From WE2.10, $X(z) = 1 + 2z^{-1}$ and $V(z) = 0.5 + z^{-1}$, therefore

$$Y(z) = X(z) \times V(z) = 0.5 + 2z^{-1} + 2z^{-2}$$

$$\therefore \quad y(n) = \{0.5, 2, 2\}$$

Using the convolution-summation operation in the time-domain the computation of $y(n)$ is shown in the following table

n	0	1	2
$x(n)$	1	2	0
$x(0)\,v(n-0)$	0.5	1	0
$x(1)\,v(n-1)$	0	1	2
$y(n)$	0.5	2	2

$$\therefore \quad y(n) = \{0.5, 2, 2\}$$

$$\therefore \quad Y(z) = 0.5 + 2z^{-1} + 2z^{-2}$$
$$= X(z) \times V(z)$$

Note: This example demonstrates that the convolution of two signals in the time-domain can be replaced by multiplication of their z-transforms.

*****

(e) ***Multiplication by*** A^n (A^n is an exponential sequence)

If $\quad \mathbf{Z}[x(n)] = X(z)$ and $g(n) = A^n \times x(n)$,

then $\quad G(z) = X(z)\Big|_{z \to \frac{z}{A}}$ (2.14)

❖ **WE2.14**

A sampled-data sequence $x(n)$ is $\{1, 2\}$, derive the z-transform of the sequence $g(n) = 0.5^n[x(n)]$.

Solution:

Applying the multiplication by A^n property with $X(z) = 1 + 2z^{-1}$ and $A = 0.5$ gives

$$G(z) = \left(1 + 2z^{-1}\right)\Big|_{z \to \frac{z}{0.5} = 2z}$$

$$= 1 + 2\left(\frac{1}{2z}\right)$$

$$= 1 + z^{-1}$$

Note: This result may be confirmed as follows:

$$g(n) = \left\{\left(0.5^0 \times 1\right), \left(0.5^1 \times 2\right)\right\} = \{1, 1\}$$

$$\therefore \quad G(z) = 1 + z^{-1}$$

*****

(f) ***Periodic Sequence***

If $x_p(n)$ is periodic and repeats every N samples, and if $\mathbf{Z}[x(n)] = X(z)$ where $x(n) = x_p(n)$ over the first period,

then $$X_p(z) = X(z)\left[\frac{z^N}{z^N - 1}\right] \qquad (2.15)$$

❖ **WE2.15**

A periodic sampled-data sequence is $\{0, 2, 1, 2, 0, 2, 1, 2 \ldots\}$, derive the z-transform of this sequence.

Solution:

The sequence repeats every four sampling periods, therefore $N = 4$, $x(n) = \{0, 2, 1, 2\}$ for the first period, and its corresponding z-transform is $X(z) = 2z^{-1} + z^{-2} + 2z^{-3}$. Substituting this into equation (2.15) gives

$$X_p(z) = \left(2z^{-1} + z^{-2} + 2z^{-3}\right)\frac{z^4}{z^4 - 1} = \frac{z\left(2z^2 + z + 2\right)}{z^4 - 1}$$

Note: This property is useful for obtaining the z-transform of a periodic sequence in closed form. The above result is the closed form of:

$$2z^{-1} + z^{-2} + 2z^{-3} + 2z^{-5} + z^{-6} + 2z^{-7} + \ldots$$

*****

(g) ***Initial and Final Values***

The initial value of a sequence, $x(0)$, can be determined from the z-transform expression using

$$x(0) = \lim_{|z| \to \infty} X(z) \tag{2.16}$$

The final value of a sequence, $x(\infty)$, can be determined from the z-transform expression using

$$x(\infty) = \lim_{|z| \to 1} \left\{ \left(1 - z^{-1}\right) X(z) \right\} \tag{2.17}$$

❖ **WE2.16**

Suppose that $X(z) = 1 + 2z^{-1} + z^{-2}$, determine the initial and final values of the corresponding sequence, $x(n)$.

Solution:

Applying equations (2.16) and (2.17) respectively gives

$$x(0) = \lim_{|z| \to \infty} \left[1 + 2z^{-1} + z^{-2}\right] = 1 + \frac{2}{\infty} + \frac{1}{\infty^2} = 1$$

$$x(\infty) = \lim_{|z| \to 1} \left[\left(1 - z^{-1}\right)\left(1 + 2z^{-1} + z^{-2}\right)\right]$$

$$= \lim_{|z| \to 1} \left[1 + z^{-1} - z^{-2} - z^{-3}\right]$$

$$= 1 + 1 - 1 - 1$$

$$= 0$$

Note: The above result can be confirmed by inspection. The initial value is 1 as it is the coefficient of z^0 and the final value is 0 as the sequence is a finite one.

*****

2.3 Inverse z-Transform

The inverse z-transform is carried out to convert the frequency-domain description of a discrete signal or system to a corresponding time-domain description. This operation can be expressed mathematically as

$$x(n) = \mathbf{Z}^{-1}[X(z)] \tag{2.18}$$

Basically there are three methods of performing the inverse z-transform, these are presented below.

(i) *Long Division Method*

In this method the z-transform of a signal or system, which is expressed as a ratio of two polynomials in z, is simply divided out to produce a power series in the form of equation (2.3) with the coefficients representing the sequence values in the time-domain, namely

$$X(z) = \frac{N(z)}{D(z)} = a_0 z^0 + a_1 z^{-1} + a_2 z^{-2} + \ldots \tag{2.19}$$

where the coefficients a_n are the values of $x(n)$.

❖ **WE2.17**

Given that the sampling period is $T = 1$s, determine $x(n)$ for

$$X(z) = \frac{z\left(1 - e^{-T}\right)}{(z-1)\left(z - e^{-T}\right)}$$

***Solution*:**

Substituting the sampling period into $X(z)$ gives

$$X(z) = \frac{0.632\,z}{(z-1)(z-0.368)} = \frac{0.632\,z}{z^2 - 1.368\,z + 0.368}$$

Dividing the numerator by the denominator using long division we have

$$\begin{array}{r|llll}
 & 0.632\,z^{-1} + 0.865\,z^{-2} + 0.950\,z^{-3} + \ldots & & & \\
z^2 - 1.368\,z + 0.368 & 0.632\,z & & & \\
 & 0.632\,z & -\,0.865 & +\,0.233\,z^{-1} & \\
 & & 0.865 & -\,0.233\,z^{-1} & \\
 & & 0.865 & -\,1.183\,z^{-1} & +\,0.318\,z^{-2} \\
 & & & 0.950\,z^{-1} & -\,0.318\,z^{-2}
\end{array}$$

$$\therefore \qquad X(z) = 0\,z^{0} + 0.632\,z^{-1} + 0.865\,z^{-2} + 0.950\,z^{-3} + \ldots$$

Therefore the values of $x(n)$ at the sampling instants ($n = 0, 1, 2, 3, \ldots$) are (0, 0.632, 0.865, 0.950, ...).

Note: The initial value of zero can be confirmed by applying the initial value theorem:

$$x(0) = \lim_{|z| \to \infty} X(z) \to \frac{\infty}{\infty(z - 0.368)} \to \frac{1}{z} \to \frac{1}{\infty} \to 0$$

and the final value can be obtained by applying the final value theorem:

$$x(\infty) = \lim_{|z| \to 1} \left(1 - z^{-1}\right) X(z) = \lim_{|z| \to 1} \frac{(z-1)0.632\,z}{z(z-1)(z-0.368)} = 1$$

*****

From WE2.17, it is seen that the long division method is a rather tedious operation. If a large number of sequence values is required, this is best achieved using a computer program. Furthermore, this method provides a **particular solution** of $x(n)$ (for a known value of T). If a closed-form solution is required, one of the following two methods should be used.

(ii) *Partial Fraction Expansion Method*

The expansion procedure presented in Section 2.1.1 is carried out to express $X(z)$ in partial fraction form. We may then refer directly to Table 2.2 (page 71) and change t to nT to obtain the corresponding $x(nT)$ expression (or $x(n)$ expression, as stated in the note on page 11).

❖ WE2.18

Use the partial fraction expansion method to confirm the calculated $x(n)$ values for WE2.17.

Solution:

$$X(z) = \frac{z\left(1 - e^{-T}\right)}{(z-1)\left(z - e^{-T}\right)} = \frac{k_0\,z}{z-1} + \frac{k_1\,z}{z - e^{-T}}$$

$$\therefore \qquad z\left(1 - e^{-T}\right) = k_0\,z\left(z - e^{-T}\right) + k_1\,z(z-1)$$

Equating coefficients of z that have equal exponents gives

$$z^2: \qquad 0 = k_0 + k_1, \qquad \therefore\ k_0 = -k_1$$

$$z^1: \qquad 1 - e^{-T} = -k_0 e^{-T} - k_1 = -k_0 e^{-T} + k_0$$

$$= -k_0\left(e^{-T} - 1\right) = k_0\left(1 - e^{-T}\right)$$

$$\therefore \qquad k_0 = 1 \quad \text{and} \quad k_1 = -1$$

$$\therefore \qquad X(z) = \frac{z}{z-1} - \frac{z}{z - e^{-T}}$$

Using Table 2.2 we obtain

$$x(n) = 1 - e^{\,nT}$$

Substituting $T = 1$s gives

n	0	1	2	3	∞
$1 - e^{-n}$	0	0.632	0.865	0.950	1

*****

(iii) ***Residue Method***

A procedure similar to that discussed in Section 2.1.2 is carried out to determine $x(n)$ by summing residues of $[X(z)z^{n-1}]$ at all poles, namely

$$x(n) = \sum_{\substack{\text{all poles} \\ \text{of } X(z)}} \text{Residues of } \left[X(z)\, z^{n-1}\right] \tag{2.20}$$

where the residue for a pole of order m at $z = x$ is

$$\text{Residue} = \frac{1}{(m-1)!} \lim_{z \to x} \left\{ \frac{d^{m-1}}{dz^{m-1}} \left[(z - x)^m\, X(z)\, z^{n-1} \right] \right\} \tag{2.21}$$

❖ WE2.19

Use the residue method to confirm the $x(n)$ expression derived in WE2.18.

***Solution*:**

$X(z)$ has two poles of order $m = 1$ at $z = 1$ and at $z = \mathrm{e}^{-T}$. By applying equation (2.21), the corresponding residues are

For pole at $z = 1$:

$$Residue = \frac{1}{0!} \lim_{z \to 1} \left\{ \frac{\mathrm{d}^0}{\mathrm{d}z^0} \left[(z-1)^1 \frac{z\left(1-\mathrm{e}^{-T}\right)}{(z-1)\left(z-\mathrm{e}^{-T}\right)} z^{n-1} \right] \right\}$$

$$= \lim_{z \to 1} \left[\frac{z\left(1-\mathrm{e}^{-T}\right) z^{n-1}}{\left(z-\mathrm{e}^{-T}\right)} \right]$$

$$= 1$$

For pole at $z = \mathrm{e}^{-T}$:

$$Residue = \frac{1}{0!} \lim_{z \to \mathrm{e}^{-T}} \left\{ \frac{\mathrm{d}^0}{\mathrm{d}z^0} \left[\left(z-\mathrm{e}^{-T}\right)^1 \frac{z\left(1-\mathrm{e}^{-T}\right)}{(z-1)\left(z-\mathrm{e}^{-T}\right)} z^{n-1} \right] \right\}$$

$$= \lim_{z \to \mathrm{e}^{-T}} \left[\frac{z\left(1-\mathrm{e}^{-T}\right) z^{n-1}}{(z-1)} \right]$$

$$= \frac{\mathrm{e}^{-T}\left(1-\mathrm{e}^{-T}\right)\left(\mathrm{e}^{-T}\right)^{n-1}}{\left(\mathrm{e}^{-T}-1\right)}$$

$$= -\mathrm{e}^{-nT}$$

$$\therefore \quad x(n) = 1 - \mathrm{e}^{-nT}$$

*****

2.4 Digital Transfer Function

The response of a linear system to an input is completely specified by the system transfer function. If the transfer function of an analogue system is $G(s)$, the corresponding digital transfer function, $G(z)$, of the corresponding digital system can be obtained by using the standard z-transform technique (see Sections

2.1.1 and 2.1.2). In general

$$G(z) = \frac{a_0 + a_1 z^{-1} + a_2 z^{-2} + \ldots + a_p z^{-p}}{1 + b_1 z^{-1} + b_2 z^{-2} + \ldots + b_q z^{-q}} = \frac{Y(z)}{X(z)} \qquad (2.22)$$

where $X(z)$ and $Y(z)$ are the z-transforms of the input and output data sequences respectively. Cross-multiplying gives

$$a_0 X(z) + a_1 X(z) z^{-1} + a_2 X(z) z^{-2} + \ldots + a_p X(z) z^{-p}$$

$$= Y(z) + b_1 Y(z) z^{-1} + b_2 Y(z) z^{-2} + \ldots + b_q Y(z) z^{-q}$$

Taking the inverse z-transform gives

$$a_0 x(n) + a_1 x(n-1) + a_2 x(n-2) + \ldots + a_p x(n-p)$$

$$= y(n) + b_1 y(n-1) + b_2 y(n-2) + \ldots + b_q y(n-q)$$

Rearranging gives:

$$y(n) = a_0 x(n) + a_1 x(n-1) + a_2 x(n-2) + \ldots + a_p x(n-p)$$

$$- b_1 y(n-1) - b_2 y(n-2) - \ldots - b_q y(n-q) \qquad (2.23)$$

This is the general difference equation introduced in Section 1.5 (see equation 1.39). The recursive form of the equation implies that the present output sample value, $y(n)$, is computed using a scaled version of the present input sample, $x(n)$, and scaled versions of previous input and output samples. This corresponds to an Infinite Impulse Response (IIR) digital signal processor.

Using z^{-1} to represent a time delay of one sampling period (T seconds), the direct form of implementation of equation (2.23) is shown in block diagram form in Figure 2.2. It is seen that a feedback path exists, and therefore it is necessary to consider whether this has any effect on system stability. If, due to feedback, any increase in the output causes further increase in the output, the system is unstable, and theoretically the output increases indefinitely. However, in practice, the output value cannot increase indefinitely, and the output will be clamped at the maximum value allowed by the digital signal processor system.

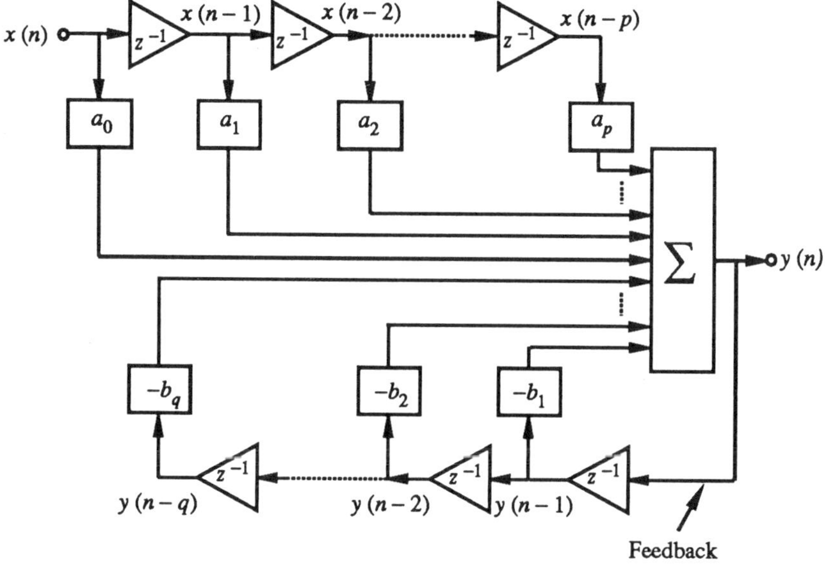

Figure 2.2 Block diagram of IIR DSP system

❖ **WE2.20**

For the IIR DSP system shown Figure 2.3, determine

(a) the digital transfer function, and
(b) calculate the first five output values and the final output value for a weighted unit-impulse input, $2\delta(t)$, for (i) $b = 0.5$ and (ii) $b = 1.5$.

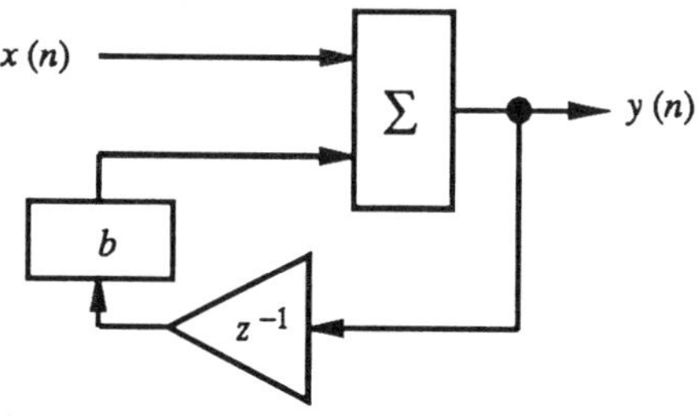

Figure 2.3

Solution:

(a) Writing the difference equation for the DSP system gives

$$y(n) = x(n) + b\,y(n-1)$$

Taking the z-transform gives

$$Y(z) = X(z) + bY(z)\,z^{-1}$$

Therefore the digital transfer function is

$$G(z) = \frac{Y(z)}{X(z)} = \frac{1}{1 - bz^{-1}} = \frac{z}{z - b}$$

(b) The z-transform of the weighted unit-impulse is 2, therefore

$$Y(z) = X(z)\,G(z) = \frac{2z}{z - b}$$

The inverse z-transform of $\frac{z}{z - \alpha}$ is α^n, therefore

$$y(n) = 2\,b^n$$

For $b = 0.5$, the output values are $y(n) = \{2, 1, 0.5, 0.25, 0.125, ... 0\}$.

For $b = 1.5$, the output values are $y(n) = \{2, 3, 4.5, 6.75, 10.125, ... \infty\}$.

Note: It is seen that the system becomes unstable when b changes from 0.5 to 1.5. The indefinite increase in the output value will eventually result in an arithmetic overflow in the DSP system.

*****

2.4.1 *Stability Considerations*

If the output signal magnitude from a DSP system, $y(n)$, is to be finite, then the magnitude of its z-transform, $Y(z)$, must be finite. The set of z values in the z-plane for which the magnitude of $Y(z)$ is finite is called the ***region of convergence***, and in contrast the set of z values in the z-plane for which the magnitude of $Y(z)$ is infinite is called the ***region of divergence***. From equation (2.3), $Y(z)$ is a function of z^{-n}. Hence the condition for $Y(z)$ to be finite is $|z| > 1$. In other words, the region of convergence for $Y(z)$ is the area outside the unit-circle in the z-plane.

❖ **WE2.21**

Determine the region of convergence for $Y(z)$ in WE2.20.

***Solution*:**
From WE2.20, $y(n) = 2b^n$. Applying equation (2.3), the corresponding z-transform is

$$Y(z) = \sum_{n=0}^{\infty} 2b^n z^{-n} = 2\sum_{n=0}^{\infty} \left(bz^{-1}\right)^n$$

Since this infinite series converges for $|bz^{-1}| < 1$, the region of convergence is $|z| > b$ as shown in Figure 2.4.

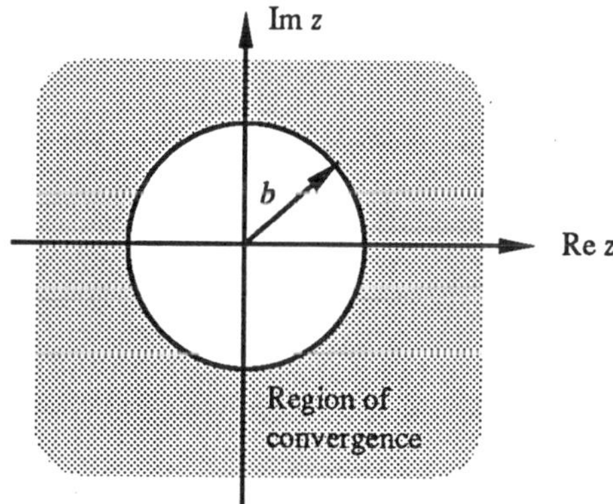

Figure 2.4

Note: Since $y(n)$ is a function of b^n, a further condition of $b < 1$ is imposed for $y(n)$ to be finite. Hence the region of convergence, $|z| > b$, reduces to $|z| > 1$.

*****

Since $Y(z) = G(z) \times X(z)$, where $G(z)$ is the digital transfer function and $X(z)$ is the z-transform of the input signal, the stability requirement of finite output for finite input implies that $G(z)$ must be finite for $|z| > 1$ (i.e. outside the unit-circle).

Consider $G(z)$ given by equation (2.22), the two polynomials can be factorised to yield

$$G(z) = \frac{f(z - z_1)(z - z_2)\cdots(z - z_p)}{(z - p_1)(z - p_2)\cdots(z - p_q)} = \frac{f\prod_{i=1}^{p}(z - z_i)}{\prod_{i=1}^{q}(z - p_i)} \qquad (2.24)$$

where f is a multiplying factor which is a real constant; z_i are called the zeros of $G(z)$ because $G(z) = 0$ for $z = z_i$, and p_i are called the poles of $G(z)$ because $G(z) = \infty$ for $z = p_i$. Hence the requirement of $G(z)$ to be finite for $|z| > 1$ implies that the poles of $G(z)$ must lie inside the unit-circle in the z-plane in a stable digital system.

❖ WE2.22

With reference to the weighted unit-impulse response of the DSP system in WE2.20, draw the pole-zero pattern and plot the output response for $b = \pm 0.5$, ± 1, ± 1.5, respectively.

Solution:

For $b = 0.5$, $Y(z) = \dfrac{2z}{z - 0.5}$ and $y(n) = 2 \times 0.5^n$

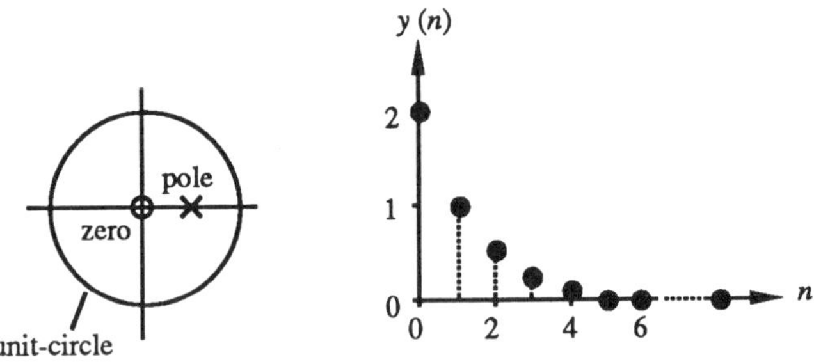

For $b = -0.5$, $Y(z) = \dfrac{2z}{z + 0.5}$ and $y(n) = 2 \times (-0.5)^n$

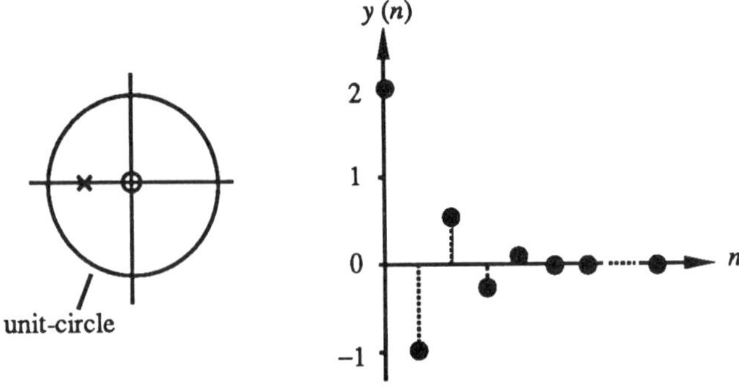

For $b = 1$, $Y(z) = \dfrac{2z}{z-1}$ and $y(n) = 2 \times 1^n$

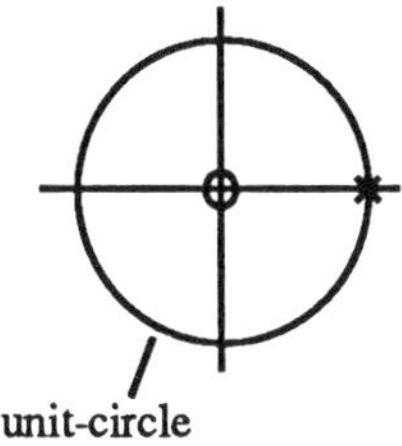

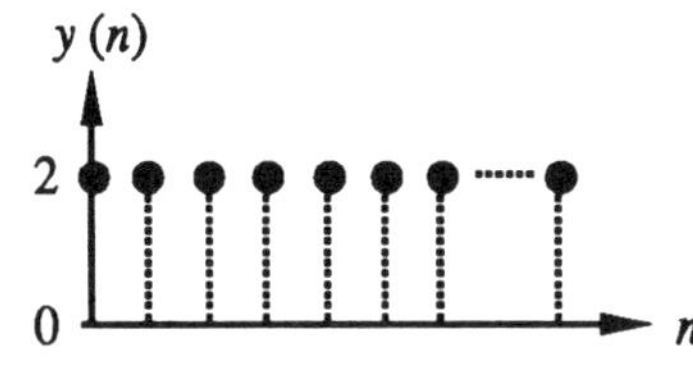

For $b = -1$, $Y(z) = \dfrac{2z}{z+1}$ and $y(n) = 2 \times (-1)^n$

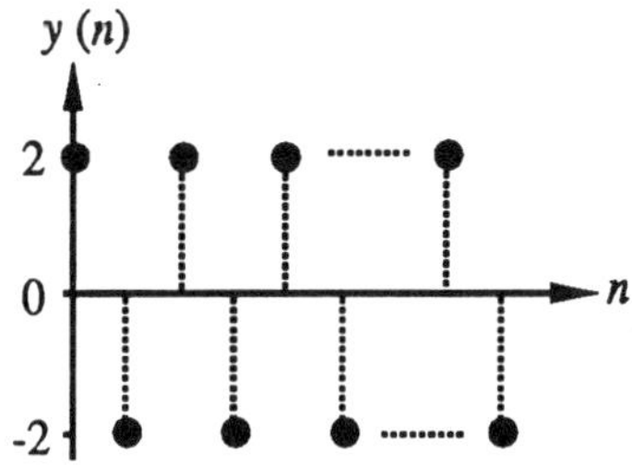

For $b = 1.5$, $Y(z) = \dfrac{2z}{z-1.5}$ and $y(n) = 2 \times 1.5^n$

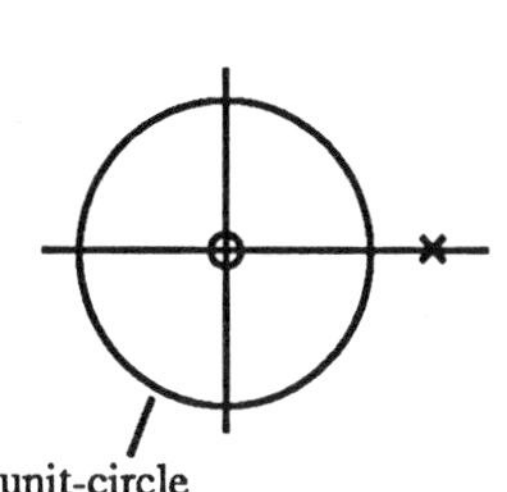

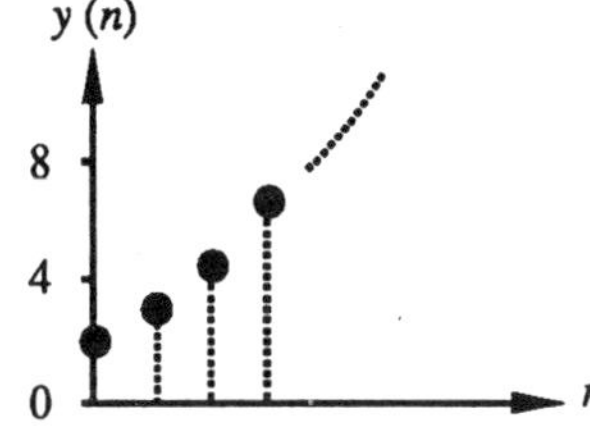

For $b = -1.5$, $Y(z) = \dfrac{2z}{z+1.5}$ and $y(n) = 2 \times (-1.5)^n$

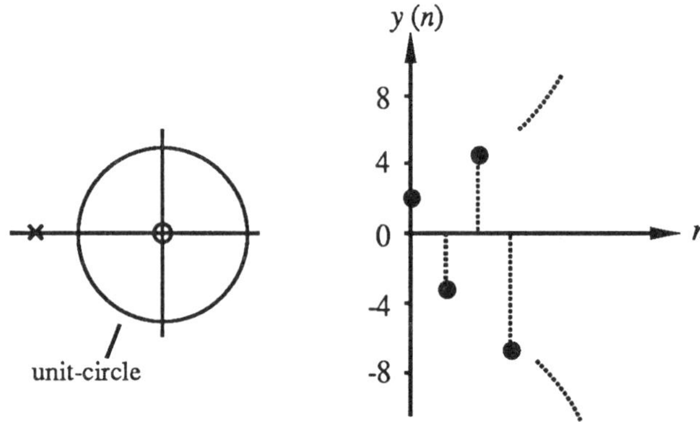

Note: When $b = \pm 1$, the pole lies on the unit-circle and the system is marginally stable.

*****

2.4.2 *Frequency Response*

The magnitude and phase of the frequency response of a digital system may be estimated by geometrical construction using

$$\left|G\left(e^{j\omega T}\right)\right| = \frac{\displaystyle\prod_{i=1}^{p}\left\{\begin{array}{l}\text{Vector magnitude from the } i_{th} \text{ zero} \\ \text{to the frequency - point on the} \\ \text{circumference of the unit - circle}\end{array}\right\}}{\displaystyle\prod_{i=1}^{q}\left\{\begin{array}{l}\text{Vector magnitude from the } i_{th} \text{ pole} \\ \text{to the frequency - point on the} \\ \text{circumference of the unit - circle}\end{array}\right\}} \tag{2.25}$$

$$\angle G\left(e^{j\omega T}\right)=\sum_{i=1}^{p}\left\{\begin{matrix}\text{Angle from the } i_{th} \text{ zero to the frequency-point}\\ \text{on the circumference of the unit-circle}\end{matrix}\right\}$$

$$-\sum_{i=1}^{q}\left\{\begin{matrix}\text{Angle from the } i_{th} \text{ pole to the frequency-point}\\ \text{on the circumference of the unit-circle}\end{matrix}\right\} \qquad (2.26)$$

❖ **WE2.23**

A digital signal processor has the digital transfer function

$$G(z)=\frac{z^2-0.25}{z^2+0.25}$$

Determine:

(a) whether the DSP system is stable, and

(b) the magnitude and phase frequency response at $\omega = k\omega_s$ for k in the range $0 \le k \le 1$.

Solution:

(a) Factorising the digital transfer function yields

$$G(z)=\frac{z^2-0.25}{z^2+0.25}=\frac{(z-0.5)(z+0.5)}{(z-j0.5)(z+j0.5)}$$

Therefore the DSP system has two poles, one at $z=-j0.5$ and the other at $z=j0.5$. Since these two poles are inside the unit-circle in the z-plane, the DSP system is stable.

(b) Substituting $e^{j\omega T}$ for z in the digital transfer function yields

$$G\left(e^{j\omega T}\right)=\frac{e^{j2\omega T}-0.25}{e^{j2\omega T}+0.25}=\frac{(\cos 2\omega T-0.25)+j\sin 2\omega T}{(\cos 2\omega T+0.25)+j\sin 2\omega T}$$

since $2\omega T=2k\omega_s T=2k\frac{2\pi}{T}T=4k\pi$

$$\therefore \quad G\left(e^{j\omega T}\right)=\frac{(\cos 4\pi k-0.25)+j\sin 4\pi k}{(\cos 4\pi k+0.25)+j\sin 4\pi k} \qquad (2.27)$$

$|G(e^{j\omega T})|$ and $\angle G(e^{j\omega T})$ may now be evaluated for various values of k, and this is best achieved using a computer program or a spreadsheet software package. The graphical output is shown below:

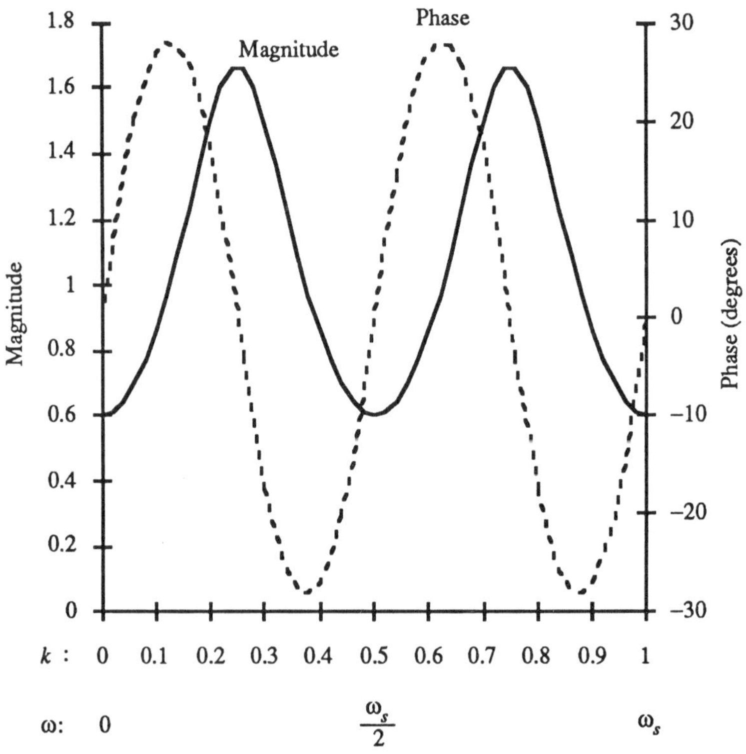

Note: The periodicity of the frequency response implies that computation is only necessary for frequencies from d.c. up to half the sampling frequency.

*****

❖ **WE2.24**

Determine, using (i) the substitution method and (ii) the geometrical construction method, the frequency response for the DSP system in WE2.23, when $k = 0.65$.

***Solution*:**

(i) Evaluation via the substitution method:

Substituting $k = 0.65$ in equation (2.27) yields

$$G\left(e^{j\omega T}\right) = \frac{((\cos\ 4 \times 0.65\pi) - 0.25) + j\sin(4 \times 0.65\pi)}{((\cos\ 4 \times 0.65\pi) + 0.25) + j\sin(4 \times 0.65\pi)}$$

$$= \frac{-0.559 + j0.951}{-0.059 + j0.951}$$

$$= \frac{1.103\angle 120.45^\circ}{0.953\angle 93.55^\circ}$$

$$= 1.157\angle 26.9^\circ$$

(ii) Evaluation via the geometrical construction method:

Since 0.65 of 2π radians is 234°, the frequency of 0.65 ω_s corresponds to the point on the unit-circle at an angle of 234° in the anti-clockwise direction with respect to the real z axis, or 36° in the clockwise direction with respect to the negative imaginary z axis.

For the pole at $z = j0.5$, the corresponding geometric configuration is shown in Figure 2.5.

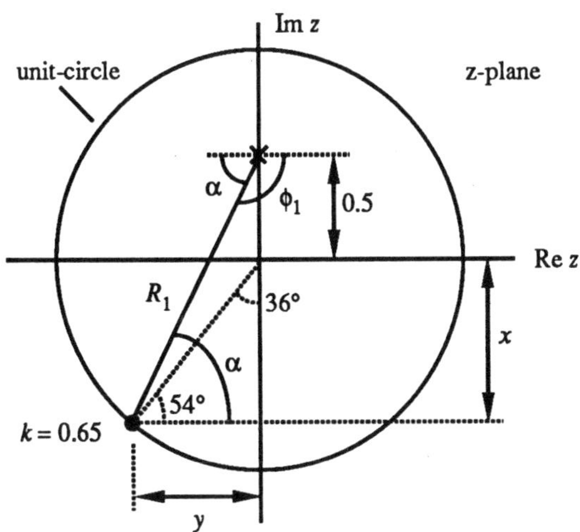

Figure 2.5

The required calculations are

$$x = \sin 54° = 0.809\ , \qquad y = \cos 54° = 0.588$$

$$R_1 = \sqrt{(0.5 + 0.809)^2 + 0.588^2} = 1.435$$

$$\alpha = \tan^{-1}\left(\frac{1.309}{0.588}\right) = 65.81°$$

$$\phi_1 = -(180° - 65.81°) = -114.19°$$

For the pole at $z = -j0.5$, the corresponding geometric configuration is shown in Figure 2.6.

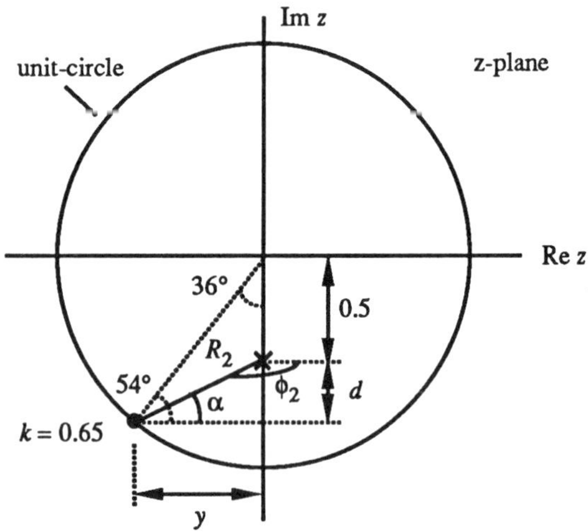

Figure 2.6

The required calculations are

$$\frac{0.5 + d}{y} = \tan\ 54°$$

$$\therefore \qquad d = y \tan 54° - 0.5$$

$$= (0.588 \times 1.3764) - 0.5$$

$$= 0.3093$$

$$R_2 = \sqrt{d^2 + y^2} = \sqrt{0.3093^2 + 0.588^2} = 0.664$$

$$\alpha = \tan^{-1}\left(\frac{d}{y}\right) = \tan^{-1}\left(\frac{0.3093}{0.588}\right) = 27.75°$$

$$\phi_2 = -(180° - 27.75°) = -152.25°$$

For the zero at $z = -0.5$, the corresponding geometric configuration is shown in Figure 2.7.

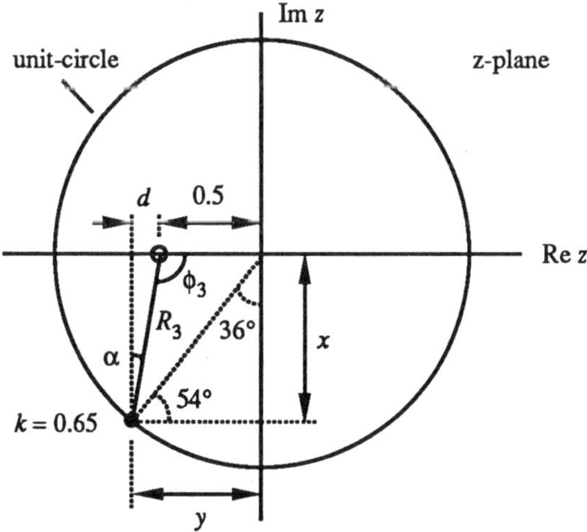

Figure 2.7

The required calculations are

$$d = y - 0.5 = 0.088$$

$$R_3 = \sqrt{d^2 + x^2} = \sqrt{0.088^2 + 0.809^2} = 0.814$$

$$\alpha = \tan^{-1}\left(\frac{d}{x}\right) = \tan^{-1}\left(\frac{0.088}{0.809}\right) = 6.2°$$

$$\phi_3 = -(90° + 6.2°) = -96.2°$$

For the zero at $z = 0.5$, the corresponding geometric configuration is shown in Figure 2.8.

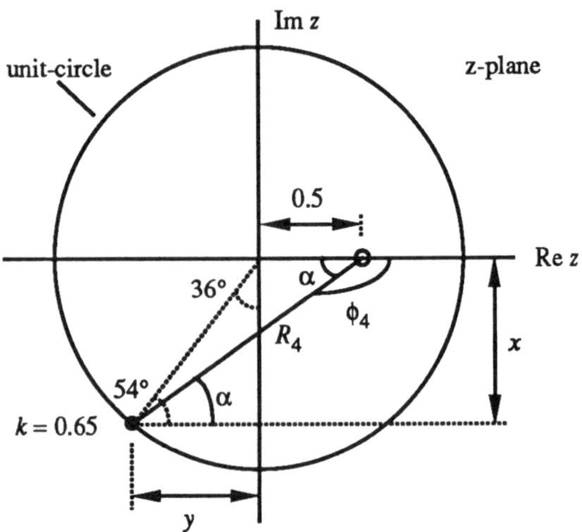

Figure 2.8

The required calculations are

$$R_4 = \sqrt{(0.5 + y)^2 + x^2} = \sqrt{(0.5 + 0.588)^2 + 0.809^2} = 1.356$$

$$\alpha = \tan^{-1}\left(\frac{x}{0.5 + y}\right) = \tan^{-1}\left(\frac{0.809}{1.088}\right) = 36.63°$$

$$\phi_4 = -(180° - 36.63°) = -143.37°$$

Substituting vector magnitudes (R values) into equation (2.25) gives

$$\left|G\left(e^{j\omega T}\right)\right| = \frac{R_3 \times R_4}{R_1 \times R_2} = \frac{0.814 \times 1.356}{1.435 \times 0.664} = 1.158$$

Substituting angles (ϕ values) into equation (2.26) gives

$$\angle G\left(e^{j\omega T}\right) = (\phi_3 + \phi_4) - (\phi_1 + \phi_2)$$

$$= (-96.2° - 143.37°) - (-114.19° - 152.25°) = 26.87°$$

Note: The geometrical construction reveals the contribution to the frequency response from each pole and zero. In this example the response at the frequency of interest is seen to be dominated by the nearest pole and zero, namely the pole at $z = -j0.5$ and the zero at $z = -0.5$.

*****

It should be noted that when the standard z-transform is used (via the residue method or Table 2.2), the frequency response of the digital transfer function, $G(e^{j\omega T})$, will generally differ from that of the analogue transfer function, $G(j\omega)$. Consider the following analogue transfer function:

$$G(s) = \frac{\alpha}{s + \alpha}$$

The frequency response for $G(s)$ is

$$G(j\omega) = \frac{\alpha}{j\omega + \alpha}$$

However $G(s)$ may be z-transformed to

$$G(z) = \frac{\alpha z}{z - e^{-\alpha T}}$$

The frequency response for $G(z)$ is

$$G\left(e^{j\omega T}\right) = \frac{\alpha e^{j\omega T}}{e^{j\omega T} - e^{-\alpha T}}$$

In many applications it is desirable that $G(j\omega)$ be faithfully modelled by $G(e^{j\omega T})$, i.e. the same frequency response. Consider the case $\omega = 0$ for both transfer functions:

$$G(j0) = \frac{\alpha}{\alpha} = 1$$

and $$G\left(e^{j0}\right) = \frac{\alpha}{1 - e^{-\alpha T}}$$

but $$e^{-\alpha T} = 1 - \alpha T + \frac{(\alpha T)^2}{2} - \frac{(\alpha T)^3}{6} + \cdots$$

$$\therefore \qquad 1 - e^{-\alpha T} = \alpha T - \frac{(\alpha T)^2}{2} + \frac{(\alpha T)^3}{6} - \cdots$$

$$\cong \alpha T \qquad \text{for} \quad \alpha T << 1$$

$$\therefore \qquad G(e^{j0}) \cong \frac{\alpha}{\alpha T} = \frac{1}{T}$$

Consequently it is necessary to multiply the digital transfer function by a factor of T to make the two systems have (ideally) the same frequency response at $\omega = 0$ (as ω increases the two frequency response functions generally diverge). That is

$$G_T(z) = G(z) \times T \tag{2.28}$$

so that $G_T(e^{j\omega T}) = G(j\omega)$ at $\omega = 0$

❖ **WE2.25**

The transfer function of an analogue R-C lowpass filter is given by

$$G(s) = \frac{1000}{s + 1000}$$

Confirm that the relationship defined by equation (2.28) is valid when the corresponding digital transfer function, $G(z)$, is required to have a frequency response that closely matches the passband characteristic of the analogue prototype filter. Also comment on (i) the theoretical value of T needed to satisfy this requirement, and (ii) a practical value of T that might be used in implementing the DSP system.

Solution:

$$G(s) = \frac{\alpha}{s + \alpha} \qquad \text{where } \alpha = 1000$$

and $$G(j\omega) = \frac{\alpha}{\alpha + j\omega}$$

For $\omega = 0$: $$G(j0) = \frac{\alpha}{\alpha + j0} = 1$$

For $\omega = \alpha$: $$G(j\alpha) = \frac{\alpha}{\alpha + j\alpha}$$

$$\left|G(\mathrm{j}\,\alpha)\right| = \frac{1}{\sqrt{2}} \qquad (-\,3\,\mathrm{dB})$$

From Table 2.2

$$G(z) = \frac{\alpha\, z}{z - \mathrm{e}^{-\alpha T}}$$

$$G_T(z) = T \times G(z) = \frac{\alpha\, T z}{z - \mathrm{e}^{-\alpha T}}$$

For $\omega = 0$ we have $z = 1$, therefore

$$\left|G_T\left(\mathrm{e}^{\,\mathrm{j}0}\right)\right| = \frac{1000\,T}{1 - \mathrm{e}^{-1000T}}$$

and this has to be equal to $|G(\mathrm{j}0)| = 1$, therefore

$$1000\,T = 1 - \mathrm{e}^{-1000T}$$

This equality holds for $T = 0$ (this answers point (i)), but the pole of $G_T(z)$ is at $z = 1$, which is directly on the stability boundary. In practice it would be necessary to relax the $T = 0$ constraint to, say, $T = 10^{-5}$ s. For this case, $G_T(z)$ becomes

$$G_T(z) = \frac{0.01\,z}{z - \mathrm{e}^{-0.01}} = \frac{0.01\,z}{z - 0.99}$$

Note that the pole has moved off, and just inside, the stability boundary.

For $\omega = 0$:

$$\left|G_T\left(\mathrm{e}^{\,\mathrm{j}0}\right)\right| = \frac{0.01 \times 1}{1 - 0.99} = 1 \qquad \text{(as required)}$$

For $\omega = \alpha$:

$$G_T\left(\mathrm{e}^{\mathrm{j}\alpha T}\right) = \frac{0.01\ \mathrm{e}^{\,\mathrm{j}0.01}}{\mathrm{e}^{\mathrm{j}0.01} - 0.99}$$

$$= \frac{0.01(\cos\,0.01 + \mathrm{j}\sin 0.01)}{(\cos\,0.01 + \mathrm{j}\sin 0.01) - 0.99}$$

$$= \frac{0.0099995\ + \mathrm{j}\,0.0001}{0.00995\ + \mathrm{j}\,0.01}$$

$$\left|G_T\left(e^{j\alpha T}\right)\right| = \frac{0.01}{0.0141} = 0.7092 \qquad (-2.985\ \text{dB})$$

Therefore $T = 10^{-5}$ s may be considered to satisfy point (ii).

*****

2.5 Bilinear z-Transform

It was stated in Section 2.4.2 that a comparison of the frequency response of the digital transfer function and the analogue transfer function is restricted to the frequency range d.c. to $f_s/2$. This restriction is removed by the bilinear z-transform which compresses the entire analogue frequency response to the digital frequency range 0 to $f_s/2$. This is useful when designing digital filters because, compared with designs obtained by the standard z-transform, the frequency response of $G(z)$ matches more closely that of $G(s)$. Furthermore, the bilinear z-transform is a straightforward design method, and it ensures that:

(a) a stable $G(s)$ transforms to a stable $G(z)$.

(b) a wideband sharp cut-off $G(s)$ characteristic transforms to a wideband sharp cut-off $G(z)$ characteristic.

(c) it matches the sampled frequency response function $|G(e^{j\omega T})|$ to the analogue frequency response function $|G(j\omega)|$ for breakpoints and zero frequency, and compresses the response at analogue frequency $\omega_a = \infty$ to sampled frequency $\omega_d = \pi/T = \omega_s/2$.

Note that in transforming $G(s)$ to $G(z)$ via the bilinear z-transform the impulse response and phase response are not preserved.

The bilinear z-transform can be considered as consisting of two mapping stages, namely from s-plane to R-plane followed by R-plane to z-plane, as illustrated in Figure 2.9.

The first stage of mapping transforms the s-plane representation of $G(s)$ to an equivalent R-plane representation by using the relationship

$$s = \frac{2}{T} \tanh\left(\frac{RT}{2}\right) \tag{2.29}$$

where $s = \pm\sigma \pm j\omega$, $R = \pm u \pm jv$, and T is the sampling period (seconds).

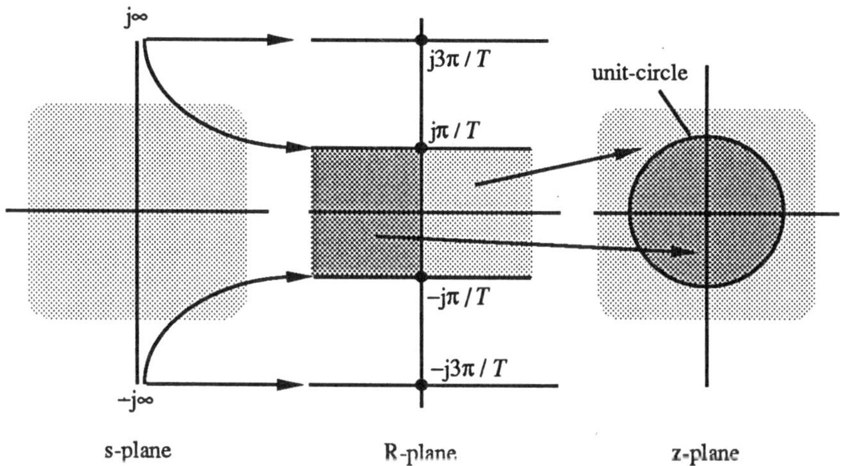

Figure 2.9 Bilinear z transform

Consider when $R = \dfrac{j\pi}{T}$, then

$$s = \frac{2}{T}\tanh\left(\frac{j\pi}{T} \times \frac{T}{2}\right) = \frac{2}{T}\tanh\left(\frac{j\pi}{2}\right)$$

but $\tanh(j\theta) = j\tan\theta$, therefore in this case we have

$$s = \frac{j2}{T}\tan\left(\frac{\pi}{2}\right) = j\infty$$

Now consider when $R = \dfrac{j\pi}{T} + j\omega_s = \dfrac{j\pi}{T} + \dfrac{j2\pi}{T} = \dfrac{j3\pi}{T}$, then

$$s = \frac{j2}{T}\tan\left(\frac{3\pi}{2}\right) = j\infty$$

Thus it is seen that the frequency range 0 to ∞ in the s-plane transforms (via equation (2.29)) to the bandlimited range 0 to π / T (0 to $\omega_s / 2$) in the R-plane. Note also that non-overlapping complementary frequency bands exist.

The second stage of mapping transforms the R-plane representation of $G(s)$ to an equivalent z-plane representation by using the relationship

$$z = e^{RT} \tag{2.30}$$

In this case, for frequency domain considerations $u = 0$, and $z = e^{j\nu T} = \cos\nu T + j\sin\nu T$. Consider when $\nu = 0$ (corresponding to $\omega_a = 0$), then $z = 1 + j0$; also consider when $\nu = \pi / T$ (corresponding to $\omega_a = \infty$) then $z = -1 + j0$. Consequently the entire s-plane frequency range 0 to ∞ is mapped to the semi-circumference of the unit-circle in the z-plane, see Figure 2.10.

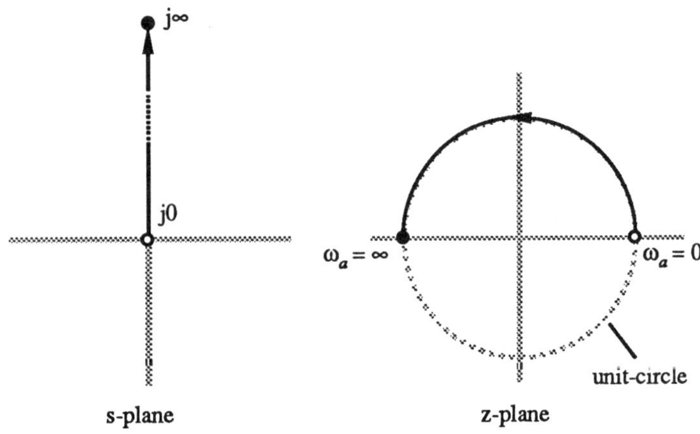

Figure 2.10 Bilinear z-transform of s-plane frequency axis

Now referring to equation (2.29), let $\dfrac{RT}{2} = jx$, then

$$s = \frac{2}{T}\tanh(jx) = \frac{j2}{T}\tan x$$

$$\therefore \quad s = \frac{j2}{T}\tan\left(\frac{RT}{j2}\right) = \frac{j2}{T}\left[\frac{\sin\left(\dfrac{RT}{j2}\right)}{\cos\left(\dfrac{RT}{j2}\right)}\right] = \frac{j2}{T}\left[\frac{\dfrac{e^{\frac{RT}{2}} - e^{-\frac{RT}{2}}}{j2}}{\dfrac{e^{\frac{RT}{2}} + e^{-\frac{RT}{2}}}{2}}\right]$$

$$= \frac{2}{T}\left[\frac{e^{\frac{RT}{2}} - e^{-\frac{RT}{2}}}{e^{\frac{RT}{2}} + e^{-\frac{RT}{2}}}\right] \times \frac{e^{\frac{RT}{2}}}{e^{\frac{RT}{2}}} = \frac{2}{T}\left[\frac{e^{RT} - 1}{e^{RT} + 1}\right]$$

$$\therefore \quad s = \frac{2}{T}\left[\frac{z-1}{z+1}\right] \tag{2.31}$$

Let us investigate further the relationship between the s-plane and z-plane frequency scales. Let $s = j\omega_a$ and let $z = e^{j\omega_d T}$ and substituting these in equation (2.31) yields

$$j\omega_a = \frac{2}{T}\left[\frac{e^{j\omega_d T} - 1}{e^{j\omega_d T} + 1}\right] = \frac{2}{T}\left[\frac{1 - e^{-j\omega_d T}}{1 + e^{-j\omega_d T}}\right] \times \left[\frac{\dfrac{e^{\left(\frac{j\omega_d T}{2}\right)}}{j2}}{\dfrac{e^{\left(\frac{j\omega_d T}{2}\right)}}{j2}}\right]$$

$$= \frac{2}{T}\left[\frac{\dfrac{\left(e^{j\omega_d \frac{T}{2}} - e^{-j\omega_d \frac{T}{2}}\right)}{j2}}{\dfrac{\left(e^{j\omega_d \frac{T}{2}} + e^{-j\omega_d \frac{T}{2}}\right)}{j2}}\right] = \frac{2}{T}\left[\frac{\sin\dfrac{\omega_d T}{2}}{\dfrac{\cos\dfrac{\omega_d T}{2}}{j}}\right]$$

$$= j\frac{2}{T}\tan\left(\frac{\omega_d T}{2}\right)$$

$$\therefore \quad \omega_a = \frac{2}{T}\tan\left(\frac{\omega_d T}{2}\right) \tag{2.32}$$

The relationship between ω_a and ω_d is non-linear due to the tan function. Consequently if a particular value of ω_d is required (say a digital filter cut-off frequency) then firstly it is ***prewarped*** (converted) to a corresponding analogue frequency value, ω_a, using equation (2.32) for a given (known) value of T. The transfer function $G(s)$ is then transformed to $G(z)$ by substituting equation (2.31) for s in $G(s)$.

❖ WE2.26

Using the bilinear z-transform method, design a lowpass digital filter having a cut-off frequency, f_{cd}, equal to 100 Hz. Check that the derived transfer function, $G(z)$, is stable. Assume that the sampling frequency is 625 Hz, and that the transfer function of the prototype denormalised lowpass analogue filter is

$$G(s) = \frac{\omega_{ca}^2}{s^2 + \sqrt{2}\,\omega_{ca}\, s + \omega_{ca}^2}$$

Solution:
Prewarping using equation (2.32) gives the analogue cut-off frequency as

$$\omega_{ca} = \frac{2}{T} \tan\left(\frac{2\pi f_{cd} T}{2}\right) = \frac{2}{T} \tan(100\pi T)$$

but $T = \frac{1}{f_s} = \frac{1}{625} = 1.6 \text{ ms}$

$$\therefore \qquad \omega_{ca} = \frac{2}{1.6 \times 10^{-3}} \tan\left(100\pi \times 1.6 \times 10^{-3}\right) = 687.2 \text{ rad/s}$$

Substituting the value of ω_{ca} into the analogue filter transfer function yields

$$G(s)_{pw} = \frac{(687.2)^2}{s^2 + \sqrt{2} \times 687.2\; s + (687.2)^2}$$

For the bilinear z-transform

$$s = \frac{2}{T}\left[\frac{z-1}{z+1}\right] = \frac{2}{1.6 \times 10^{-3}}\left[\frac{z-1}{z+1}\right] = 1250\left[\frac{z-1}{z+1}\right]$$

Now substituting for s in $G(s)_{pw}$ gives the following digital filter transfer function:

$$G(z) = \frac{(687.2)^2}{1250^2\left[\frac{(z-1)^2}{(z+1)^2}\right] + \sqrt{2} \times 687.2 \times 1250\left[\frac{z-1}{z+1}\right] + (687.2)^2}$$

$$= \frac{z^2 + 2z + 1}{6.88\, z^2 - 4.62\, z + 1.74}$$

Solving the denominator quadratic equation we obtain the pole positions to check for stability:

$$z_{poles} = \frac{-(-4.62) \pm \sqrt{(-4.62)^2 - (4 \times 6.88 \times 1.74)}}{2 \times 6.88}$$

$$= 0.336 \pm j0.374$$

Since the poles lie inside the unit-circle in the z-plane, $G(z)$ is stable.

*****

2.6 Chirp z-Transform

In Section 2.4.2 it was shown that the computation of the frequency response of a digital system is carried out by substituting $e^{j\omega T}$ for z in the digital transfer function. Since $e^{j\omega T}$ is equivalent to $1\angle\omega T$, the frequency response was actually evaluated by using points on the unit-circle in the z-plane. There is nothing to stop the frequency response being evaluated using other points on different contours in the z-plane. Different contours will produce different shapes of frequency reponse. A contour passing through, or close to, positions of poles and zeros will produce very sharp peaks and troughs in the frequency response. Such contours are desirable in spectrum analysis of signals or systems, because sharp peaks and troughs allow poles and zeros to be located precisely, which in turn allow signals or systems to be modelled accurately. The evaluation of the z-transform of signals, $X(z)$, or systems, $G(z)$, at points along an arbitrary contour is accomplished by the chirp z-transform.

For the chirp z-transform, the value of an N-sample sequence at a point k on a contour in the z-plane is given by

$$X(z_k) = \sum_{n=0}^{N-1} x(n)\, z_k^{-n} \tag{2.33}$$

where z_k is defined as

$$z_k = \left(r_0 e^{j\omega_0 T}\right)\left(R_0 e^{j\Delta\omega T}\right)^k \tag{2.34}$$

Figure 2.11 shows three possible contours of z_k. When $k = 0$, the first bracketed term in equation (2.34) defines the first point of a contour at $r_0\angle\omega_0 T$. As k increases, the points follow a contour spiraling toward the origin if the constant $R_0 < 1$, but they follow a contour spiraling away from the origin if $R_0 > 1$. The contour forms a circle of radius r_0 if $R_0 = 1$ and becomes the unit-circle if $r_0 = R_0 = 1$. The spacing between points is determined by $\Delta\omega T$.

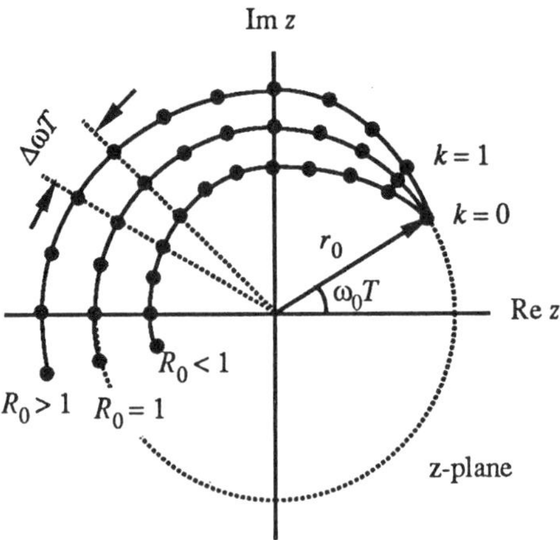

Figure 2.11 Three possible contours for chirp z-transform

Substituing equation (2.34) for z_k in equation (2.33) yields

$$X(z_k) = \sum_{n=0}^{N-1} x(n)\, A^{-n}\, W^{-nk} \tag{2.35}$$

where $\quad A = r_0\, e^{j\omega_0 T}$ (2.36)

and $\quad W = R_0\, e^{j\Delta\omega T}$ (2.37)

Since $\quad nk = \frac{1}{2}\left[n^2 + k^2 - (k-n)^2 \right]$ equation (2.35) can be expressed as

$$X(z_k) = W^{-\frac{k^2}{2}} \sum_{n=0}^{N-1} \left[x(n)\, A^{-n}\, W^{-\frac{n^2}{2}} \right] W^{\frac{(k-n)^2}{2}}$$

i.e. $$X(z_k) = W^{-\frac{k^2}{2}} \sum_{n=0}^{N-1} p(n)\; q(k-n) \tag{2.38}$$

where $\quad p(n) = x(n)\, A^{-n}\, W^{-\frac{n^2}{2}}$ and $q(n) = W^{\frac{n^2}{2}}$

Thus from equation (2.38) it is seen that the chirp z-transform can, basically, be implemented as a convolution operation.

❖ **WE2.27**

Sampling of an analogue signal at a frequency of 10 kHz produces the sequence {1, −0.66946, 0.3665, 0.00132, −0.01475, 0.00097, 0.00052, −0.00008, −0.00002}. Compute the chirp z-transform at 91 points, with equal angular spacing between them, from 0° to 180° on the semi-circumference of circles with radii of 1, 0.8, 0.6, 0.4 and 0.2, and determine the transfer function of the digital system capable of generating the given sequence in response to an applied unit-impulse input.

Solution:

Since the chirp z-transform is evaluated along the semi-circumference of circles starting from 0°, $\omega_0 = 0$ and $R_0 = 1$. Furthermore, 91 equally spaced points from 0° to 180° correspond to points separated by 2° (0.035 rad) with k incrementing from 0 to 90. Since $\Delta\omega T = 0.035$ rad, this angular spacing yields a frequency spacing $\Delta f \cong 56$ Hz. Also $N = 9$ for the given number of samples in the sequence. Substituting these data values into equation (2.33) gives

$$X(z_k) = \sum_{n=0}^{8} x(n)\left(r_0 \, e^{j0.035k}\right)^{-n}$$

$$= \sum_{n=0}^{8} \frac{x(n)}{r_0^{\,n}}\left[\cos 0.035\,kn - j\sin 0.035\,kn\right]$$

The magnitude response, $|X(z_k)|$, may now be evaluated for $k = 0, 1, 2, \ldots 90$ when $r_0 = 1, 0.8, 0.6, 0.4, 0.2$ respectively, and this is best achieved using a computer program or a spreadsheet software package. The graphical output produced is shown in Figure 2.12.

From the graphs shown in Figure 2.12, it is seen that a significant trough, which corresponds to a zero location of the transfer function, occurs at 60° on the curve for $r_0 = 0.6$; and a dominant peak, which corresponds to a pole location of the transfer function, occurs at 100° on the curve for $r_0 = 0.2$. Since the transfer function of digital systems has real coefficients, poles and zeros must occur in complex-conjugate pairs. Consequently there must be another zero at $0.6\angle{-60^\circ}$ and another pole at $0.2\angle{-100^\circ}$.

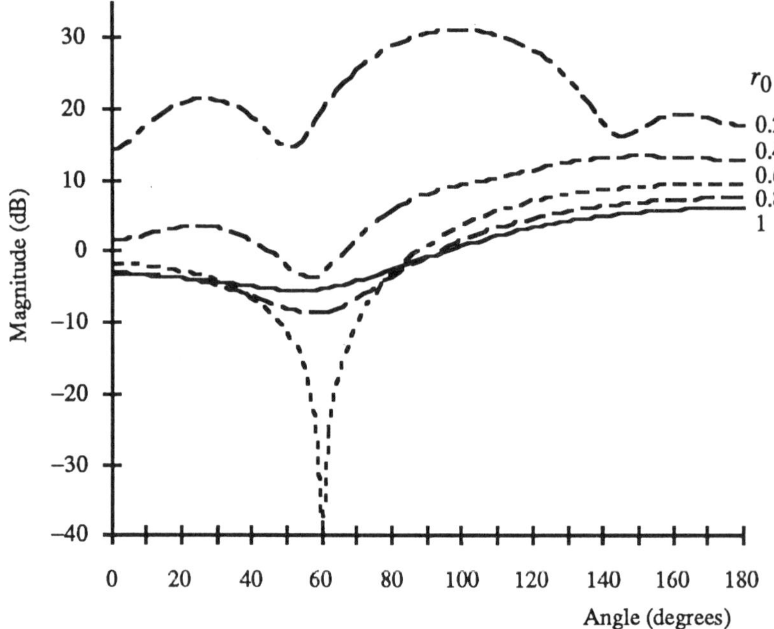

Figure 2.12

The transfer function of the digital system is

$$G(z) = \frac{(z - 0.6\angle 60°)(z - 0.6\angle -60°)}{(z - 0.2\angle 100°)(z - 0.2\angle -100°)}$$

$$= \frac{(z - 0.3 - j0.51962)(z - 0.3 + j0.51962)}{(z + 0.03473 - j0.19696)(z + 0.03473 + j0.19696)}$$

$$= \frac{z^2 - 0.6z + 0.36}{z^2 + 0.06946z + 0.04}$$

Since the z-transform of the unit-impulse is 1, the output sequence for a unit-impulse input can be obtained directly by taking the inverse z-transform of the above transfer function. Applying the long division method discussed in Section 2.3(i) produces the given sequence, and consequently confirms the correct identification of $G(z)$.

*****

2.7 Case Study: Notch Filter Design

A ***notch filter*** is a band-stop filter used to remove undesirable frequencies from a signal.

Aim:

The aim of this case study is to demonstrate how a number of the principles presented in this chapter may be used to design a digital notch filter. The purpose of this filter is to eliminate an interference signal and prevent it from distorting a measurement-transducer signal.

Problem:

A particular measurement-transducer outputs a sinewave voltage of amplitude 0.2 V at a frequency of 20 Hz. This signal, after being transmitted through a short cable to a digital instrumentation system, is sampled at 200 Hz and digitised by an A/D converter. The digitised signal is found to have the repeat sequence {0, 0.9, 0.2, −0.6, 0.1, 0.8, −0.1, −1, −0.2, 0.7, 0, −0.7, 0.2, 1, 0.1, −0.8, −0.1, 0.6, −0.2, −0.9}. Figure 2.13 shows the first 41 samples.

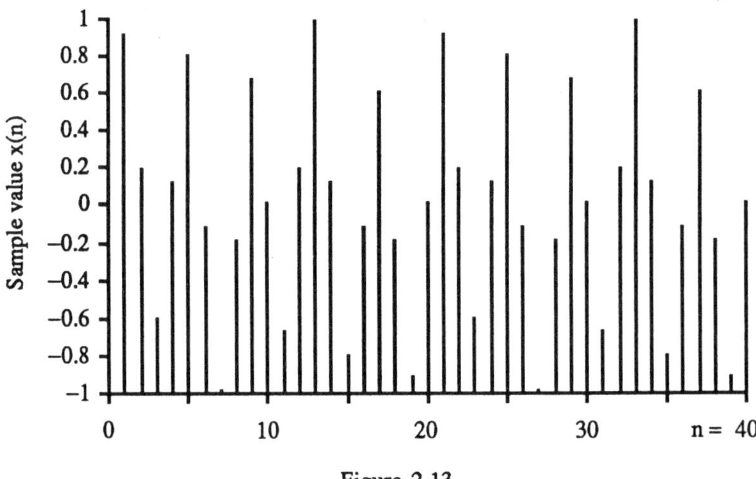

Figure 2.13

From Figure 2.13, it is seen that the digitised signal does not resemble the expected digitised 20 Hz sinewave, which should repeat at an interval of 10 samples. Identify the interference source(s) and design a suitable digital notch filter to eliminate the measurement-transducer signal distortion.

Method:

(a) Signal Analysis
With reference to Figure 2.13, although it is clear that the problem is caused by interference, it is difficult to identify the interference source(s) in the time-domain. Hence the first step is to carry out spectrum analysis of the digitised signal in the digital frequency domain to identify the interference frequency or frequencies.

(b) Notch Filter Design
The next step after identifying the interference source is to design a notch filter to remove the interference signal. Filters can be designed by the placement of poles and zeros in the z-plane. A pole has the effect of passing and amplifying a signal and a zero has the effect of stopping and attenuating a signal. Hence the notch filter can be designed by placing the zero at the point on the circumference of the unit-circle corresponding to the interference frequency. The pole is placed near to the zero to reduce the attenuation effect of the zero on the wanted signal.

(c) Design Confirmation
The final step is to confirm the design by checking that the time-domain output sequence of the notch filter corresponds to the expected digitised sinewave at 20 Hz.

Execution of the Method:

(a) Signal Analysis
The spectrum analysis can be performed by applying equation (2.3) to the digitised signal $x(n)$ to obtain its z-transform $X(z)$, followed by substituting $e^{j\omega T}$ for z in $X(z)$. That is

$$X(z) = \sum_{n=0}^{\infty} x(n)\, z^{-n}$$

followed by

$$\left|X\left(e^{j\omega T}\right)\right| = \left|\sum_{n=0}^{\infty} x(n)\, e^{-j\omega nT}\right|$$

$$= \left|\sum_{n=0}^{\infty} x(n)[\cos \omega nT - j\sin \omega nT]\right|$$

$$= \sqrt{\left[\sum_{n=0}^{\infty} x(n)\cos \omega nT\right]^2 + \left[\sum_{n=0}^{\infty} x(n)\sin \omega nT\right]^2}$$

However, as the summation limit in the above equations goes from 0 to ∞ and the digitised signal is an infinite periodic sequence, there is a problem of how many samples should be included in the above equation. While the computation complexity increases as the number of samples increase, the error in the spectrum analysis increases as the number of samples included decrease. On a closer look at Figure 2.13, the digitised signal is seen to have a period of 20 samples. Hence the approach is to start from 20 samples and increases the number of samples by multiples of 20 until there is no change in the positions of the main lobes in the signal spectrum. The spectrum of the digitised signal from d.c. up to 100 Hz (half the sampling frequency) is shown in Figure 2.14 for 20 and 80 samples. Further increase in the number of samples does not change the positions of the main lobes.

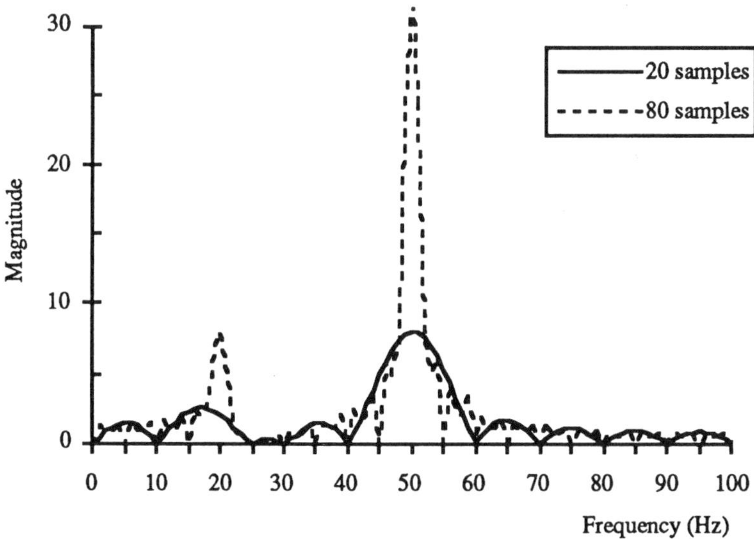

Figure 2.14

As shown in Figure 2.14, there are two main lobes in the spectrum of the digitised signal – one is centred at 20 Hz, which corresponds to the output signal from the transducer; the other is centred at 50 Hz, which can now be identified as the interference signal due to *mains pick-up*.

(b) Notch Filter Design

To remove mains pick-up, a zero must be placed at the point on the circumference of the unit circle $z = e^{j2\pi 50/200} = e^{j\pi/2} = 1\angle 90°$, i.e. the point located at the intersection of the positive imaginary axis and the circumference of the unit-circle. As poles and zeros must occur in complex-conjugate pairs, there must be another zero at $1\angle -90°$, i.e. located at the intersection of the negative imaginary axis and the circumference of the unit-circle. Choices are now open for the number of poles and their positions. For simplicity, a pair of complex-conjugate poles is placed near to the zeros on the negative and positive imaginary axes respectively, namely at the points $z = 0.9e^{\pm j\pi/2}$. Hence the transfer function of the notch filter is

$$G(z) = \frac{\left(z - e^{\frac{j\pi}{2}}\right)\left(z - e^{-\frac{j\pi}{2}}\right)}{\left(z - 0.9\,e^{\frac{j\pi}{2}}\right)\left(z - 0.9\,e^{-\frac{j\pi}{2}}\right)}$$

$$= \frac{\left(z - \cos\frac{\pi}{2} - j\sin\frac{\pi}{2}\right)\left(z - \cos\frac{\pi}{2} + j\sin\frac{\pi}{2}\right)}{\left(z - 0.9\cos\frac{\pi}{2} - j\,0.9\sin\frac{\pi}{2}\right)\left(z - 0.9\cos\frac{\pi}{2} + j\,0.9\sin\frac{\pi}{2}\right)}$$

$$= \frac{z^2 + 1}{z^2 + 0.81}$$

The magnitude response of the notch filter, $|G(z)|$, evaluated by substituting $e^{j\omega T}$ for z in the above transfer function, is shown in Figure 2.15.

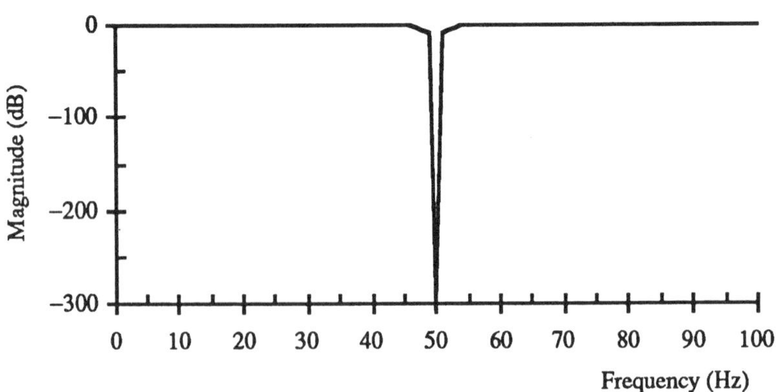

Figure 2.15

The computed value of $|G(z)|$ is approximately 1.1 or 0.83 dB at 20 Hz and exceeds −300 dB at 50 Hz. It is seen from Figure 2.15 that the magnitude response is symmetric with respect to 50 Hz, this is due to the poles lying at the same angular position as the zeros. However, placing the 'root-pole' at an angular position less than 90° causes less attenuation for frequencies lower than 50 Hz, and more attenuation for frequencies above 50 Hz, and therefore the magnitude response is correspondingly asymmetrical. Similarly, an asymmetrical magnitude response is produced when the 'root-pole' is placed at an angular position greater than 90°. This leads to a more complex transfer function with extra z-terms due to the non-zero coefficients.

To implement the notch filter, the numerator and denominator of the transfer function is multiplied by z^{-2} to give

$$G(z) = \frac{1 + z^{-2}}{1 + 0.81z^{-2}} = \frac{Y(z)}{X(z)}$$

Cross-multiplying and rearranging terms gives

$$Y(z) = X(z) + X(z)z^{-2} - 0.81Y(z)z^{-2}$$

Taking the inverse z-transform gives

$$y(n) = x(n) + x(n-2) - 0.81y(n-2)$$

This difference equation can be realised in the direct form of implementation as shown in Figure 2.16.

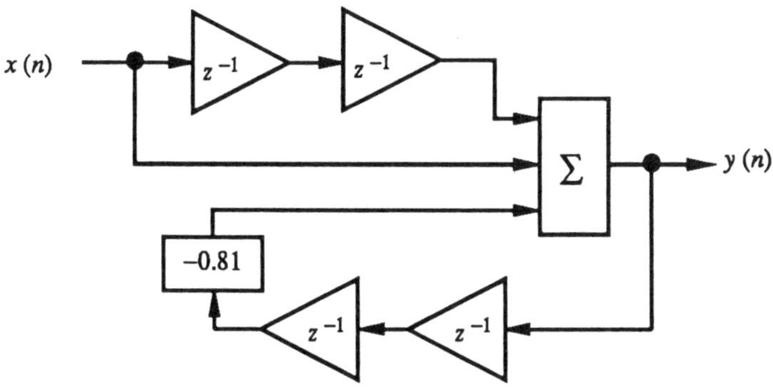

Figure 2.16

(c) Design Confirmation
To confirm the removal of the mains pick-up, the output sequence of the notch filter is computed by using the difference equation. Figure 2.17 shows the first 61 samples of the output sequence.

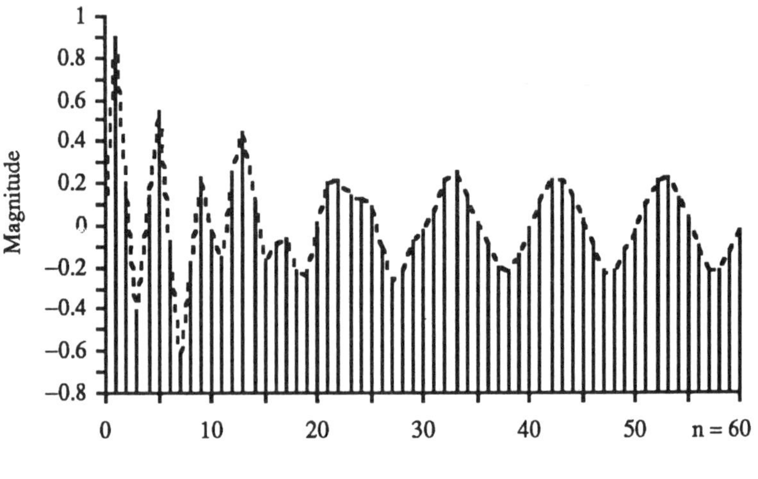

Figure 2.17

It is seen from Figure 2.17 that after an initial transient, the output sequence resembles a digitised sinewave. The periodic time, τ_p, is equal to $10 \times T$, where T is the sampling period equal to $1/f_s = 1/200 = 5$ ms. Therefore the frequency of the digitised sinewave is

$$f_p = \frac{1}{\tau_p} = \frac{1}{10 \times 5 \times 10^{-3}} = 20 \text{ Hz}$$

The transient duration can be reduced by increasing the distance between the 'root-pole' and the circumference of the unit-circle, however this causes a widening of the notch filter stopband.

Problems

P2.1

An input sequence corresponding to a sampled signal is $\{6, 0.2, -11.4, 0, 2.7\}$. What is the z-transform of this sequence?

P2.2

Using the residue method determine the z-transform of

(a) $X(s) = \dfrac{1}{s + \alpha}$ $\qquad (x(t) = e^{-\alpha t})$

(b) $X(s) = \dfrac{2}{s^3}$ $\quad (x(t) = t^2)$

(c) $X(s) = \dfrac{1}{(s+\alpha)^2}$ $\quad (x(t) = t\,e^{-\alpha t})$

P2.3
Use the following z-transform pair

$$X(s) = \frac{1}{s+\alpha} \quad \leftrightarrow \quad X(z) = \frac{z}{z - e^{-\alpha T}}$$

to derive the z-transform of

(a) $x(t) = e^{-\alpha t} - e^{-\beta t}$

(b) $x(t) = \cos\ \omega t$

(c) $x(t) = \sin\ \omega t$

P2.4
Use the standard z-transform to derive the transfer function, $G(z)$, corresponding to the circuit shown in Figure P2.4:

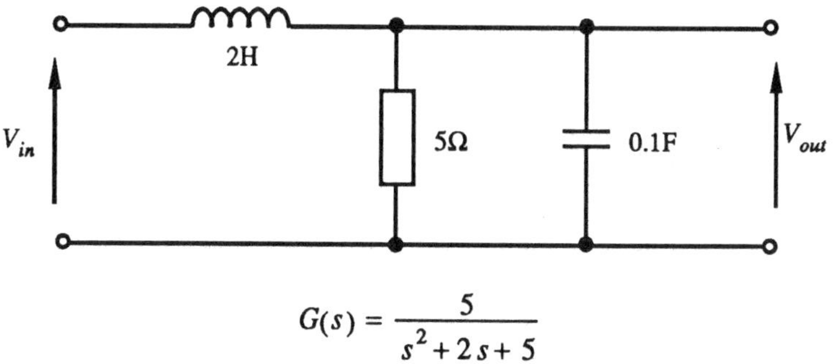

$$G(s) = \frac{5}{s^2 + 2s + 5}$$

Figure P2.4

P2.5
For the transfer function $G(z)$ derived in P2.4, calculate the impulse response values for n in the range $0 \le n \le 3$. Compare these calculated values with the corresponding impulse response values of the L-R-C circuit. The sampling frequency is 10Hz. Comment on the comparative values.

P2.6

(a) For the circuit shown in Figure P2.6 derive the continuous-time expression for the step response when the step input magnitude is k volts.

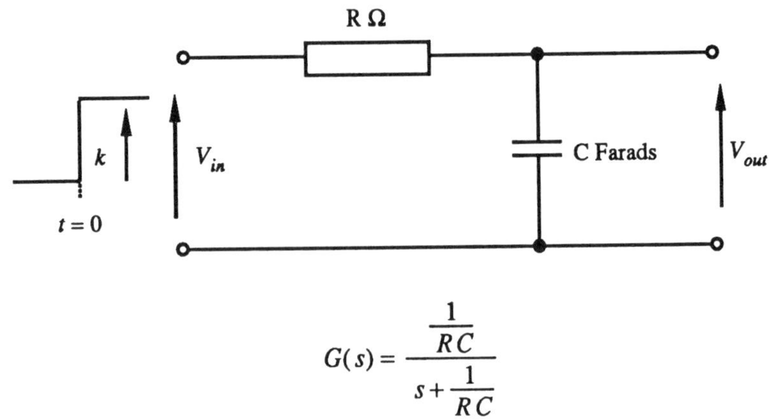

$$G(s) = \frac{\frac{1}{RC}}{s + \frac{1}{RC}}$$

Figure P2.6

(b) The circuit is to be modelled as a sampled-data system, derive the required discrete-time expression for the step response. However, note that in this case

$$Y(z) = \mathbf{Z}[G(s)] \times \mathbf{Z}\left[\frac{k}{s}\right]$$

$$Y(z) \neq \mathbf{Z}\left[\frac{k}{s} \times G(s)\right]$$

(c) Use the expression derived in Part (b) to evaluate the step response when R = 1MΩ, C = 1μF, $k = 2$V and $f_s = 50$Hz (sampling frequency), for n in the range $0 \le n \le 3$. Confirm the calculated values using the principle of discrete-time convolution.

P2.7

(a) For the circuit shown in Figure P2.7 derive the equivalent discrete-time expression for the circuit output response, $y(n)$, when $x(t) = e^{-2t}$ and $f_s = 50$Hz (sampling frequency).

(b) Use the expression derived in Part (a) to evaluate the output response for n in the range $0 \le n \le 3$. Confirm the calculated values using the principle of discrete-time convolution.

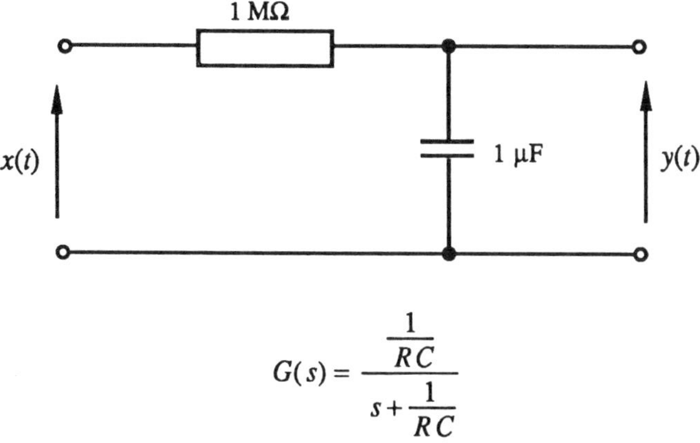

$$G(s) = \frac{\frac{1}{RC}}{s + \frac{1}{RC}}$$

Figure P2.7

P2.8

Using (i) the residue method, (ii) partial fraction expansion method, and (iii) long division method, determine the inverse z-transform of

(a) $X(z) = \dfrac{z+3}{z-0.25}$

(b) $X(z) = \dfrac{z^2}{z^2 - 1.5z + 0.5}$

(c) $X(z) = \dfrac{1.8z(z+0.1667)}{z^2 - 0.4z - 0.05}$

Verify the results in each case for n in the range $0 \le n \le 3$. What conclusion may be deduced from (i)(a)?

P2.9

The transfer function of a digital filter is

$$G(z) = \frac{(z+0.5)}{(z+0.25)}$$

Derive:

(a) a general expression for the filter's unit-step response (refer to note given in P2.6(b)); evaluate it at the first four sampling instants, and
(b) a general expression for the filter's unit-impulse response; use it in the convolution-summation representation to verify the unit-step values calculated in part (a).

P2.10

A digital filter has a transfer function

$$G(z) = \frac{z^2 - 0.5z - 0.05}{z^2 + 0.1z - 0.2}$$

Determine:

(a) The location of the filter's poles and zeros in the z-plane.
(b) Whether the filter is stable.
(c) A general expression for the filter's unit-impulse response.
(d) The filter's linear difference equation.
(e) The frequency response of the filter at a frequency equal to half of the sampling frequency.

P2.11

Using the prototype analogue denormalised filter of WE2.26 with a cut-off frequency of 6 kHz and a sampling frequency of 24 kHz, derive the corresponding transfer function, $G(z)$, of the equivalent digital filter by applying the bilinear z-transform method.

Determine:

(a) The z-plane pole-zero locations.
(b) The linear difference equation of the filter.
(c) The block diagram representation of the filter.

Verify that the derived digital filter has the desired d.c. gain and 6 kHz cut-off frequency.

P2.12

Using the bilinear z-transform design method, determine the digital filter transfer function, $G(z)$, corresponding to the following specification.

> *Specification:*
> A highpass digital filter having a cut-off frequency $f_{cd} = 100\text{Hz}$ and sampling period $T = 1.6\text{ms}$. The design is to be based on the denormalised analogue prototype filter

$$G(s) = \frac{s^2}{s^2 + \sqrt{2}\,\omega_{ca}\,s + \omega_{ca}^2}$$

Determine:

(a) The z-plane pole-zero locations.
(b) The linear difference equation of the filter.
(c) The block diagram representation of the filter.

Verify that the derived digital filter has the desired d.c. gain and 100 Hz cut-off frequency.

P2.13

A DSP system under test has a 'root-zero' and a 'root-pole' lying on circles with radii of 0.6 and 0.3 respectively and located between 80° and 100°. Applying a unit-impulse test signal to the DSP system produces the sequence {1, 0, 0.27, 0, −0.0243, 0, 0.0022}. Determine the transfer function of the DSP system under test by computing the chirp z-transform at five equally spaced points on the two circles.

3 The Discrete Fourier Transform

3.1 Introduction

As discussed in Section 1.1.2, the design of a DSP system basically involves two fundamental tasks, namely, the analysis of the input signal and the design of a processing system to give the desired output. There are several different mathematical tools for carrying out these two tasks. A time-domain approach was presented in Chapter 1, where a sampled input signal was represented by a weighted unit-impulse train and a DSP system was described by either a general difference equation or a unit-impulse response. A frequency-domain approach based on the z-transform was presented in Chapter 2, where an infinite data sequence was converted to an algebraic equation and a DSP system was described compactly by a transfer function; the former enables the frequency spectrum of a signal to be estimated and the latter enables the stability and the frequency response of a DSP system to be assessed.

This chapter introduces another frequency-domain approach based on the Fourier transform. One reason for studying this frequency domain approach is the availability of the Fast Fourier Transform (FFT), which enables the spectral properties of a signal and the frequency response of a DSP system to be estimated rapidly. The FFT also allows some time-domain signal processing operations to be performed equivalently in the frequency-domain with considerable reduction in computation time.

3.2 Discrete Fourier Series

It is extremely useful if an arbitrary discrete signal, $x(n)$, can be approximated as a weighted sum of some elementary sequences (known mathematically as basis functions), because such an approximation will enable the output of a linear time-invariant DSP system to be easily predicted by just adding up the discrete output signals in response to the individual elementary sequences constituting the discrete input signal. That is

$$x(n) = \sum_{r=-\infty}^{\infty} C_r \, \beta_r(n) \tag{3.1}$$

where C_r are the weighting coefficients describing the contribution of the elementary sequences, $\beta_r(n)$, in constructing $x(n)$.

In 1807 Jean Baptiste Joseph Fourier proposed discrete sine and cosine sequences as the elementary sequences. The frequencies of the discrete sine and cosine sequences are integer multiples of the fundamental frequency of the periodic sequence, $x(n)$. This choice of elementary sequences is known as the Fourier series representation for periodic sequences and the C_r values are called the Fourier series coefficients. Figure 3.1 illustrates a periodic discrete signal represented as the sum of a constant (d.c.) sequence, $x_1(n)$, and two discrete sinusoidal sequences, $x_2(n)$ and $x_3(n)$. Figure 3.1 also shows the use of a simple spectral diagram to display the magnitude and phase of C_r plotted against the frequency of the elementary sinusoidal sequences.

With the signal of $(1 + \sin 2\pi 5000nT + 2\cos 2\pi 10000nT)$ being sampled at 80 kHz, the spectra in Figure 3.1 show that $|C_r|$ is non-zero at 0 Hz, ± 5 kHz, ± 10 kHz and at integer multiples of ± 80 kHz, ± (80 ± 5) kHz, ± (80 ± 10) kHz (these are complementary spectra as a result of sampling at 80 kHz). In particular, the d.c. sequence is represented at 0 Hz and at integer multiples of the sampling frequency with the same amplitude and zero phase; the sine sequence is represented at ± 5 kHz and at its complementary spectra frequencies with half amplitude and phases of $\pm \pi/2$; and the cosine sequence is represented at ± 10 kHz and at its complementary spectra frequencies with half amplitude and zero phase. The spectra repeat *ad infinitum*, and are centred about integer multiples of 80 kHz.

With discrete sine and cosine sequences expressed equivalently and compactly using discrete complex exponential sequences, the discrete Fourier series of a periodic sequence can be written as

$$x(n) = \sum_{r=-\infty}^{\infty} C_r \, e^{j r \omega_o n T} \tag{3.2}$$

where T is the sampling period and ω_o is the ***fundamental radian frequency***. If N is the number of samples in each period of the periodic sequence, then ω_o is given by

$$\omega_o = 2\pi f_o = \frac{2\pi}{NT} \tag{3.3}$$

Substituting equation (3.3) into equation (3.2) gives

$$x(n) = \sum_{r=-\infty}^{\infty} C_r \, e^{j 2\pi r n / N} \tag{3.4}$$

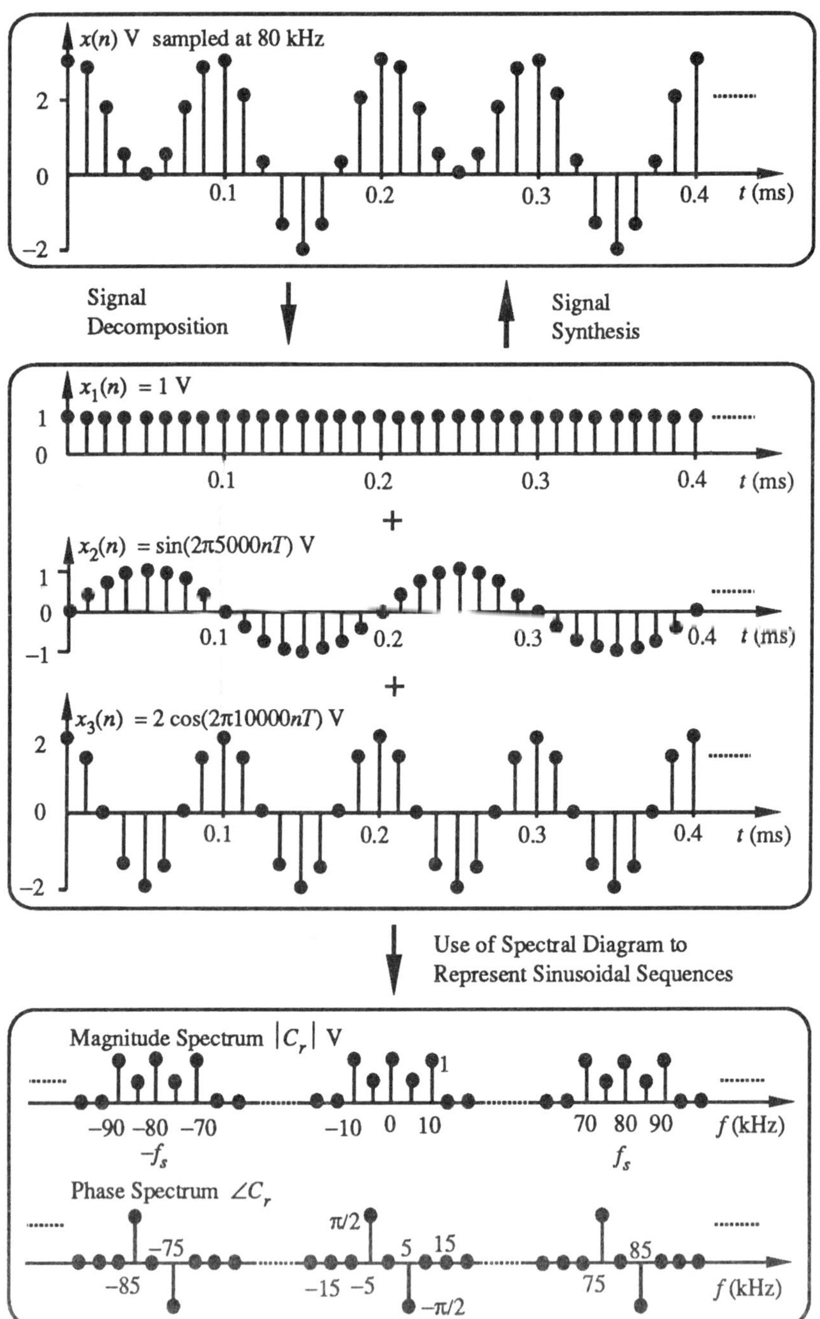

Figure 3.1 Fourier series representation of a periodic discrete signal

Since the function $e^{j2\pi rn/N}$ is periodic with a period of 2π, there are only N distinct magnitude values derived from the terms

$$e^{j0},\ e^{j2\pi/N},\ e^{j4\pi/N},\ \ldots,\ e^{j2\pi(N-1)/N}$$

This implies a periodic frequency spectrum for a discrete signal as shown in Figure 3.1 and as discussed in Section 1.2.1, and consequently it is sufficient to use N consecutive terms, leading to the finite series

$$x(n) = \sum_{r=0}^{N-1} C_r\, e^{j2\pi rn/N} \tag{3.5}$$

The Fourier series coefficients, C_r, can now be determined by multiplying both sides of equation (3.5) by $e^{-j2\pi qn/N}$, where q is an integer, and summing from 0 to $N-1$. This gives

$$\sum_{n=0}^{N-1} x(n)\, e^{-j2\pi qn/N} = \sum_{n=0}^{N-1} e^{-j2\pi qn/N} \sum_{r=0}^{N-1} C_r\, e^{j2\pi rn/N}$$

Interchanging the order of the summations on the right hand side gives

$$\sum_{n=0}^{N-1} x(n)\, e^{-j2\pi qn/N} = \sum_{r=0}^{N-1} C_r \sum_{n=0}^{N-1} e^{j2\pi \frac{n}{N}(r-q)} \tag{3.6}$$

For $r = q$, the second summation on the right hand side of equation (3.6) becomes

$$\sum_{n=0}^{N-1} e^{j2\pi \frac{n}{N}(r-q)} = \sum_{n=0}^{N-1} e^{(n \times 0)} = N \tag{3.7}$$

For $r \neq q$, using the following geometric sequence closed form relationship

$$\sum_{n=0}^{N-1} a^n = \frac{1 - a^N}{1 - a} \qquad \text{for} \quad a \neq 1$$

the second summation on the right hand side of equation (3.6) becomes

$$\sum_{n=0}^{N-1} e^{j\frac{2\pi}{N}n(r-q)} = \frac{1 - e^{j2\pi(r-q)}}{1 - e^{j\frac{2\pi}{N}(r-q)}}$$

$$= \frac{1 - [\cos\ 2\pi(r-q) + \mathrm{j}\sin\ 2\pi(r-q)]}{1 - \mathrm{e}^{\mathrm{j}\frac{2\pi}{N}(r-q)}}$$

$$= \frac{1 - [1+0]}{1 - \mathrm{e}^{\mathrm{j}\frac{2\pi}{N}(r-q)}} = 0 \qquad (3.8)$$

Using the results of equations (3.7) and (3.8) in equation (3.6) gives

$$\sum_{n=0}^{N-1} x(n)\ \mathrm{e}^{-\mathrm{j}2\pi q n/N} = N \sum_{r=0}^{N-1} C_r$$

Since the above equation is only non-zero for $r = q$, it reduces to

$$\sum_{n=0}^{N-1} x(n)\ \mathrm{e}^{-\mathrm{j}2\pi q n/N} = N \times C_q$$

Changing index q to r yields

$$C_r = \frac{1}{N} \sum_{n=0}^{N-1} x(n)\ \mathrm{e}^{-\mathrm{j}2\pi r n/N} \qquad (3.9)$$

Since C_r is a complex number, it can be expressed in terms of its magnitude, $|C_r|$, and phase $\angle C_r$. A plot of a set of $|C_r|$ values versus frequency and a plot of a set of $\angle C_r$ values versus frequency are commonly known respectively as the magnitude spectrum and the phase spectrum of a digital sequence. Furthermore, the line spectra are repetitive every f_s Hz, and over each repetitive interval there are N frequency points separated by the fundamental frequency, f_o Hz. (see Figure 3.1).

Equations (3.5) and (3.9) are known as the **Discrete Fourier Series (DFS) pair** for periodic digital sequences, which relate the time and frequency domains. Equation (3.5) enables a digital sequence to be synthesised using a set of C_r values, and equation (3.9) enables a digital sequence to be analysed in terms of its frequency components.

❖ **WE 3.1**

An amplitude-modulated signal having a carrier frequency of 10 kHz, a modulating signal frequency of 2.5 kHz, and a modulation depth of 0.6 may be expressed as

$$x(t) = [1 + 0.6 \sin(2\pi 2500\, t)]\cos(2\pi 10000\, t) \quad \text{V}$$

If this signal is sampled at a frequency of 40 kHz, sketch the sampled digital signal, and its magnitude/frequency spectrum.

***Solution*:**

With the sampling frequency $f_s = 40$ kHz and the lowest frequency component $f_o = 2.5$ kHz, the sampled amplitude-modulated signal will repeat at an interval of $N = f_s / f_o = 16$ samples, or every 0.4 ms $(= 1/f_o)$.

The discrete values of the sampled amplitude-modulated signal over one period are:

t (ms)	0	0.025	0.05	0.075	0.1	0.125	0.15	0.175
n	0	1	2	3	4	5	6	7
$x(n)$ V	1	0	−1.4	0	1.6	0	−1.4	0

t (ms)	0.2	0.225	0.25	0.275	0.3	0.325	0.35	0.375
n	8	9	10	11	12	13	14	15
$x(n)$ V	1	0	−0.6	0	0.4	0	−0.6	0

The sampled digital signal is shown in the following figure:

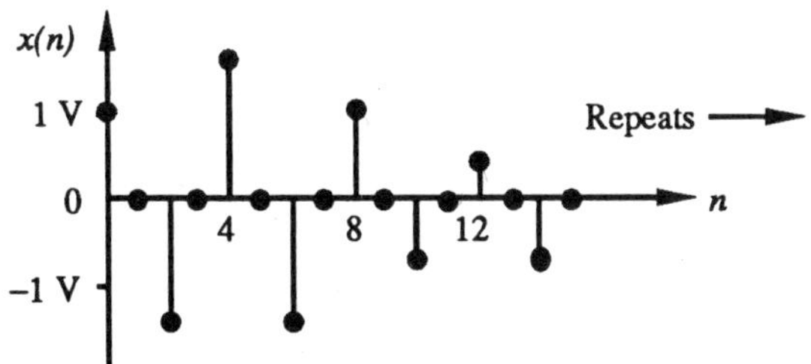

Expanding equation (3.9) to compute C_r gives

$$C_r = \frac{1}{N}\left\{ \sum_{n=0}^{N-1} x(n)\cos\left(\frac{2\pi}{N} rn\right) - j\sum_{n=0}^{N-1} x(n)\sin\left(\frac{2\pi}{N} rn\right)\right\} \quad \text{V}$$

The sixteen Fourier series coefficients obtained are:

r	0	1	2	3	4	5	6	7
C_r (V)	0	0	0	j 0.15	0.5	−j 0.15	0	0
$\|C_r\|$ (V)	0	0	0	0.15	0.5	0.15	0	0
$\angle C_r$	0	0	0	$\pi/2$	0	$-\pi/2$	0	0

r	8	9	10	11	12	13	14	15
C_r (V)	0	0	0	j 0.15	0.5	−j 0.15	0	0
$\|C_r\|$ (V)	0	0	0	0.15	0.5	0.15	0	0
$\angle C_r$	0	0	0	π/2	0	−π/2	0	0

With each C_r value separated by the fundamental frequency of 2.5 kHz, the magnitude/frequency spectrum of the sampled amplitude modulated signal is shown below:

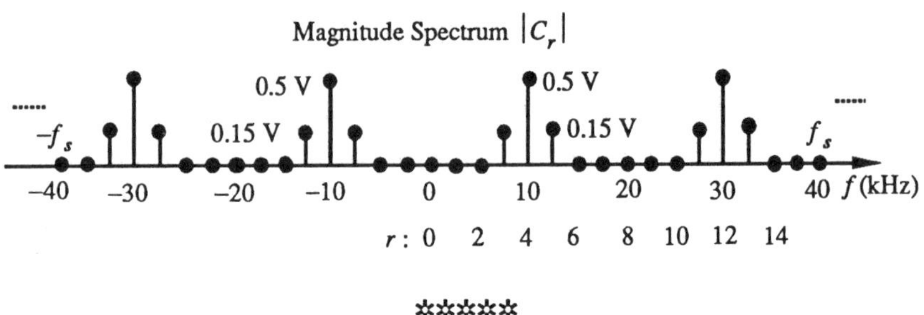

*****

3.3 Discrete-time Fourier Transform

The DFS approach can be extended to aperiodic (non-periodic) discrete signals, which are most likely to be encountered in practice, by increasing the signal period without limit. As N increases towards infinity (to create a non-periodic discrete signal) the spacing between successive C_r terms given by equation (3.9) becomes closer due to N appearing in the denominator of the exponential function, and the amplitude of C_r becomes smaller due to the multiplier $1/N$. If C_r is multiplied by a scaling factor N, then the product $N \times C_r$ remains finite when $C_r \rightarrow 0$ as $N \rightarrow \infty$. By denoting the $N \times C_r$ product as $X(\mathrm{j}\,\omega)$, equations (3.5) and (3.9) can be rewritten respectively for aperiodic discrete signals as

$$x(n) = \sum_{r=0}^{N-1} \frac{X(\mathrm{j}\,\omega)}{N}\, \mathrm{e}^{\mathrm{j}\,2\pi r n/N} \tag{3.10}$$

and
$$X(\mathrm{j}\,\omega) = N \times C_r = \sum_{n=0}^{N-1} x(n)\, \mathrm{e}^{-\mathrm{j}\,2\pi r n/N} \tag{3.11}$$

Since, from equation (3.3), $N = 2\pi/(\omega_o T)$, equations (3.10) and (3.11) become

$$x(n) = \frac{1}{2\pi} \sum_{r=0}^{N-1} X(\mathrm{j}\,\omega)\, \mathrm{e}^{\mathrm{j}\,r\omega_o nT}\, \omega_o T \tag{3.12}$$

$$X(j\,\omega) = \sum_{n=0}^{N-1} x(n)\, e^{-j\,r\,\omega_o\,n\,T} \tag{3.13}$$

The effects of the limit $N \rightarrow \infty$ in equation (3.12) are:

(a) the discrete frequencies, $r\omega_o$, merge to become a continuous frequency, and may therefore be replaced by ω,

(b) the spacing between the consecutive spectral components, ω_o, approaches zero and may therefore be replaced by $d\omega$, and

(c) since the spectrum of a digital signal repeats itself over every 2π interval, the summation becomes integration with $\pm\pi$ as the limits.

Furthermore, for convenience, by normalising the independent variable of integration to ωT, equation (3.12) becomes

$$x(n) = \frac{1}{2\pi} \int_{-\pi}^{\pi} X(j\,\omega)\, e^{j\,\omega\,n\,T}\, d(\omega T) \tag{3.14}$$

Similarly applying the limit $N \rightarrow \infty$ to equation (3.13) yields

$$X(j\,\omega) = \sum_{n=-\infty}^{\infty} x(n)\, e^{-j\,\omega\,n\,T} \tag{3.15}$$

where the summation is not replaced by integration because $x(n)$ is a discrete sequence, and the summation limits are extended to $\pm\infty$ because $x(n)$ is now infinitely long.

Equations (3.14) and (3.15) are known as the **Discrete-time Fourier Transform (DTFT) pair** for aperiodic digital sequences which relate the time and frequency domains.

❖ **WE 3.2**

A rectangular pulse is sampled to produce the following sequence

$$x(n) = \begin{cases} A & 0 \le n \le L-1 \\ 0 & \text{otherwise} \end{cases}$$

(a) Derive the expression that defines the DTFT of $x(n)$.

(b) If the sampling frequency is set to 10 kHz to give $L = 5$, and the pulse amplitude A is 0.5 V, plot the magnitude and phase spectra by using the results obtained in (a).

(c) Use the inverse DTFT to verify $x(n)$ for $L = 3$ and $A = 1$ V.

Solution:

(a) Taking the DTFT of the sequence gives

$$X(\mathrm{j}\,\omega) = \sum_{n=-\infty}^{\infty} x(n)\,\mathrm{e}^{-\mathrm{j}\,\omega n T} = \sum_{n=0}^{L-1} A\,\mathrm{e}^{-\mathrm{j}\,\omega n T} = A\sum_{n=0}^{L-1} \mathrm{e}^{-\mathrm{j}\,\omega n T}$$

Applying the geometric series summation formula, $\sum_{n=0}^{L-1} x^n = \frac{1-x^L}{1-x}$, yields

$$X(\mathrm{j}\,\omega) = A\left(\frac{1-\mathrm{e}^{-\mathrm{j}\,\omega T L}}{1-\mathrm{e}^{-\mathrm{j}\,\omega T}}\right)$$

$$= A\left(\frac{\mathrm{e}^{-\mathrm{j}\frac{\omega T L}{2}}}{\mathrm{e}^{-\mathrm{j}\frac{\omega T}{2}}}\right)\left(\frac{\mathrm{e}^{\mathrm{j}\frac{\omega T L}{2}} - \mathrm{e}^{-\mathrm{j}\frac{\omega T L}{2}}}{\mathrm{e}^{\mathrm{j}\frac{\omega T}{2}} - \mathrm{e}^{-\mathrm{j}\frac{\omega T}{2}}}\right)$$

$$= A\,\mathrm{e}^{-\mathrm{j}\frac{\omega T (L-1)}{2}}\left(\frac{\sin\left(\frac{\omega T L}{2}\right)}{\sin\left(\frac{\omega T}{2}\right)}\right)$$

(b) Substituting $L = 5$, $A = 0.5$ V and $T = 1/10^4$ in the above equation, the magnitude of $X(\mathrm{j}\omega)$ is

$$|X(\mathrm{j}\,\omega)| = \sqrt{\mathrm{Re}\{X(\mathrm{j}\,\omega)\}^2 + \mathrm{Im}\{X(\mathrm{j}\,\omega)\}^2}$$

$$= 0.5\left|\frac{\sin\dfrac{5\times\omega}{2\times 10^4}}{\sin\dfrac{\omega}{2\times 10^4}}\right| \text{ V} \qquad \text{for } \omega \neq 0$$

A simple way to obtain the $|X(\mathrm{j}\omega)|$ value at $\omega = 0$ is to substitute $\omega = 0$ and $A = 0.5$ V in

$$X(\mathrm{j}\,\omega) = A\sum_{n=0}^{L-1} \mathrm{e}^{-\mathrm{j}\,\omega n T}$$

to yield

$$|X(0)| = \left| 0.5 \sum_{n=0}^{4} e^{n \times 0} \right| = 2.5\,\text{V}$$

and the phase of $X(\mathrm{j}\omega)$ is

$$\angle X(\mathrm{j}\,\omega) = \tan^{-1} \frac{\operatorname{Im}\{X(\mathrm{j}\,\omega)\}}{\operatorname{Re}\{X(\mathrm{j}\,\omega)\}}$$

With these equations, a computer program, or a spreadsheet software package, can be used to generate the magnitude and phase spectra shown below:

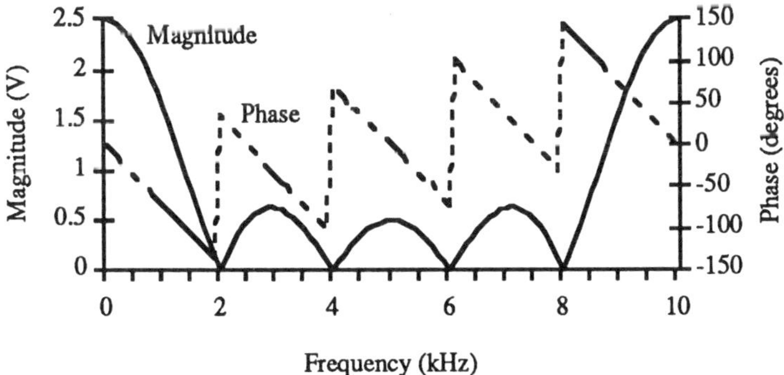

Observe that the maximum value of the main lobe is $0.5 \times L = 0.5 \times 5 = 2.5$ and there are $L - 2 = 5 - 2 = 3$ side-lobes. This spectrum is repetitive in every 10 kHz interval.

(c) The DTFT of $x(n)$ with $L = 3$ and $A = 1$ V is given by

$$X(\mathrm{j}\,\omega) = A \sum_{n=0}^{L-1} e^{-\mathrm{j}\,\omega n T} = 1 + e^{-\mathrm{j}\omega T} + e^{-\mathrm{j}2\omega T}$$

Taking the inverse DTFT of $X(\mathrm{j}\omega)$ gives

$$x(n) = \frac{1}{2\pi} \int_{-\pi}^{\pi} X(\mathrm{j}\,\omega)\; e^{\mathrm{j}\,\omega n T}\; \mathrm{d}(\omega T)$$

$$= \frac{1}{2\pi} \int_{-\pi}^{\pi} \left\{1 + e^{-\mathrm{j}\,\omega T} + e^{-\mathrm{j}2\omega T}\right\} e^{\mathrm{j}\,\omega n T}\; \mathrm{d}(\omega T)$$

$$= \frac{1}{2\pi}\left[\frac{e^{j n\omega T}}{j n} + \frac{e^{j(n-1)\omega T}}{j(n-1)} + \frac{e^{j(n-2)\omega T}}{j(n-2)}\right]_{-\pi}^{\pi}$$

$$= \frac{1}{2\pi}\left[\frac{2\sin n\pi}{n} + \frac{2\sin((n-1)\pi)}{n-1} + \frac{2\sin((n-2)\pi)}{n-2}\right]$$

For $n = 0$, the above expression reduces to

$$x(0) = \frac{1}{2\pi}\left[\frac{2\sin n\pi}{n}\right] = \frac{\sin n\pi}{n\pi}\ \text{V}$$

By applying l'Hôpital's rule we obtain $\lim\limits_{n \to 0} \frac{\sin n\pi}{n\pi} = 1$, giving $x(0) = 1$ V.

Similarly, substituting other values of n into the inverse DTFT of $X(j\omega)$ yields $x(1) = x(2) = 1$ V and $x(n) = 0$ V for $n > 2$, which is identical to the defined sequence for $L = 3$ and $A = 1$ V.

*****

3.4 Discrete Fourier Transform (DFT)

Although equation (3.15) gives the frequency spectrum of a signal, there are two implementation problems in practice. The first problem is associated with the limits of the summation which extend from $-\infty$ to $+\infty$, implying the length of the signal must be infinitely long. The second problem is associated with the frequency variable ω which is continuous, implying there is an infinite number of frequency points to be computed. Both problems result in the requirement for infinite time to produce the result.

To overcome the first problem, the limits of the summation are reduced, thereby truncating an infinitely long signal to a finite-length signal. This is known as ***windowing*** because only a portion of the actual discrete signal is available for the transform operation, as illustrated in Figure 3.2(a). The length of the windowed sequence is known as the ***record length***.

To overcome the second problem, the number of frequency points to be computed is restricted to a finite number. For ease in computation, the selected frequency points should be spaced evenly over the range 0 to f_s. If the windowed sequence of the actual discrete signal is regarded as one full period of a periodic signal, as shown in Figure 3.2(b), then it can be analysed as a discrete Fourier series as discussed in Section 3.2, and the DFS of the extended periodic windowed sequence with N samples per period will result in a repetitive line spectrum, consisting of N frequency points separated by a fundamental frequency of $1/(NT)$, or f_s/N, as shown in Figure 3.2(c).

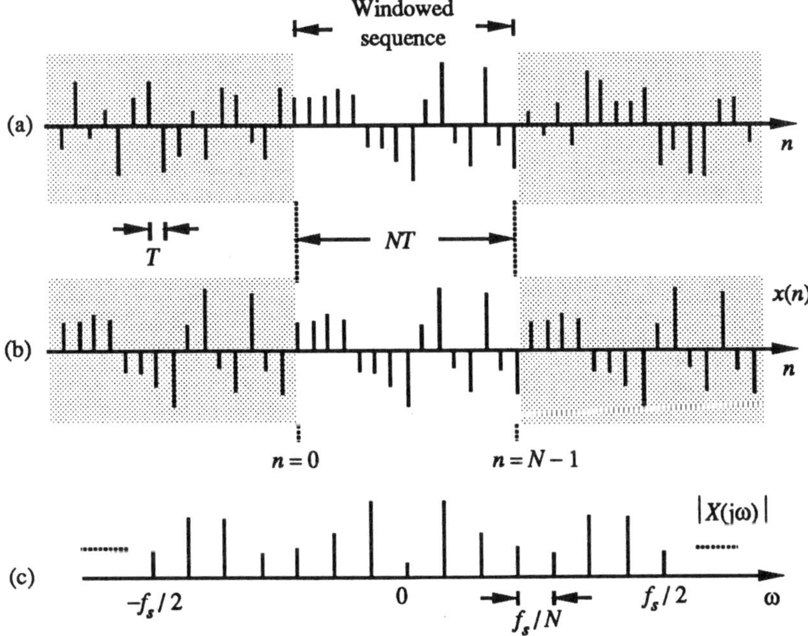

Figure 3.2 (a) Actual sequence
(b) Extended periodic windowed sequence
(c) Magnitude spectrum of (b)

Taking into account the implementation issues outlined above, equation (3.15) can be expressed in a new form to give the **Discrete Fourier Transform (DFT)**, that is

$$X_r = \sum_{n=0}^{N-1} x(n) e^{-j \frac{2\pi r}{N} n} \tag{3.16}$$

where (a) the continuous frequency spectrum $X(j\omega)$ in equation (3.15) is replaced by a discrete frequency spectrum X_r, (b) the infinite summation in equation (3.15) is replaced by one with finite limits from 0 to $(N-1)$, and (c) the continuous frequency variable ω in equation (3.15) is replaced by a finite number of frequencies located at $2\pi r/(NT)$, with $r = 0, 1, 2, \ldots, (N-1)$. In spectrum analysis the fundamental frequency, ω_o, which represents the increment between successive frequency points, is referred to as the ***frequency resolution***.

Similarly, equation (3.14) can be expressed in a new form to give the inverse DFT (IDFT) as

$$x(n) = \frac{1}{N} \sum_{r=0}^{N-1} X_r \, e^{j\frac{2\pi r}{N}n} \tag{3.17}$$

where (a) $X(j\omega)$ and ω in equation (3.14) are replaced respectively by X_r and a finite number of frequency points located at $2\pi r/(NT)$, and (b) the integral with limits of $\pm\pi$ is replaced by the summation with limits from 0 to $(N-1)$. For notational convenience, equations (3.16) and (3.17), may be rewritten respectively as

$$X_r = \sum_{n=0}^{N-1} x(n)\, W^{rn} \tag{3.18}$$

$$x(n) = \frac{1}{N} \sum_{r=0}^{N-1} X_r W^{-rn} \tag{3.19}$$

$$\text{where } W = e^{-j\frac{2\pi}{N}} \tag{3.20}$$

❖ **WE 3.3**

Plot the magnitude and phase spectrum of the sampled-data sequence {2, 0, 0, 1}, which was obtained using a sampling frequency of 20 kHz, and verify the DFT result using the IDFT.

Solution:

Applying equation (3.18), the DFT computations obtained using the given samples are:

$$X_0 = \sum_{n=0}^{3} x(n) = 2 + 0 + 0 + 1 = 3 = 3\angle 0°$$

$$X_1 = \sum_{n=0}^{3} x(n)\, e^{-j\frac{2\pi}{4}n} = \sum_{n=0}^{3} x(n)\, e^{-j\frac{\pi}{2}n}$$

$$= 2 + 0 + 0 + e^{-j\frac{3\pi}{2}} = 2 + \cos\frac{3\pi}{2} - j\sin\frac{3\pi}{2}$$

$$= 2 + j = 2.236\angle 26.57°$$

$$X_2 = \sum_{n=0}^{3} x(n)\,e^{-j\frac{4\pi}{4}n} = \sum_{n=0}^{3} x(n)\,e^{-j\pi n}$$

$$= 2 + 0 + 0 + e^{-j3\pi} = 2 + \cos\,3\pi - j\sin\,3\pi$$

$$= 1 = 1\angle 0°$$

$$X_3 = \sum_{n=0}^{3} x(n)\,e^{-j\frac{6\pi}{4}n} = \sum_{n=0}^{3} x(n)\,e^{-j\frac{3\pi}{2}n}$$

$$= 2 + 0 + 0 + e^{-j\frac{9\pi}{2}} = 2 + \cos\,\frac{9\pi}{2} - j\sin\,\frac{9\pi}{2}$$

$$- 2 - j = 2.236\angle -26.57°$$

Applying equation (3.3) yields the frequency resolution of

$$f_o = \frac{1}{NT} = \frac{f_s}{N} = \frac{20\ \text{kHz}}{4} = 5\ \text{kHz}$$

The magnitude and phase spectrum can be plotted as shown below:

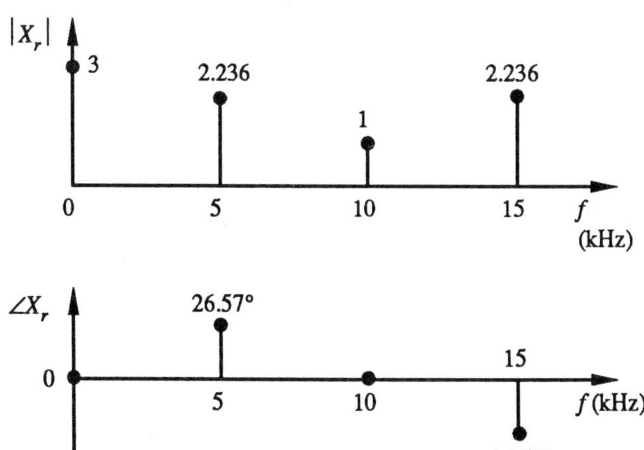

We may verify the DFT results of {3, 2 + j, 1, 2 – j} using equation (3.19):

$$x(0) = \frac{1}{4}\sum_{r=0}^{3} X_r = \frac{1}{4}[3 + (2 + j) + 1 + (2 - j)] = 2$$

$$x(1) = \frac{1}{4}\sum_{r=0}^{3} X_r\, e^{j\frac{2\pi}{4}r} = \frac{1}{4}\sum_{r=0}^{3} X_r\, e^{j\frac{\pi}{2}r}$$

$$= \frac{1}{4}\left\{3 + (2+j)e^{j\frac{\pi}{2}} + e^{j\pi} + (2-j)e^{j\frac{3\pi}{2}}\right\}$$

$$= \frac{1}{4}\left\{3 + (2+j)\left(\cos\frac{\pi}{2} + j\sin\frac{\pi}{2}\right) + (\cos\pi + j\sin\pi)\right.$$
$$\left. + (2-j)\left(\cos\frac{3\pi}{2} + j\sin\frac{3\pi}{2}\right)\right\}$$

$$= \frac{1}{4}\{3 + (2+j)j - 1 + (2-j)(-j)\} = 0$$

$$x(2) = \frac{1}{4}\sum_{r=0}^{3} X_r\, e^{j\frac{4\pi}{4}r} = \frac{1}{4}\sum_{r=0}^{3} X_r\, e^{j\pi r}$$

$$= \frac{1}{4}\{3 + (2+j)e^{j\pi} + e^{j2\pi} + (2-j)e^{j3\pi}\}$$

$$= \frac{1}{4}\{3 + (2+j)(\cos\pi + j\sin\pi) + (\cos 2\pi + j\sin 2\pi)$$
$$+ (2-j)(\cos 3\pi + j\sin 3\pi)\}$$

$$= \frac{1}{4}\{3 + (2+j)(-1) + 1 + (2-j)(-1)\} = 0$$

$$x(3) = \frac{1}{4}\sum_{r=0}^{3} X_r\, e^{j\frac{6\pi}{4}r} = \frac{1}{4}\sum_{r=0}^{3} X_r\, e^{j\frac{3\pi}{2}r}$$

$$= \frac{1}{4}\left\{3 + (2+j)e^{j\frac{3\pi}{2}} + e^{j3\pi} + (2-j)e^{j\frac{9\pi}{2}}\right\}$$

$$= \frac{1}{4}\left\{3 + (2+j)\left(\cos\frac{3\pi}{2} + j\sin\frac{3\pi}{2}\right) + (\cos 3\pi + j\sin 3\pi)\right.$$
$$\left. + (2-j)\left(\cos\frac{9\pi}{2} + j\sin\frac{9\pi}{2}\right)\right\}$$

$$= \frac{1}{4}\{3 + (2+j)(-j) - 1 + (2-j)(j)\} = 1$$

Hence, as expected, the IDFT of the DFT produces the original sequence values.

*****

The calculation procedures demonstrated in WE3.3 can be implemented as a software program. Figure 3.3 shows a basic flowchart for the direct implementation of the DFT.

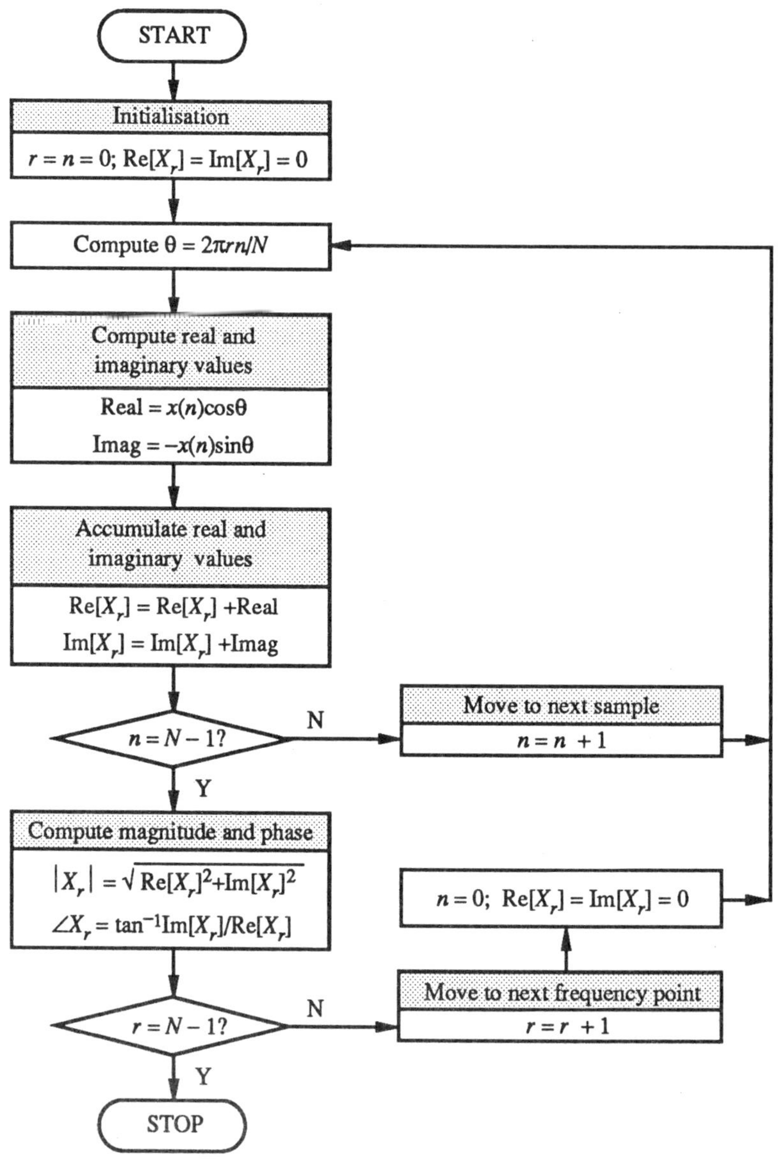

Figure 3.3 Flowchart for direct DFT implementation

By comparing equations (3.18) and (3.19), we see that the differences between the IDFT and the DFT for a real signal are the additional multiplier of $1/N$, the complex weighting coefficients and the sign of the exponent, consequently the flowchart for the direct implementation of the IDFT can be obtained by modifying Figure 3.3, producing the resulting flowchart shown in Figure 3.4

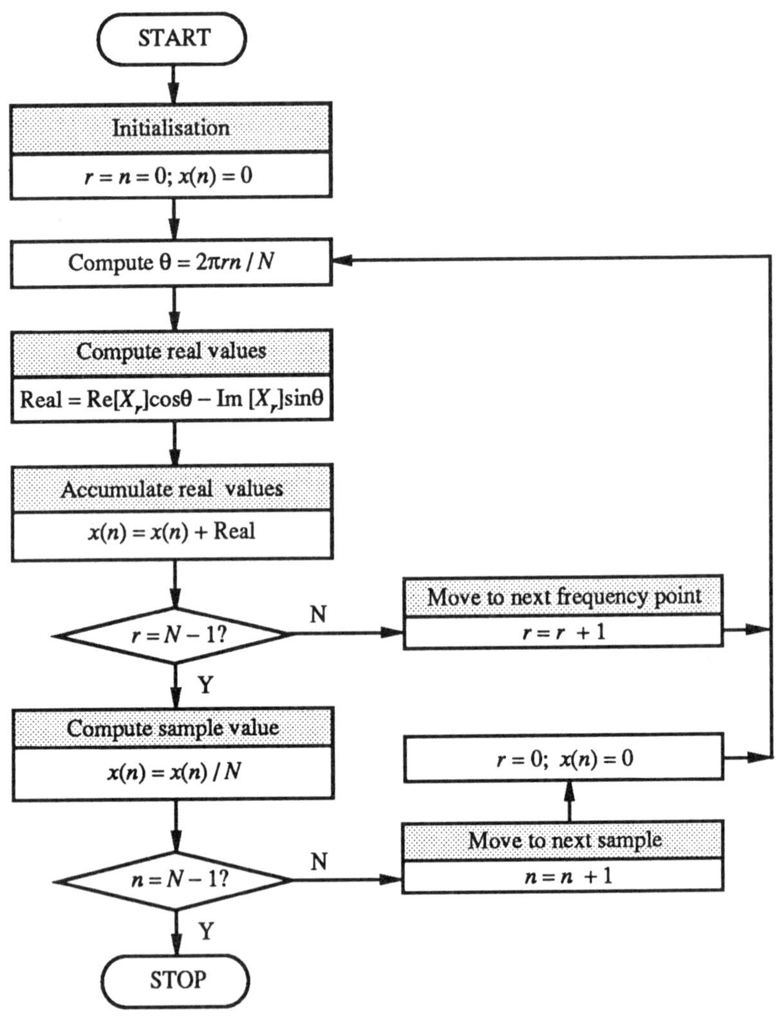

Figure 3.4 Flowchart for direct IDFT implementation

3.5 Relationships

(a) *Discrete and Continuous Fourier Series*

The discrete Fourier series discussed in Section 3.2 can be extended to derive the corresponding Fourier series representation of a periodic continuous signal. With the discrete sampling instant, nT, replaced by the continuous time variable, t, and the discrete signal, $x(n)$, replaced by the continuous signal, $x(t)$, in equation (3.2), the continuous Fourier series is therefore given by

$$x(t) = \sum_{r=-\infty}^{\infty} C_r \, e^{j r \omega_0 t} \tag{3.21}$$

Equation (3.21) is a function of the continuous time variable, t, and compared with the case for the discrete Fourier series, it no longer gives a finite set of distinct frequency magnitude values. Since the summation limits are $\pm\infty$, the spectrum of $x(t)$ is non-repetitive, i.e. complementary spectra do not exist.

Similarly, with (i) the interval of the discrete sequence, N, replaced by the period of the continuous signal, τ, (ii) summation replaced by integration, (iii) $2\pi n/N$ replaced by $\omega_0 t$ (since $2\pi n/N = 2\pi nT/(NT) = \omega_0 t$ by applying equation (3.3) and by replacing nT with t), and (iv) $x(n)$ replaced by $x(t)$ in equation (3.9), the Fourier series coefficients of a continuous signal are given by

$$C_r = \frac{1}{\tau} \int_0^{\tau} x(t) \, e^{-j r \omega_0 t} \, dt \tag{3.22}$$

❖ **WE 3.4**

Sketch the magnitude spectrum for the amplitude-modulated signal given in WE3.1.

Solution:

Expressing the given signal, $x(t)$, in the same form as equation (3.21) by replacing sine and cosine functions with exponential functions, gives

$$x(t) = [1 + 0.6 \sin(2\pi 2500\, t)] \cos(2\pi 10000\, t)$$

$$= \left[1 + \frac{0.6}{2j}\left(e^{j2\pi 2500\, t} - e^{-j2\pi 2500\, t}\right)\right] \frac{1}{2}\left(e^{j2\pi 10000 t} + e^{-j2\pi 10000\, t}\right)$$

$$= j0.15\, e^{-j2\pi 12500\, t} + 0.5\, e^{-j2\pi 10000\, t} - j0.15\, e^{-j2\pi 7500\, t}$$

$$+ j0.15\, e^{j2\pi 7500\, t} + 0.5\, e^{j2\pi 10000\, t} - j0.15\, e^{j2\pi 12500\, t}$$

Hence the Fourier series coefficients are 0.5 at ± 10 kHz, j 0.15 at 7.5 kHz and − 12.5 kHz, and − j 0.15 at − 7.5 kHz and 12.5 kHz respectively. The magnitude spectrum is sketched below.

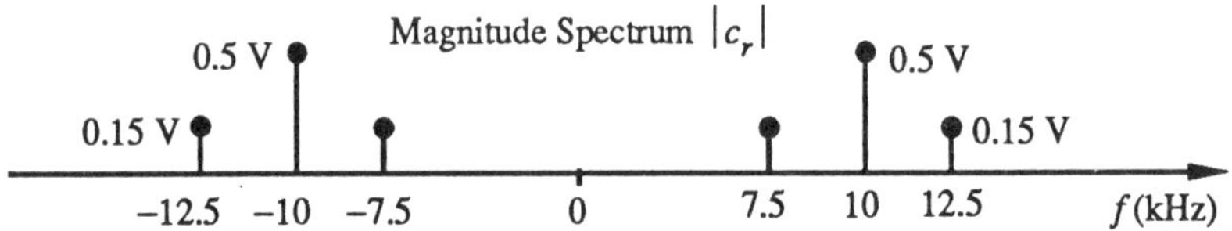

Compared with the magnitude spectrum in WE3.1, it is seen that the removal of the sampling process results in the removal of the complementary spectra and produces a non-repetitive spectrum for the continuous signal.

*****

(b) ***Discrete-time and Continuous Fourier Transform***

The discrete-time Fourier transform discussed in Section 3.3 can be extended to derive the corresponding Fourier transform of an aperiodic continuous signal. For equation (3.15) with nT replaced by t, $x(n)$ replaced by $x(t)$, and the summation replaced by integration, the continuous Fourier transform is

$$X(j\,\omega) = \int_{-\infty}^{\infty} x(t)\, e^{-j\,\omega\,t}\, dt \qquad (3.23)$$

Similarly for equation (3.14), with nT replaced by t, $x(n)$ replaced by $x(t)$, the integration limits replaced by $\pm\infty$ because the spectrum of the continuous signal is no longer periodic, and by normalising the independent variable of integration to ω, the continuous inverse Fourier transform is

$$x(t) = \frac{1}{2\pi} \int_{-\infty}^{\infty} X(j\,\omega)\, e^{j\,\omega\,t}\, d\omega \qquad (3.24)$$

❖ **WE 3.5**

Determine the Fourier transform of a rectangular pulse defined as

$$x(t) = \begin{cases} 0.5\ \text{V} & \text{for } 0 \le t \le 0.5 \text{ ms} \\ 0\ \text{V} & \text{otherwise} \end{cases}$$

Solution:

Applying equation (3.23) gives

$$X(j\,\omega) = \int_{0}^{0.0005} 0.5\, e^{-j\,\omega\,t}\, dt$$

$$= 0.5\left[\frac{e^{-j\omega t}}{-j\omega}\right]_0^{0.0005} = -\frac{0.5}{j\omega}\left[e^{-j0.0005\omega} - 1\right]$$

$$= -\frac{0.5\,e^{-j0.00025\omega}}{j\omega}\left[e^{-j0.00025\omega} - e^{j0.00025\omega}\right]$$

$$= 0.00025\ e^{-j0.00025\omega}\ \frac{\sin 0.00025\,\omega}{0.00025\,\omega}\quad \mathrm{V/Hz}$$

For the above equation a computer program or a spreadsheet software package can be used to generate the magnitude-density spectrum as shown below:

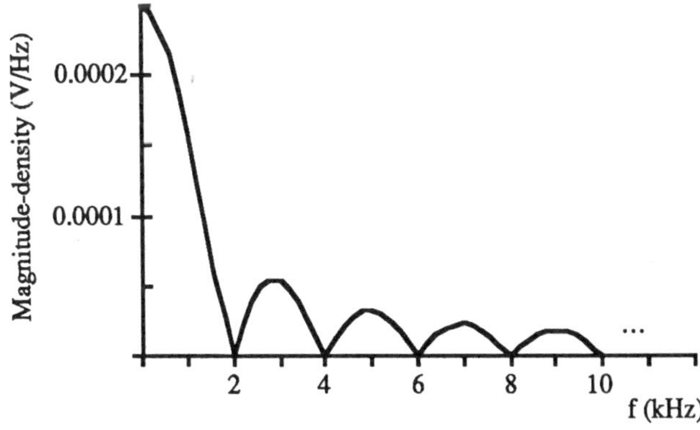

This magnitude-density spectrum may be compared with the magnitude spectrum obtained in WE3.2(b), because the specified continuous rectangular pulse signal sampled at a rate of 10,000 samples per second (f_s = 10 kHz) produces identical rectangular pulse sequence values for A = 0.5 V. Although both spectra have zero value at multiples of 2 kHz, the magnitude-density spectrum for the rectangular pulse is seen to be non-repetitive with an infinite number of side-lobes successively decreasing in magnitude as frequency increases, whereas the magnitude spectrum for the discrete rectangular pulse sequence is repetitive every f_s Hz. Furthermore the amplitude values in the two spectra are seen to relate to each other by a scaling factor equal to the sampling frequency (or equivalently the sampling period). Taking the maximum values of the main lobes in the two spectra as an example, we have 0.00025 V/Hz = 2.5 V / 10 kHz. This relationship was shown in Figure 1.5.

(c) *DFT and z-Transform*

As discussed in Section 2.1, the z-transform of a finite-length discrete signal is given by

$$X(z) = \sum_{n=0}^{N-1} x(n)\, z^{-n}$$

where $z = e^{sT} = e^{(\pm\sigma\pm j\omega)T}$. If $\sigma = 0$, the z-transform is evaluated on the unit-circle, that is,

$$X(z) = X\left(e^{j\omega T}\right) = \sum_{n=0}^{N-1} x(n)\, e^{-j\omega nT}$$

Furthermore, if $\omega = 2\pi r/(NT)$, the z-transform becomes

$$X(z) = X\left(e^{j\frac{2\pi r}{N}}\right) = \sum_{n=0}^{N-1} x(n)\, e^{-j\frac{2\pi r}{N}n} \tag{3.25}$$

Since this equation is identical to equation (3.16) for the DFT, then it follows that the DFT corresponds to the z-transform evaluated at N equally spaced points on the unit-circle in the z-plane.

3.6 Useful DFT Properties

The DFT possesses a number of properties which are useful for simplifying computations in signal analysis and synthesis processes, and also when interpreting results. Some useful DFT properties are presented and demonstrated in this section using worked examples.

(a) *Periodicity*

If we compute the DFT (equation (3.16)) of a discrete-time signal sequence, $x(n)$, the corresponding DFT sequence values, X_r, repeat with an interval N, that is

$$X_r = X_{r+N} \qquad \text{for DFT} \tag{3.26}$$

If we compute the IDFT (equation (3.17)) of a discrete-frequency spectrum sequence, X_r, the corresponding IDFT sequence values, $x(n)$, repeat with a period of N, that is

$$x(n) = x(n+N) \qquad \text{for IDFT} \tag{3.27}$$

❖ **WE 3.6**

In WE3.3 the DFT of the sampled-data sequence {2, 0, 0, 1} was shown to be {3, 2 + j, 1, 2 − j}. Verify (a) $x(7) = x(3)$, and (b) $X_{12} = X_0$.

Solution:

(a) Substituting $N = 4$, and $n = 7$ into equation (3.17) gives

$$x(7) = \frac{1}{4}\sum_{r=0}^{3} X_r\, e^{j\frac{2\pi}{4}7r} = \frac{1}{4}\sum_{r=0}^{3} X_r\, e^{j\frac{7\pi}{2}r}$$

Substituting the X_r values into the above equation gives

$$x(7) = \frac{1}{4}\left\{3 + (2+j)e^{j\frac{7\pi}{2}} + e^{j\,7\pi} + (2-j)e^{j\frac{21\pi}{2}}\right\}$$

$$= \frac{1}{4}\Big\{3 + (2+j)\left(\cos\frac{7\pi}{2} + j\sin\frac{7\pi}{2}\right) + (\cos 7\pi + j\sin 7\pi)$$

$$+ (2-j)\left(\cos\frac{21\pi}{2} + j\sin\frac{21\pi}{2}\right)\Big\}$$

$$= \frac{1}{4}\{3 + (2+j)(-j) + (-1) + (2-j)\,j\} = 1$$

$$= x(3)$$

(b) Substituting $N = 4$, and $r = 12$ into equation (3.16) gives

$$X_{12} = \sum_{n=0}^{3} x(n)\, e^{-j\frac{2\pi}{4}12n} = \sum_{n=0}^{3} x(n)\, e^{-j6\pi n}$$

Substituting the $x(n)$ values into the above equation gives

$$X_{12} = 2 + e^{-j\,18\pi} = 2 + \cos 18\pi - j\sin 18\pi = 2 + 1 = 3$$

$$= X_0$$

*****

(b) ***Circular Shift***

Shifting a finite discrete-time signal sequence $x(n)$ by k sample intervals can be regarded as a circular rotation of the samples. For example, a circular shift of the data sequence {0, 1, 2, 3, 4, 5} two places to the right creates the sequence {4, 5, 0, 1, 2, 3}. The circular shift property of the DFT states

If $\quad y(n) = x(n-k)$

then $\quad Y_r = X_r\, W^{rk} \qquad (3.28)$

where $W = e^{-j2\pi/N}$

❖ **WE 3.7**

Derive the DFT of the sampled-data sequence {0, 0, 1, 2}, and compute the corresponding amplitude and the phase spectrum.

Solution:

This sampled-data sequence is the one used in WE3.3 but having been circularly shifted to the right by 3 sample intervals ($k = 3$). Hence applying the circular shift property, the DFT of this sample-data sequence is

$$Y_r = X_r\, e^{-j\frac{2\pi}{N}rk} = X_r\, e^{-j\frac{2\pi}{4}3r} = X_r\, e^{-j\frac{3\pi}{2}r}$$

However, from WE3.3 $X_r = \{3, 2+j, 1, 2-j\}$, therefore

$$Y_r = \left\{3, (2+j)e^{-j\frac{3\pi}{2}}, e^{-j3\pi}, (2-j)e^{-j\frac{9\pi}{2}}\right\}$$

$$= \left\{3, (2+j)\left(\cos\frac{3\pi}{2} - j\sin\frac{3\pi}{2}\right), (\cos 3\pi - j\sin 3\pi),\right.$$

$$\left.(2-j)\left(\cos\frac{9\pi}{2} - j\sin\frac{9\pi}{2}\right)\right\}$$

$$= \{3, (2+j)(j), -1, (2-j)(-j)\}$$

$$= \{3, -1+j2, -1, -1-j2\}$$

The corresponding amplitude spectrum is given by

$$|Y_r| = \{\sqrt{9}, \sqrt{5}, \sqrt{1}, \sqrt{5}\} = \{3, 2.236, 1, 2.236\}$$

and the corresponding phase spectrum is given by

$$\angle Y_r = \left\{ \tan^{-1}\left(\frac{0}{3}\right), \tan^{-1}\left(\frac{2}{-1}\right), \tan^{-1}\left(\frac{0}{-1}\right), \tan^{-1}\left(\frac{-2}{-1}\right) \right\}$$

$$= \{0°, 116.57°, 180°, 243.43°\}$$

Note that $\tan^{-1}[0/(-1)] = 180°$ because the imaginary part of the complex number is 0 and because the real part of the complex number (–1) lies on the negative real axis in the complex plane.

The amplitude and phase spectrum corresponding to the original unshifted sequence {2, 0, 0, 1} was shown in WE3.3 to be {3, 2.236, 1, 2.236} and {0°, 26.57°, 0°, 333.43°} respectively. Hence the circular shift of a discrete signal does not change the amplitude spectrum, but only introduces a phase shift of $-(2\pi k/N)r$ in the phase spectrum. The phase shift introduced in this worked example is seen to be $\{0°, -270°, -2\times 270°, -3\times 270°\}$, which is equivalent to $\{0°, 90°, 180°, 270°\}$.

*****

(c) *Symmetry*
This is a useful property which eliminates the need to compute half minus one of the DFT values.

If $x(n)$ is real

then $X_{N-r} = X_r^*$ (3.29)

where X_r^* is the complex conjugate of X_r. Equation (3.29) implies

(a) $\mathrm{Re}[X_r] = \mathrm{Re}[X_{N-r}]$

(b) $\mathrm{Im}[X_r] = -\mathrm{Im}[X_{N-r}]$

(c) $\angle X_r = \angle(-X_{N-r})$

❖ **WE 3.8**
Using the symmetry property derive the DFT of the sampled data sequence {1, 0, 2, 4.5}

Solution:
Applying equation (3.16) the first three DFT values are

$$X_0 = \sum_{n=0}^{3} x(n) = 1 + 0 + 2 + 4.5 = 7.5 = 7.5\angle 0°$$

$$X_1 = \sum_{n=0}^{3} x(n)\, e^{-j\frac{2\pi}{4}n} = \sum_{n=0}^{3} x(n)\, e^{-j\frac{\pi}{2}n}$$

$$= 1 + 0 + 2\, e^{-j\pi} + 4.5\, e^{-j\frac{3\pi}{2}}$$

$$= 1 + 2(\cos\ \pi - j\sin\ \pi) + 4.5\left(\cos\ \frac{3\pi}{2} - j\sin\ \frac{3\pi}{2}\right)$$

$$= -1 + j\,4.5 = 4.61\angle 102.53^\circ$$

$$X_2 = \sum_{n=0}^{3} x(n)\, e^{-j\pi n} = 1 + 0 + 2\, e^{-j2\pi} + 4.5\, e^{-j3\pi}$$

$$= 1 + 2\,(\cos\ 2\pi - j\sin\ 2\pi) + 4.5(\cos\ 3\pi - j\sin\ 3\pi)$$

$$= -1.5 = 1.5\angle 180^\circ$$

Applying the symmetry property, the last DFT value is

$$X_3 = X_{4-1} = X_1^{*} = -1 - j4.5 = 4.61\angle -102.53^\circ$$

*****

(d) *Linearity*

The linearity property may be stated formally as

If $\quad y(n) = ax(n) + bv(n)$

then $\quad Y_r = aX_r + bV_r \qquad (3.30)$

❖ WE 3.9

Given $x(n)$ is $\{2, 0, 0, 1\}$ and $v(n)$ is $\{0, 0, 1, 2\}$, show that $Y_r = 0.5X_r + 2V_r$ when $y(n) = 0.5x(n) + 2v(n)$.

Solution:

Substituting $x(n)$ and $v(n)$ sequences into the given $y(n)$ equation yields

$$\begin{aligned} y(n) &= 0.5\{2, 0, 0, 1\} + 2\{0, 0, 1, 2\} \\ &= \{1, 0, 0, 0.5\} + \{0, 0, 2, 4\} \\ &= \{1, 0, 2, 4.5\} \end{aligned}$$

The DFT of $y(n)$ was shown to be $\{7.5, -1 + j4.5, -1.5, -1 - j4.5\}$ in WE3.8.

Furthermore the DFT of $x(n)$ was shown to be $\{3, 2+j, 1, 2-j\}$ in WE3.3 and the DFT of $v(n)$ was shown to be $\{3, -1 + j2, -1, -1 - j2\}$ in WE3.7. Substituting these values into the given Y_r equation yields

$$\begin{aligned}
Y_r &= 0.5\{3,\ 2+j,\ 1,\ 2-j\} + 2\{3,\ -1+j\,2,\ -1,\ -1-j\,2\} \\
&= \{1.5,\ 1+j\,0.5,\ 0.5,\ 1-j\,0.5\} + \{6,\ -2+j\,4,\ -2,\ -2-j\,4\} \\
&= \{7.5,\ -1+j\,4.5,\ -1.5,\ -1-j\,4.5\}
\end{aligned}$$

The results are the same as those obtained previously.

3.7 Fast Fourier Transform (FFT)

The direct implementation of the DFT (Figure 3.3) involves a large number of multiplications, additions and trigonometric function evaluations. Consequently, from an implementation point of view, it is not practical to handle a large set of input samples in real-time as demonstrated in the following worked example.

❖ WE 3.10

A DSP system based on a floating-point processor is capable of performing a multiply-and-add instruction in one machine cycle of 50 ns. Suppose that the system is used to implement the DFT directly, and is required to output the DFT of 512 input sample points within an interval of 64 samples. Estimate the maximum sampling frequency, if sine and cosine functions are precomputed and stored in a look-up table.

Solution:

Expressing equation (3.16) in real and imaginary parts, the equation for the direct implementation of the 512-point DFT of a real signal is given by

$$X_r = \sum_{n=0}^{511} x(n) \cos\left(\frac{2\pi}{512} rn\right) - j\sum_{n=0}^{511} x(n) \sin\left(\frac{2\pi}{512} rn\right)$$

$$\text{for } r = 0, 1, 2, \ldots 511$$

With 512 possible sine values and 512 possible cosine values precomputed just once at the start of the program and stored in a look-up table, the computation at each frequency point requires 512 multiplications and 511 additions for both the real part and the imaginary part, which can be implemented by executing the multiply-and-add instruction 2×512 times. Since there are 512 frequency points to be computed, the total number of multiply-and-add instructions required to be executed is 2×512^2. If the execution times for indexing, testing, branching, data fetching and storing are ignored, the total time taken to compute the DFT is $2 \times 512^2 \times 50$ ns = 26.21 ms. Since the DFT is to be output at an interval of 64 samples, the maximum sampling period is 26.21 ms/64 = 0.4095 ms and the maximum sampling frequency is 1/0.4095 ms = 2442 Hz.

Note: From this example, it can be deduced that the direct implementation of an N-point DFT requires $2N^2$ multiplications and $2(N-1)N$ additions.

*****

WE3.10 clearly shows the impracticality of the direct implementation of the DFT for processing long data sequences in real-time. To reduce the time required to compute the DFT, the **Fast Fourier Transform** (FFT) was developed by eliminating redundant calculations inherent in the direct implementation of the DFT. The most important FFT technique is based on a decimation process whereby the DFT is decomposed into smaller DFTs. This decimation process can be performed in either the time-domain or the frequency-domain.

3.7.1 Decimation-in-Time FFT

The decimation-in-time FFT (DIT FFT) is a process of dividing the N-point DFT into two ($N/2$)-point DFTs by splitting the input samples into even and odd indexed samples. The two ($N/2$)-point DFTs are then further divided in the same way into four ($N/4$)-point DFTs, and this decomposition process continues until 2-point DFTs are obtained. This approach is described below.

Dividing equation (3.18) into two $N/2$-point DFTs by splitting the input samples into even and odd indexed samples yields

$$X_r = \sum_{n=0}^{\frac{N}{2}-1} x(2n)W^{2nr} + \sum_{n=0}^{\frac{N}{2}-1} x(2n+1)\,W^{(2n+1)r}$$

$$= \sum_{n=0}^{\frac{N}{2}-1} x(2n)W^{2nr} + W^r \sum_{n=0}^{\frac{N}{2}-1} x(2n+1)W^{2nr}$$

$$= E_r + W^r O_r \tag{3.31}$$

where $x(2n)$ and $x(2n+1)$ represent the even and the odd indexed sequences respectively; the former gives $\{x(0),\ x(2),\ x(4),\ \ldots\ x(N-2)\}$ and the latter gives $\{x(1),\ x(3),\ x(5),\ \ldots\ x(N-1)\}$ as n is incremented from 0 to $N/2-1$; E_r and O_r are the DFTs of the even and the odd indexed sequences respectively.

Although equation (3.31) still needs to be evaluated N times for r varying from 0 to $N-1$, each summation only needs to be computed $N/2$ times for r varying from 0 to $N/2-1$, because E_r and O_r are repetitive with an interval of $N/2$ (refer to periodicity property). Consequently, the original DFT computation time is reduced by approximately 50%. Furthermore it may be noted that

$$W^{\frac{N}{2}+r} = \mathrm{e}^{-\mathrm{j}\frac{2\pi}{N}\left(\frac{N}{2}+r\right)} = \mathrm{e}^{-\mathrm{j}\pi}\,\mathrm{e}^{-\mathrm{j}\frac{2\pi}{N}r}$$

$$= (\cos\pi - \mathrm{j}\sin\pi)\mathrm{e}^{-\mathrm{j}\frac{2\pi}{N}r} = -W^{r}$$

and consequently by restricting r to the range 0 to $(N/2)-1$ equation (3.31) can be rewritten in two parts (with one part for the first half of the frequency points and the other part for the second half), that is

$$\left.\begin{aligned} X_r &= E_r + W^r O_r \\ X_{\frac{N}{2}+r} &= E_r - W^r O_r \end{aligned}\right\} \quad \text{for } r = 0, 1, 2, \ldots \frac{N}{2} - 1 \qquad (3.32)$$

odd.

The implementation of equation (3.32) for an 8-point DFT can be shown as a **butterfly diagram**, see Figure 3.5. Each butterfly takes a pair of inputs and generates a pair of outputs. For example, for the E_0 and O_0 input pair, the output pair from the butterfly is X_0 and X_4.

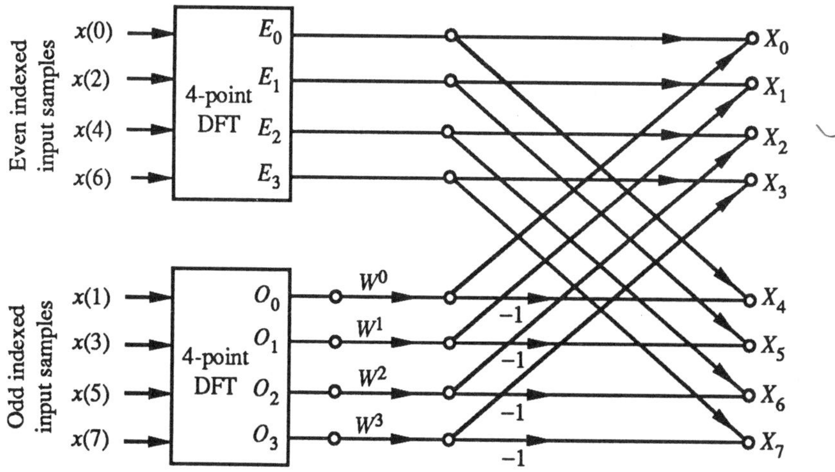

Figure 3.5 Butterfly diagram for 8-point DFT with one decimation stage

❖ **WE 3.11**

Repeat WE3.10 so that the 512-point DFT is implemented by one decimation stage.

Solution:

With reference to equation (3.32), clearly the first summation, E_r, and the second summation, O_r, need only be evaluated once. For each value of r, 256 multiplications and 255 additions are required for the real part and the imaginary part of both the E_r and O_r summations. The two summations can be implemented by executing the multiply-and-add instruction 4×256 times. Also four multiplications and two additions are required to multiply O_r (a complex number) by W^r (also a complex number). We then add/subtract the product to/from E_r, which can be implemented by executing the multiply-and-add instruction 2×4 times. Since r ranges from 0 to 255, the total number of multiply-and-add instructions required is $(4 \times 256 + 8) \times 256$. If the execution time of indexing, testing, branching, data fetching and storing are ignored, the total time taken to compute the DFT is $(4 \times 256^2 + 8 \times 256) \times 50$ ns = 13.21 ms. Since the DFT is to be output at an interval of 64 samples, the maximum sampling period is 13.21 ms/64 = 0.206 ms, and therefore the maximum sampling frequency is 1/0.206 ms = 4854 Hz.

Compared with the result for WE3.10, it is seen that the sampling frequency is nearly doubled due to the nearly 50% reduction in the computation time.

*****

Applying the same decomposition technique again to divide two $N/2$-point DFTs into four $N/4$-point DFTs by splitting the even and the odd indexed sequences into four sub-sequences, the first term (the DFT of the even indexed sequence) of equation (3.31) becomes

$$E_r = \sum_{n=0}^{\frac{N}{4}-1} x(4n)W^{4nr} + \sum_{n=0}^{\frac{N}{4}-1} x(4n+2)\,W^{(4n+2)r}$$

$$= \sum_{n=0}^{\frac{N}{4}-1} x(4n)W^{4nr} + W^{2r} \sum_{n=0}^{\frac{N}{4}-1} x(4n+2)\,W^{4nr}$$

$$= EE_r + W^{2r}\,EO_r \tag{3.33}$$

where $x(4n)$ and $x(4n+2)$ respectively represent the even and the odd indexed sub-sequences of the original even indexed sequence; the former gives $\{x(0), x(4), x(8), \ldots x(N-4)\}$ and the latter gives $\{x(2), x(6), x(10), \ldots x(N-2)\}$ as n is incremented from 0 to $(N/4) - 1$; EE_r and EO_r are the DFTs of the even-even indexed and the even-odd indexed sub-sequences respectively.

Similarly the second term (the DFT of the odd indexed sequence) of equation (3.31) becomes

$$W^r O_r = \sum_{n=0}^{\frac{N}{4}-1} x(4n+1)\, W^{(4n+1)r} + \sum_{n=0}^{\frac{N}{4}-1} x(4n+3) W^{(4n+3)r}$$

where $x(4n+1)$ and $x(4n+3)$ respectively represent the even and the odd indexed sub-sequences of the original odd indexed sequence; the former gives $\{x(1), x(5), x(9), \dots x(N-3)\}$ and the latter gives $\{x(3), x(7), x(11), \dots x(N-1)\}$ as n is incremented from 0 to $(N/4) - 1$.

Dividing both sides of the above equation by W^r gives

$$O_r = \sum_{n=0}^{\frac{N}{4}-1} x(4n+1) W^{4nr} + W^{2r} \sum_{n=0}^{\frac{N}{4}-1} x(4n+3) W^{4nr}$$

$$= OE_r + W^{2r}\, OO_r \tag{3.34}$$

where OE_r and OO_r are the DFTs of the odd-even and the odd-odd indexed sub-sequences respectively.

Although equations (3.33) and (3.34) are required to be evaluated $N/2$ times for r varying from 0 to $(N/2) - 1$, each summation only needs to be computed $N/4$ times for r varying from 0 to $(N/4) - 1$, because EE_r, EO_r, OE_r and OO_r are repetitive with an interval of $N/4$. This results in a further saving in the computation time. Furthermore it may be noted that

$$W^{2\left(\frac{N}{4}+r\right)} = \mathrm{e}^{-\mathrm{j}\frac{2\pi}{N}\left(\frac{N}{2}+2r\right)} = \mathrm{e}^{-\mathrm{j}\pi}\, \mathrm{e}^{-\mathrm{j}\frac{2\pi}{N}2r} = -\, W^{2r}$$

and consequently by restricting r to the range 0 to $(N/4) - 1$, equations (3.33) and (3.34) can be rewritten in two parts, that is

$$\left.\begin{aligned} E_r &= EE_r + W^{2r}\, EO_r \\ E_{\frac{N}{4}+r} &= EE_r - W^{2r}\, EO_r \\ O_r &= OE_r + W^{2r}\, OO_r \\ O_{\frac{N}{4}+r} &= OE_r - W^{2r}\, OO_r \end{aligned}\right\} \quad \text{for } r = 0, 1, 2, \dots \frac{N}{4} - 1 \tag{3.35}$$

The implementation of equation (3.35) for an 8-point DFT is shown as stage 2 in Figure 3.6.

The same decomposition technique can be applied again to divide four $N/4$-point DFTs into eight $N/8$-point DFTs, until 2-point DFTs are obtained. Each decomposition stage doubles the number of separate DFTs, but halves the number of points per DFT. In computing an N-point DFT, with $N = 2^y$ (y is a positive integer), this decimation process can be repeated y (or $\log_2 N$) times. Figure 3.6 shows the complete implementation of the DIT FFT for an 8-point DFT. The number of computation stages is seen to be 3 since $8 = 2^3$.

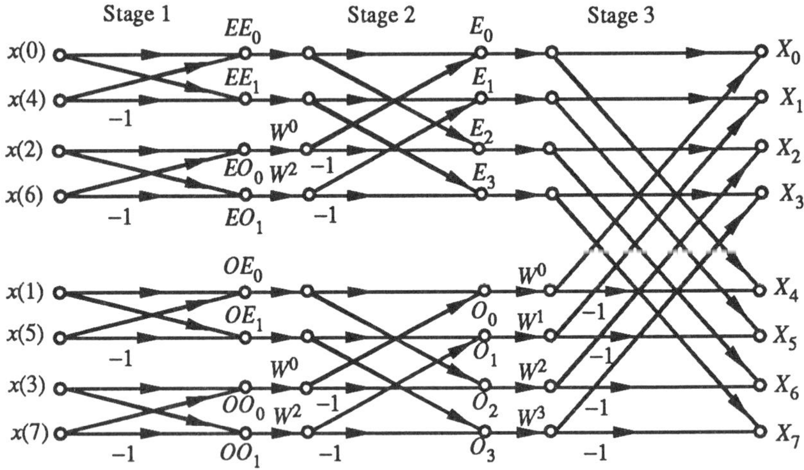

Figure 3.6 Butterfly diagram for 8-point DIT FFT

Figure 3.6 shows that stage 1 requires N additions/subtractions and the other two stages require N complex additions/subtractions (or $2N$ additions/subtractions) and $N/2$ complex multiplications (or $2N$ ordinary multiplications and N additions/subtractions, since each complex multiplication requires 4 ordinary multiplications and 2 additions/subtractions). Since there are $\log_2 N$ stages for an N-point FFT, the total number of multiplications is $2N(\log_2 N - 1)$ and the total number of additions is $3N(\log_2 N - 1) + N$. This can be compared with the $2N^2$ multiplications and $2(N - 1)N$ additions required for the direct implementation of the DFT.

❖ WE 3.12

Repeat WE3.10 if the 512-point DFT is fully implemented by employing the DIT FFT algorithm.

***Solution*:**
Except for stage 1, each stage requires 256 complex multiplications (or 4×256 ordinary multiplications) and 2×256 additions/subtractions. If each complex multiplication is implemented by executing the multiply-and-add instruction 4 times, the number of multiply-and-add instructions required to be executed at each stage is 4×256. Furthermore the complex additions at each stage (except stage 1) also require the addition instruction to be executed 2×512 times. The total number of computation stage is $\log_2 512 = 9$ and stage 1 requires only 512 additions. If the execution time of the addition instruction is assumed to be the same as the multiply-and-add instruction, then the computation time required is

$$[(4 \times 256 + 2 \times 512) \times 8 + 512] \times 50 \text{ ns} = 0.8448 \text{ ms}.$$

Since the DFT is to be output at an interval of 64 samples, the maximum sampling period is 0.8448 ms/64 = 13.2 μs and the maximum sampling frequency is 1/13.2 μs = 75.757 kHz. This compares with 2442 Hz for the direct implementation of the DFT, giving a 31-fold increase in the computation speed.

******

❖ WE 3.13
Draw the butterfly diagram of a 4-point DIT FFT and use it to verify the DFT of the sequence {2, 0, 0, 1} obtained in WE3.3.

***Solution*:**
Given that $N = 4$, we have

$$W^r = e^{-j\frac{2\pi}{N}r} = e^{-j\frac{2\pi}{4}r} = e^{-j\frac{\pi}{2}r}$$

therefore

$$W^0 = 1 \quad \text{and} \quad W^1 = e^{-j\frac{\pi}{2}} = \cos\left(\frac{\pi}{2}\right) - j\sin\left(\frac{\pi}{2}\right) = -j$$

Substituting the above W^r values into the butterfly diagram of the 4-point DIT FFT yields

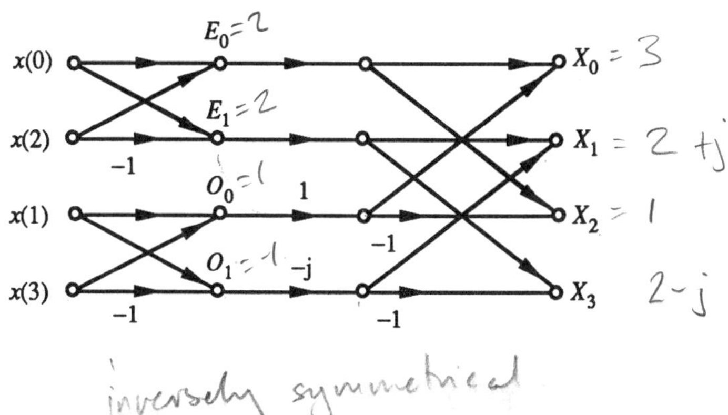

Computing each butterfly node output in the above diagram gives

$$E_0 = x(0) + x(2) = 2 + 0 = 2 \qquad E_1 = x(0) - x(2) = 2 - 0 = 2$$

$$O_0 = x(1) + x(3) = 0 + 1 = 1 \qquad O_1 = x(1) - x(3) = 0 - 1 = -1$$

$$X_0 = E_0 + O_0 = 2 + 1 = 3 \qquad X_1 = E_1 + (-\mathrm{j})O_1 = 2 + (-\mathrm{j})(-1) = 2 + \mathrm{j}$$

$$X_2 = E_0 - O_0 = 2 - 1 = 1 \qquad X_3 = E_1 - (-\mathrm{j})O_1 = 2 - (-\mathrm{j})(-1) = 2 - \mathrm{j}$$

These results are identical to those obtained in WE3.3.

*****

3.7.2 Implementation Aspects of Decimation-in-Time FFT

In practice, the data sequence appears at the input of a DSP system in a natural order, i.e. $x(0)$, $x(1)$, $x(2)$, ... Looking at Figure 3.6, we see that a different order is required to present the input data sequence to the DIT FFT processor. For example, the computation of the first butterfly is seen to require $x(0)$ and $x(4)$. To enable computation of the $N/2$ butterflies in the first stage to be carried out conveniently by fetching input data from consecutive memory locations, it is necessary to shuffle the input data sequence to give the required order. This shuffling can be achieved by a ***bit-reversal*** operation, which reverses the digits of the binary representation of the index, n, to obtain the required order, as illustrated in Figure 3.7.

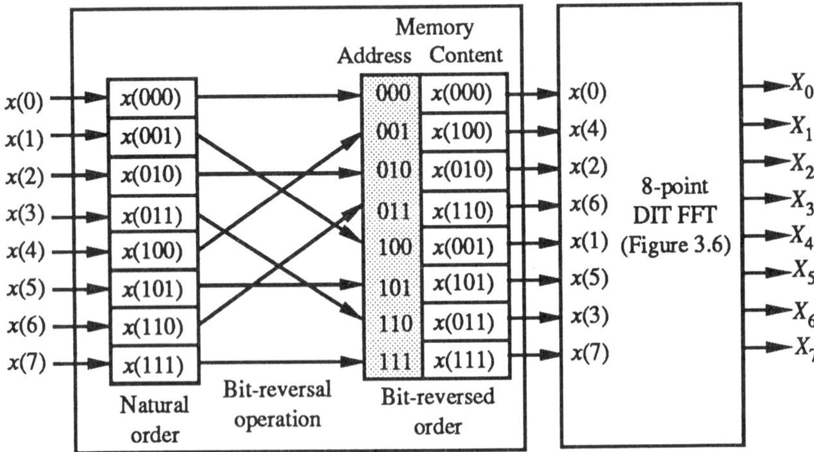

Figure 3.7 Data sequence re-ordering by bit-reversal

The flowchart shown in Figure 3.8 provides a way to implement the bit-reversal operation.

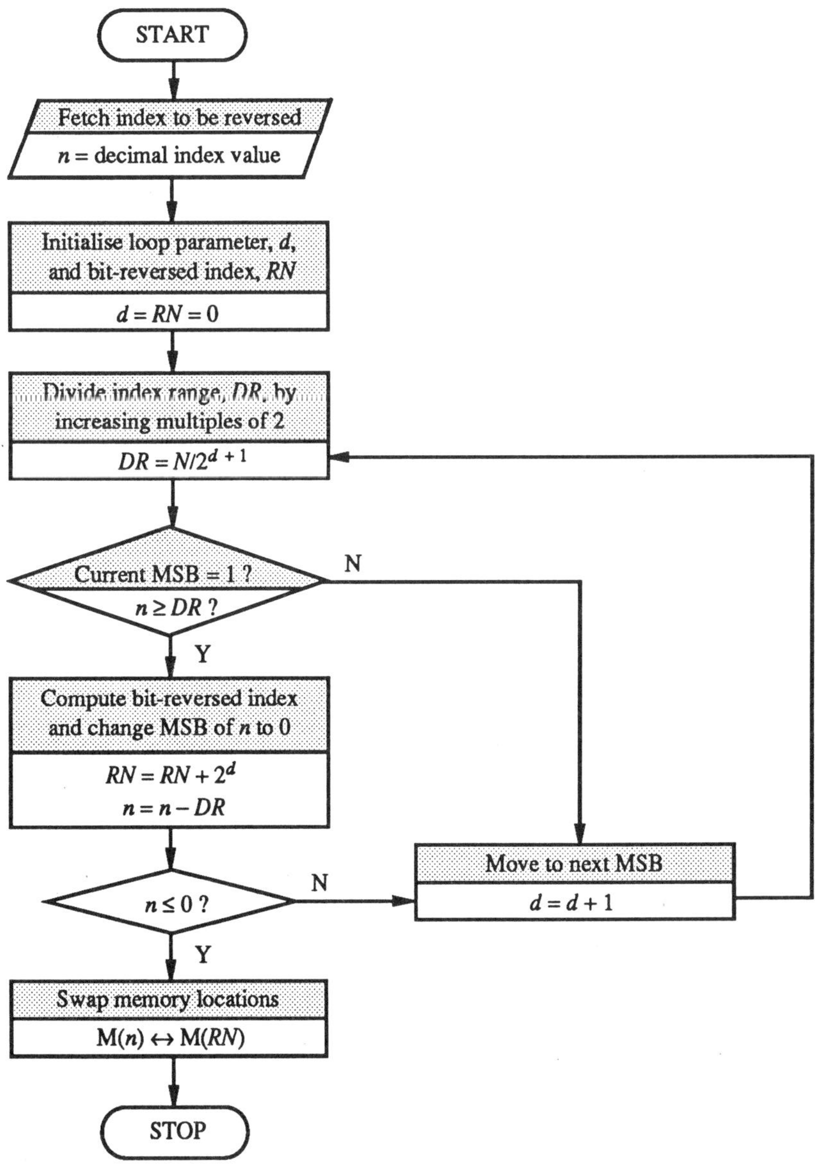

Figure 3.8 Bit-reversal flowchart

The basic principle of the bit-reversal operation can be described by using $x(10)$ of a 16-point DIT FFT as an example. Let the digits of the binary representation of the decimal index be denoted by $b_3b_2b_1b_0$. Following through the flowchart, with $N = 16$ and $d = 0$, the index number 10 will initially be compared with 8 (= $16/2^1$), this is in fact testing whether b_3 (MSB) of the binary representation is 1 or 0 by comparing 1010 with 1000. Since 10 is greater than 8 implying that $b_3 = 1$, $2^0 = 1$ is added to the bit-reversed index. Bit b_2 is then tested by subtracting 8 from the original index number to remove the MSB, and by incrementing d to 1, the result of the subtraction is compared with 4 (= $16/2^2$) or 0100 in binary. Since $(10 - 8) = 2$, which is less than 4, implying that b_2 (next MSB) is zero, nothing is added to the bit-reversed index and d is incremented to 2 to enable the test of b_1. Since the next test gives $2 = 16/2^3$ implying that b_1 is 1, $2^2 = 4$ is added to the bit-reversed index to give it a value of 5. The next subtraction results in $n = 0$ and the program exits the loop by swapping the contents in memory locations having binary addresses of 0101 and 1010. To summarise the above operation mathematically, the program executes the following bit-reversal equation

$$\text{Bit-reversed index} = \sum_{i=0}^{L} b_i \, 2^{L-i} \tag{3.36}$$

With the swapping operation performed at the end of the bit-reversal program, it implies (a) the bit-reversal program needs to be executed only $N/2$ times on either the lower half or the upper half of the index numbers for an N-point DIT FFT, and (b) it is an **in-place operation** requiring no additional memory locations.

Many general purpose DSP devices now offer a special bit-reversed addressing mode, which eliminates the need to swap memory locations, and enables the input data sequence to be accessed directly in bit-reversed order without any time penalty.

With the input sequence properly shuffled by using the bit-reversed procedure, the DIT FFT can be implemented with three nested loops as shown in Figure 3.9.

(a) Loop 1: *Compute butterfly with the same W^r factor*
In this innermost loop, variables t and b provide the locations of the array elements corresponding to the input pair and the output pair of the butterfly to be computed. Referring back to Figure 3.6, it is seen that the node separation between the input pair and between the output pair of a butterfly increases by a factor of 2 as the stage number increases (1 node apart in stage 1, 2 nodes apart in stage 2 and 4 nodes apart in stage 3), hence $b = t + 2^{s-1}$, where s is the stage number.

R and I are two variables providing two temporary storage locations for real and imaginary parts of the product of W^r and the bottom input of the butterfly.

The actual computation of each butterfly is then performed in-place with the computed output pair saved in the same array locations originally occupied by the input pair, M(t) and M(b). This is possible because the values of each input pair are used only once in the execution of the whole DIT FFT. For example, in Figure 3.6, after the input pair, $x(1)$ and $x(5)$, are used to form the output pair OE_0 and OE_1, $x(1)$ and $x(5)$ are not required in the computation of any other butterflies. Hence OE_0 and OE_1 can be saved in the same memory locations occupied by $x(1)$ and $x(5)$. The use of this in-place computation minimises memory requirements.

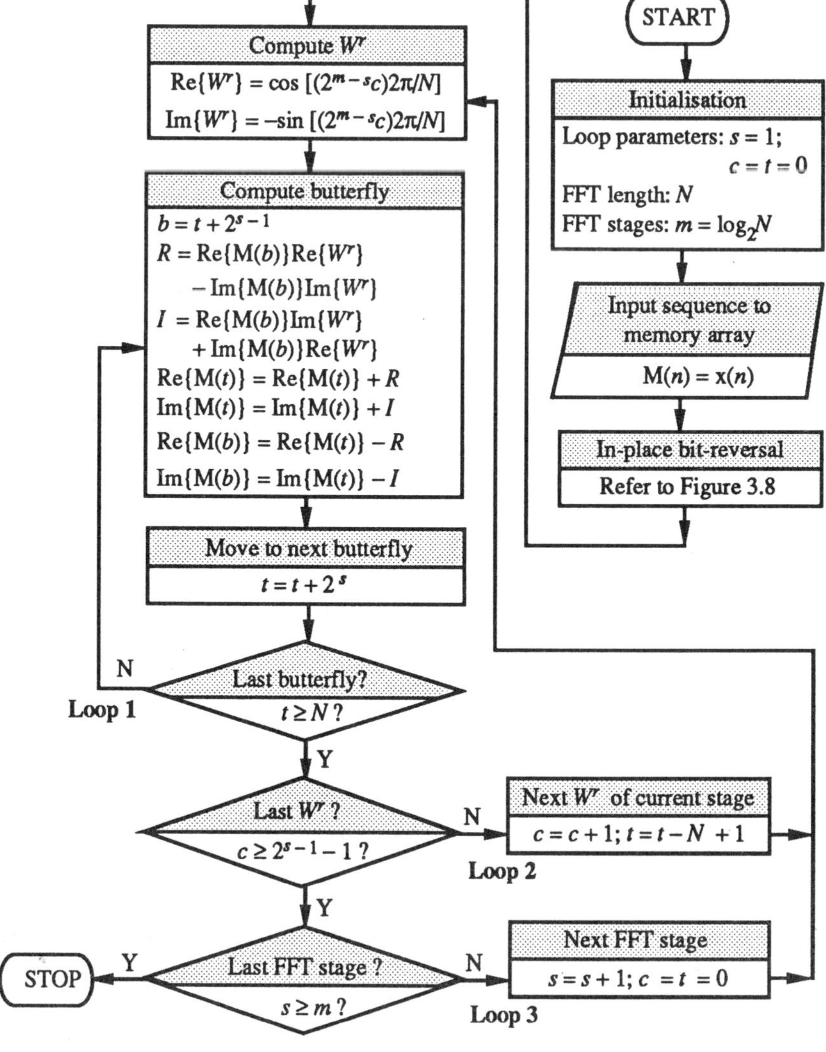

Figure 3.9 Flowchart for an N-point DIT FFT

Referring back to Figure 3.6, it is seen that the separation between two nearest butterflies associated with the same W^r factor in a stage is 2^s (2 nodes in stage 1, 4 nodes in stage 2), hence t is incremented by 2^s to provide the location of the array element corresponding to the top input of the next butterfly associated with the same W^r factor, and the loop is repeated until $t \geq N$, which implies that t has stepped through all butterflies associated with the same W^r factor.

(b) Loop 2: *Compute all butterflies in a stage*
This loop computes each W^r factor in a stage and passes it to Loop 1. Referring back to Figure 3.6, it is seen that there are 2^{s-1} distinct W^r factors per stage, namely 1 in stage 1, 2 in stage 2 and 4 in stage 3. Parameter c is compared with $2^{s-1} - 1$, and if c is less than $2^{s-1} - 1$, implying more W^r factors to be computed, c is incremented and used to compute the next W^r factor, otherwise it exits the loop and moves to the next stage.

(c) Loop 3: *Compute all stages*
In this outer loop, s steps from 1 through to m, (the total number of stages), to enable the computation of the whole DIT FFT to be carried out stage-by-stage.

Since the IDFT equation is similar to the DFT equation, apart from the additional multiplier of $1/N$ and the sign of the exponent, the flowchart for the DIT FFT can be adapted for the implementation of the inverse FFT (IFFT) by replacing $x(n)$ with X_n, changing the sign of the $\mathrm{Im}\{W^r\}$ equation, and dividing the output values from the last FFT stage by N.

3.7.3 Decimation-in-Frequency FFT

In contrast to the DIT FFT which decomposes the DFT by recursively splitting the input samples in the time-domain into smaller sub-sequences, the decimation-in-frequency FFT (DIF FFT) decomposes the DFT by recursively splitting the sequence elements in the frequency-domain into smaller sub-sequences. This approach is described below.

Dividing equation (3.18) into two $N/2$-point DFTs by splitting the input samples into two halves yields

$$X_r = \sum_{n=0}^{\frac{N}{2}-1} x(n)W^{nr} + \sum_{n=\frac{N}{2}}^{N-1} x(n)W^{nr}$$

$$= \sum_{n=0}^{\frac{N}{2}-1} x(n)W^{nr} + \sum_{n=0}^{\frac{N}{2}-1} x\left(n+\frac{N}{2}\right) W^{\left(n+\frac{N}{2}\right)r}$$

$$= \sum_{n=0}^{\frac{N}{2}-1} x(n)\, W^{nr} + \sum_{n=0}^{\frac{N}{2}-1} x\left(n+\frac{N}{2}\right) W^{\frac{N}{2}r}\, W^{nr}$$

Since $W^{\frac{N}{2}r} = e^{-j\frac{2\pi}{N}\frac{N}{2}r} = \cos(\pi r) - j\sin(\pi r) = (-1)^r$, we obtain

$$X_r = \sum_{n=0}^{\frac{N}{2}-1} x(n) W^{nr} + \sum_{n=0}^{\frac{N}{2}-1} x\left(n+\frac{N}{2}\right)(-1)^r\, W^{nr}$$

$$= \sum_{n=0}^{\frac{N}{2}-1} \left[x(n) + (-1)^r\; x\left(n+\frac{N}{2}\right)\right] W^{nr}$$

Decomposing the sequence in the frequency domain, X_r, into an even indexed subsequence X_{2k} and an odd indexed subsequence X_{2k+1}, where $k = 0, 1, 2, \ldots, (N/2) - 1$, yields

$$X_{2k} = \sum_{n=0}^{\frac{N}{2}-1} \left[x(n) + (-1)^{2k}\; x\left(n+\frac{N}{2}\right)\right] W^{2kn}$$

$$= \sum_{n=0}^{\frac{N}{2}-1} \left[x(n) + x\left(n+\frac{N}{2}\right)\right] W^{2kn} = \sum_{n=0}^{\frac{N}{2}-1} a_n\, W^{2kn} \qquad (3.37)$$

$$X_{2k+1} = \sum_{n=0}^{\frac{N}{2}-1} \left[x(n) + (-1)^{2k+1}\; x\left(n+\frac{N}{2}\right)\right] W^{(2k+1)n}$$

$$= \sum_{n=0}^{\frac{N}{2}-1} \left[\left(x(n) - x\left(n+\frac{N}{2}\right)\right) W^{n}\right] W^{2kn} = \sum_{n=0}^{\frac{N}{2}-1} \left[b_n\, W^{n}\right] W^{2kn}$$

(3.38)

The same decomposition technique can be applied again to divide equations (3.37) and (3.38) into two halves of $N/4$-point DFTs to obtain X_{4k}, X_{4k+2}, X_{4k+1} and X_{4k+3} for $k = 0, 1, 2, \ldots, (N/4) - 1$, and applied again until 2-point DFTs are reached. Figure 3.10 shows the butterfly diagram for the 8-point DIF FFT.

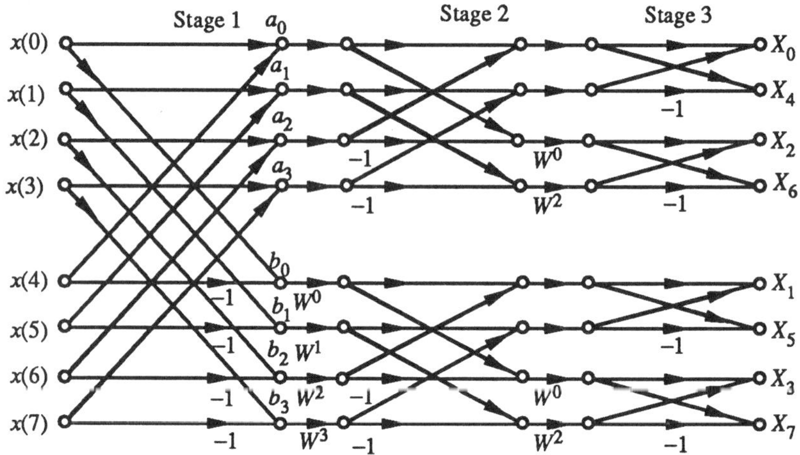

Figure 3.10 Butterfly diagram for 8-point DIF FFT

In contrast to Figure 3.6, Figure 3.10 shows that the DIF FFT has its input values in natural order and the output values are in bit-reversed order. However, the DIT and DIF algorithms can be computed in-place and require the same number of mathematical operations.

❖ WE 3.14

Draw the butterfly diagram of a 4-point inverse DIF FFT and use it to verify the DFT results {3, 2 + j, 1, 2 − j) obtained in WE3.13 for the given input sequence {2, 0, 0, 1}.

Solution:

Due to the similarities between the DFT and the IDFT, the inverse 4-point DIF FFT butterfly diagram can be obtained from the corresponding DIT FFT diagram in WE3.13 by making the following modifications: (a) reversing the butterfly diagram, (b) swapping the data input samples with the FFT outputs, (c) scaling the FFT input values by 1/4, and (d) changing the sign of the imaginary part of the W^r term. These modifications give

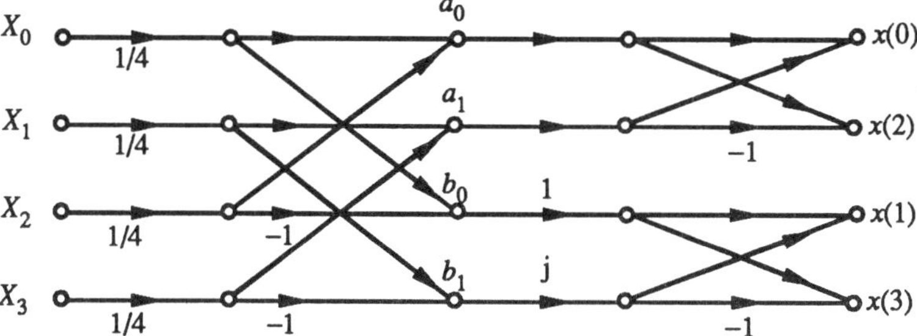

Computing each butterfly node output in the above diagram gives

$$a_0 = \frac{1}{4}\left(X_0 + X_2 \right) = \frac{1}{4}(3 + 1) = 1$$

$$a_1 = \frac{1}{4}\left(X_1 + X_3 \right) = \frac{1}{4}[(2 + j) + (2 - j)] = 1$$

$$b_0 = \frac{1}{4}\left(X_0 - X_2 \right) = \frac{1}{4}(3 - 1) = \frac{1}{2}$$

$$b_1 = \frac{1}{4}\left(X_1 - X_3 \right) = \frac{1}{4}[(2 + j) - (2 - j)] = \frac{j}{2}$$

$$x(0) = a_0 + a_1 = 1 + 1 = 2$$

$$x(1) = b_0 + j\, b_1 = \frac{1}{2} + j\,\frac{j}{2} = 0$$

$$x(2) = a_0 - a_1 = 1 - 1 = 0$$

$$x(3) = b_0 - j\, b_1 = \frac{1}{2} - j\,\frac{j}{2} = 1$$

*****

3.8 Convolution Revisited

In Section 1.5.2, the convolution-summation of two discrete sequences was introduced and was used to determine the output sequence of a linear time-invariant system in response to any given input sequence. In Section 2.2, the convolution-summation of two discrete signals in the time-domain was shown to be equivalent to the product of their z-transforms. In Section 3.5(c), the DFT was shown to correspond to the z-transform evaluated on the unit-circle. Consequently, we may expect a relationship similar to that between the z-transform and convolution to exist between the DFT and convolution. Indeed such a relationship does exist between the DFT and the convolution of two periodic sequences of the same length, and this is known as ***circular convolution.***

If two periodic sequences with the same period are to be convolved, the infinite summation limit for the convolution operation, equation (1.43), has to be reduced to fit the period of the sequences, otherwise the convolution result may diverge to infinity as more and more sample pairs from the two periodic sequences are included in the convolution operation. Hence the convolution of two periodic sequences $x(n)$ and $h(n)$ with the same length N is given by

$$y(n) = \sum_{k=0}^{N-1} x(k)\, h(n-k) = x(n) \circledast h(n) \tag{3.39}$$

where $\circledast$ is used to denote the circular convolution operation of the two sequences. Figure 3.11 illustrates the process of circular convolution of two periodic sequences having the same length of eight. The eight periodic samples of $x(n)$ are equally spaced around the inner circle in a counter-clockwise direction, and the eight periodic samples of $h(n)$ are equally spaced around the outer circle in a clockwise direction. The successive convolution values are obtained by rotating the outer circle one sample at a time, followed by multiplying the values sitting on two circles with the same angular position, and finally summing the products.

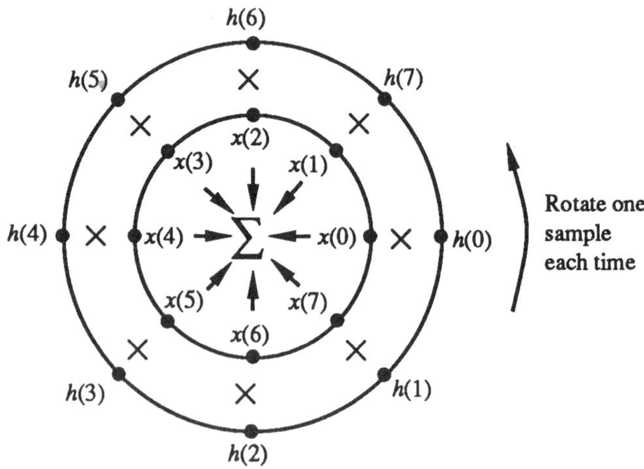

Figure 3.11 Circular convolution of two 8-sample sequences

The differences between circular convolution and the convolution operation introduced in Section 1.5.2, commonly referred to as ***linear convolution***, are illustrated in the following worked example.

❖ **WE 3.15**

Given that $x(n) = \{2, 0, 0, 1\}$ and $h(n) = \{4, 3, 2, 1\}$, perform (a) linear convolution, and (b) circular convolution of the two sequences.

Solution:

(a) Using the second method illustrated in WE1.19, linear convolution of the two given sequences is shown in the following table:

n	−3	−2	−1	0	1	2	3	4	5	6	≥7
$x(n)$	0	0	0	2	0	0	1	0	0	0	0
$h(-(k-n))$	1	2	3	4	→						
				2×4+ 0×3+ 0×2+ 0×1	0×4+ 2×3+ 0×2+ 0×1	0×4+ 0×3+ 2×2+ 0×1	1×4+ 0×3+ 0×2+ 2×1	0×4+ 1×3+ 0×2+ 0×1	0×4+ 0×3+ 1×2+ 0×1	0×4+ 0×3− 0×2− 1×1	0×4+ 0×3+ 0×2+ 0×1
$y(n)$	0	0	0	= 8	= 6	= 4	= 6	= 3	= 2	= 1	= 0

(b) Similarly circular convolution of the two sequences is shown in the following table:

n	0	1	2	3	
$x(n)$	2	0	0	1	$y(n)$
$h(-(k))$	4	1	2	3	$2\times4+0\times1+0\times2+1\times3=11$
$h(-(k-1))$	3	4	1	2	$2\times3+0\times4+0\times1+1\times2=8$
$h(-(k-2))$	2	3	4	1	$2\times2+0\times3+0\times4+1\times1=5$
$h(-(k-3))$	1	2	3	4	$2\times1+0\times2+0\times3+1\times4=6$

Note: The resulting sequence produced by linear convolution differs from that produced by circular convolution, not only in the sequence values but also in the sequence length. While linear convolution results in an aperiodic sequence with a length of $2N-1$ (i.e. 7 in this case), circular convolution results in a periodic sequence having a length of N (i.e. 4 in this case). However, if three zeros were padded (added) at the end of the two given sequences, $x(n)$ and $h(n)$, for circular convolution, the sequence values will be the same as those produced by linear convolution.

In general, the linear convolution of two sequences $x(n)$ and $h(n)$ with lengths of N and M respectively will yield a sequence $y(n)$ with a length of $M+N-1$, as shown in WE1.19. To implement linear convolution using circular convolution, $M-1$ and $N-1$ zeros are padded at the end of $x(n)$ and $h(n)$ respectively.

*****

3.8.1 DFT Properties of Circular Convolution

(a) ***Time-domain Circular Convolution***
This property may be formally stated as

If $y(n) = x(n) \circledast h(n)$

then $Y_r = X_r H_r$ (3.40)

where Y_r, X_r and H_r are the DFTs of $y(n)$, $x(n)$ and $h(n)$, respectively.

❖ **WE 3.16**

(a) Design a system in the form of a block diagram to implement circular convolution using the DFT and IDFT.
(b) Verify the design using the two data sequences given in WE3.15.
(c) If a DSP system based on a floating-point processor, capable of performing a multiply-and-add instruction in 50 ns, is used to implement circular convolution of two 512-point sequences, estimate the computation time required for (i) the direct form of implementation, and (ii) for the FFT form of implementation.

Solution:
(a) The block diagram below shows a system which can perform circular convolution using the DFT and IDFT. This is the implementaion of equation (3.40).

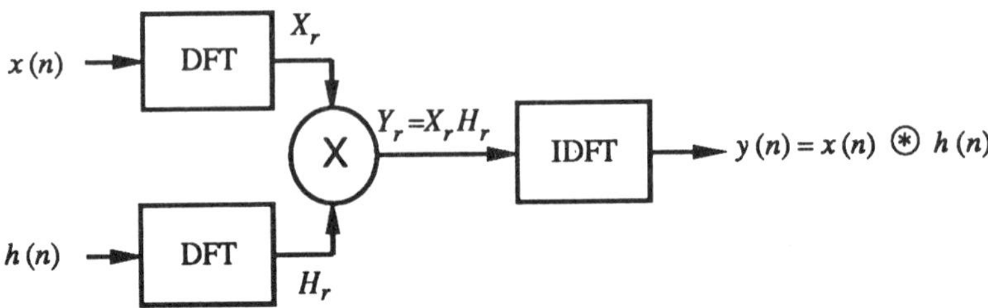

(b) As shown in WE3.3, the DFT of $x(n)$ is $\{3, 2 + \mathrm{j}, 1, 2 - \mathrm{j}\}$. Using the butterfly diagram of the 4-point DIT FFT in WE3.13, the DFT values of $h(n)$ are

$$H_0 = E_0 + O_0 = [h(0) + h(2)] + [h(1) + h(3)]$$
$$= [4 + 2] + [3 + 1] = 10$$

$$H_1 = E_1 - \mathrm{j}\, O_1 = [h(0) - h(2)] - \mathrm{j}[h(1) - h(3)]$$
$$= [4 - 2] - \mathrm{j}[3 - 1] = 2 - \mathrm{j}2$$

$$H_2 = E_0 - O_0 = [h(0) + h(2)] - [h(1) + h(3)]$$
$$= [4 + 2] - [3 + 1] = 2$$

$$H_3 = E_1 + j\,O_1 = [h(0) - h(2)] + j[h(1) - h(3)]$$
$$= [4 - 2] + j[3 - 1] = 2 + j2$$

$$Y_r = X_r H_r = \{3, 2 + j, 1, 2 - j\}\{10, 2 - j2, 2, 2 + j2\}$$
$$= \{30, 6 - j2, 2, 6 + j2\}$$

Using the butterfly diagram of the 4-point inverse DIF FFT in WE3.14, the IDFT values of Y_r are

$$y(0) = a_0 + a_1 = \frac{1}{4}\left[Y_0 + Y_2\right] + \frac{1}{4}\left[Y_1 + Y_3\right]$$
$$= \frac{1}{4}[30 + 2] + \frac{1}{4}[(6 - j2) + (6 + j2)] = 11$$

$$y(1) = b_0 + j\,b_1 = \frac{1}{4}\left[Y_0 - Y_2\right] + j\frac{1}{4}\left[Y_1 - Y_3\right]$$
$$= \frac{1}{4}[30 - 2] + j\,\frac{1}{4}[(6 - j2) - (6 + j2)] = 8$$

$$y(2) = a_0 - a_1 = \frac{1}{4}\left[Y_0 + Y_2\right] - \frac{1}{4}\left[Y_1 + Y_3\right]$$
$$= \frac{1}{4}[30 + 2] - \frac{1}{4}[(6 - j2) + (6 + j2)] = 5$$

$$y(3) = b_0 - j\,b_1 = \frac{1}{4}\left[Y_0 - Y_2\right] - j\frac{1}{4}\left[Y_1 - Y_3\right]$$
$$= \frac{1}{4}[30 - 2] - j\,\frac{1}{4}[(6 - j2) - (6 + j2)] = 6$$

Since the output, $y(n)$, of the block diagram in (a), agrees with that produced by the circular convolution in WE3.15(b), the design has been verified.

(c) In the circular convolution table in WE3.15(b), the direct implementation of circular convolution of two 4-point sequences was shown to require $4^2 = 16$ multiplications and $4(4 - 1) = 12$ additions. It follows that the direct implementation of two 512-point sequences will require 512^2 multiplications and $512(512 - 1)$ additions, and will therefore require the execution of the multiply-and-add instruction 512^2 times. If the execution time of indexing, testing, branching, data fetching and storing are ignored, the total time taken to compute the circular convolution is $512^2 \times 50$ ns = 13.11 ms.

The indirect implementation of circular convolution was shown in (a) to require the multiplication of two DFTs and one IDFT. In WE3.12, the computation time for a 512-point FFT was shown to be 0.8448 ms. Since the inverse IDFT can be computed using the same algorithm as for the FFT, the time required to compute two DFTs and one IDFT using the FFT is 3×0.8448 ms. The multiplication of two DFT outputs is a complex one which requires a total of 4×512 multiplications and 2×512 additions, and can be implemented by executing the multiply-and-add instruction 4×512 times. Hence the total computation time for the indirect implementation is

$$(3 \times 0.8448)\ \text{ms} + (4 \times 512 \times 50)\ \text{ns} = 2.6368\ \text{ms}$$

It can therefore be concluded that the indirect form of implementation of circular convolution based on the FFT is 13.11/2.6368 = 4.97 times faster than the direct form of implementation. Furthermore, if one of the sequences is the impulse response of a DSP system and if the FFT of the impulse response is precomputed and stored, then the total computation time for the indirect form of implementation will be reduced to

$$(2 \times 0.8448)\ \text{ms} + (4 \times 512 \times 50)\ \text{ns} = 1.792\ \text{ms}.$$

*****

(b) ***Frequency-domain Circular Convolution***

This property may be formally stated as

If $$Y_r = \frac{1}{N}\left(X_r \circledast H_r \right)$$

then $$y(n) = x(n)\ h(n) \tag{3.41}$$

where Y_r, X_r and H_r are the DFTs of $y(n)$, $x(n)$ and $h(n)$, respectively.

❖ **WE 3.17**

Use the two sequences and their DFTs obtained in WE3.16 to verify the frequency-domain circular convolution property.

Solution:

The product of $x(n)$ and $h(n)$ is

$$y(n) = x(n)\ h(n) = \{2, 0, 0, 1\}\{4, 3, 2, 1\} = \{8, 0, 0, 1\}$$

and the circular convolution of X_r and H_r using equation (3.41) is shown in the following table:

r	0	1	2	3	
X_r	3	$2+j$	1	$2-j$	Y_r
$H_{(-(k))}$	10	$2+j2$	2	$2-j2$	$[3 \times 10 + (2+j)(2+j2) + 1 \times 2 + (2-j)(2-j2)]/4 = 9$
$H_{(-(k-1))}$	$2-j2$	10	$2+j2$	2	$[3\,(2-j2) + (2+j)\,10 + 1\,(2+j2) + (2-j)\,2]/4 = 8+j$
$H_{(-(k-2))}$	2	$2-j2$	10	$2+j2$	$[3 \times 2 + (2+j)(2-j2) + 1 \times 10 + (2-j)(2+j2)]/4 = 7$
$H_{(-(k-3))}$	$2+j2$	2	$2-j2$	10	$[3\,(2+j2) + (2+j)\,2 + 1\,(2-j2) + (2-j)\,10]/4 = 8-j$

Taking the IDFT of Y_r by using the butterfly diagram for the 4-point inverse DIF FFT in WE3.14 yields

$$y(0) = a_0 + a_1 = \frac{1}{4}\left[Y_0 + Y_2\right] + \frac{1}{4}\left[Y_1 + Y_3\right]$$
$$= \frac{1}{4}[9 + 7] + \frac{1}{4}[(8 + j) + (8 - j)] = 8$$

$$y(1) = b_0 + j\,b_1 = \frac{1}{4}\left[Y_0 - Y_2\right] + j\frac{1}{4}\left[Y_1 - Y_3\right]$$
$$= \frac{1}{4}[9 - 7] + j\,\frac{1}{4}[(8 + j) - (8 - j)] = 0$$

$$y(2) = a_0 - a_1 = \frac{1}{4}\left[Y_0 + Y_2\right] - \frac{1}{4}\left[Y_1 + Y_3\right]$$
$$= \frac{1}{4}[9 + 7] - \frac{1}{4}[(8 + j) + (8 - j)] = 0$$

$$y(3) = b_0 - j\,b_1 = \frac{1}{4}\left[Y_0 - Y_2\right] - j\frac{1}{4}\left[Y_1 - Y_3\right]$$
$$= \frac{1}{4}[9 - 7] - j\,\frac{1}{4}[(8 + j) - (8 - j)] = 1$$

This sequence is the same as the product of $x(n)$ and $h(n)$.

*****

3.8.2 Fast Convolution by Signal Segmentation

In some practical applications, such as filtering, it is required to implement the linear convolution of a finite impulse response sequence of a DSP system with an input sequence. As shown in WE3.15, circular convolution can be used to implement the linear convolution by padding $N - 1$ zeros to the end of the impulse response sequence of length M and by padding $M - 1$ zeros to the end of the input signal of length N respectively. Although the indirect implementation of circular convolution based on the FFT offers computational advantages, as demonstrated in WE3.16(c), it has characteristic delays since the output cannot be generated until the entire input signal is received. Consequently, as the signal gets longer, not only does the delay get longer, but also the FFT implementation and the size of the memory required become impractical. One way to perform fast convolution for a long input sequence is to segment it into blocks and to obtain the final convolution output sequence by combining the partial convolution results generated from each block. Two signal segmentation methods, namely the ***overlap-save*** and the ***overlap-add*** methods, are presented in this section.

(a) ***Overlap-save Method***
This method is illustrated in Figure 3.12:

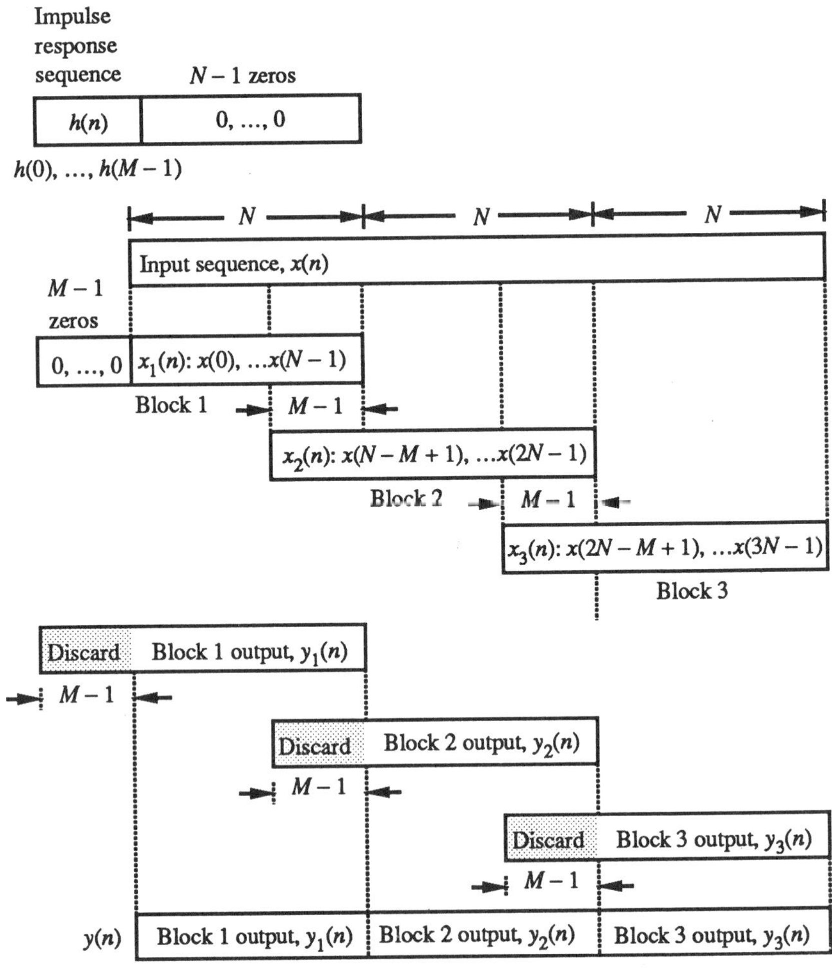

Figure 3.12 Overlap-save method

The overlap-save method is performed by the following procedures:

(i) Padding $N-1$ zeros to the end of the impulse response sequence, $h(n)$, of length M to obtain a sequence of length $M+N-1=L$, and perform an L-point FFT of the padded impulse response sequence and store the FFT output values.

(ii) Perform an L-point FFT on the selected data block, where each data block begins with the last $M-1$ values in the previous data block, except the first data block which begins with $M-1$ zeros.

(iii) Multiply the stored FFT output sequence obtained in (i) by the FFT output sequence of the selected data block obtained in (ii).
(iv) Perform an L-point IFFT on the product sequence obtained in (iii).
(v) Save the last N values of the IFFT obtained in (iv) for output, i.e. discard the first $M - 1$ values of the IFFT.
(vi) Move to (ii) for the next data block.

❖ WE 3.18

The unit-impulse response sequence of an FIR digital filter is $\{3, 2, 1\}$. Use the overlap-save method to determine its output sequence in response to the repeating input sequence $\{2, 0, -2, 0, 2, 1, 0, -2, -1, 0,\}$.

Solution:

The length of the impulse response, M, is 3. If the length of the FFT/IFFT operation, L, is selected to be $2^3 = 8$, then $N = L - M + 1 = 8 - 3 + 1 = 6$, and the segmentation of the input sequence results in the data blocks shown below:

n	−2	−1	0	1	2	3	4	5	6	7	8	9	10	11	...
$x(n)$			2	0	−2	0	2	1	0	−2	−1	0	2	0	...
$x_1(n)$	0	0	2	0	−2	0	2	1							
$x_2(n)$							2	1	0	−2	−1	0	2	0	
$x_3(n)$													2	0	...

Stages (ii), (iii) and (iv) of the procedure (the indirect implementation of circular convolution using the FFT) are demonstrated below using the direct implementation of circular convolution. Note however it should be understood that in practice the indirect form of implementation would be used since it offers speed advantages when processing long sequences.

Circular convolution of data block $x_1(n)$ with $h(n)$ padded with $N - 1$ zeros is shown below:

$x_1(n)$	0	2	0	−2	0	2	1	0	0	2	0	−2	0	2	1
$h(-(k-n))$	0	0	0	0	0	1	2	3	→						
$y_1(n)$								4	1	6	4	−4	−4	4	7

Circular convolution of data block $x_2(n)$ with $h(n)$ padded with $N - 1$ zeros is shown below:

$x_2(n)$	1	0	−2	−1	0	2	0	2	1	0	−2	−1	0	2	0
$h(-(k-n))$	0	0	0	0	0	1	2	3	→						
$y_2(n)$								8	7	4	−5	−7	−4	5	4

Discarding the first two values and saving the last six values of each circular convolution result yields the output sequence as shown below:

n	−2	−1	0	1	2	3	4	5	6	7	8	9	10	11	...
$y_1(n)$	4	1	6	4	−4	−4	4	7							
$y_2(n)$							8	7	4	−5	−7	−4	5	4	
$y_3(n)$													X	X	...
$y(n)$			6	4	−4	−4	4	7	4	−5	−7	−4	5	4	...

*****

(b) *Overlap-add Method*

This method is illustrated in Figure 3.13:

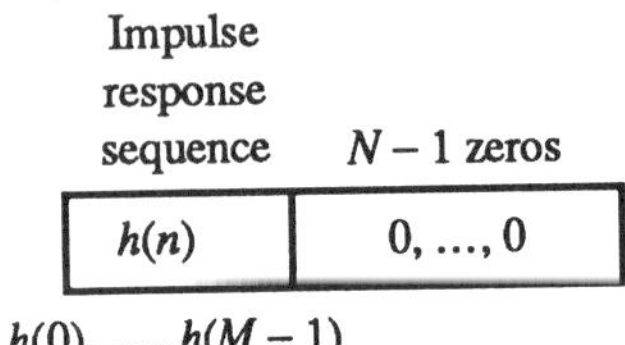

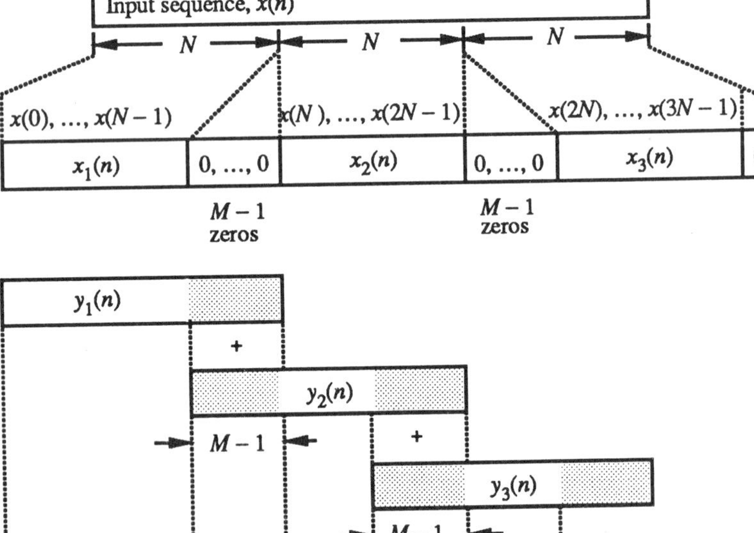

Figure 3.13 Overlap-add method

The overlap-add method is performed by the following procedures:

(i) Padding $N-1$ zeros to the end of the impulse response sequence, $h(n)$, of length M to obtain a sequence of length $M+N-1=L$, and perform an L-point FFT of the padded impulse response sequence and store the FFT output values.
(ii) Perform an L-point FFT on the selected data block, where each data block consists of N input data values and $M-1$ zeros.
(iii) Multiply the stored FFT output sequence obtained in (i) by the FFT output sequence of the selected data block obtained in (ii).
(iv) Perform an L-point IFFT on the product sequence obtained in (iii).
(v) Overlap the first $M-1$ IFFT values obtained in (iv) with the last $M-1$ IFFT values for the previous block and perform addition to produce the $y(n)$ output values.
(vi) Move to (ii) for the next data block.

❖ **WE 3.19**

Repeat WE3.18 by using the overlap-add convolution method.

Solution:

With the length of the FFT/IFFT operation, L, set to 8, the segmentation of the input sequence with the required zero padding is shown below:

n	0	1	2	3	4	5	6	7	8	9	10	11	12	13	...
$x(n)$	2	0	−2	0	2	1	0	−2	−1	0	2	0	−2	0	...
$x_1(n)$	2	0	−2	0	2	1	0	0							
$x_2(n)$							0	−2	−1	0	2	0	0	0	
$x_3(n)$													−2	0	...

Stages (ii), (iii) and (iv) of the procedure (the indirect implementation of circular convolution using the FFT) are demonstrated below using the direct implementation of circular convolution. Note however it should be understood that in practice the indirect form of implementation would be used since it offers speed advantages when processing long sequences.

Circular convolution of data blocks $x_1(n)$ and $x_2(n)$ with $h(n)$ padded with five zeros is shown below:

$x_1(n)$	0	−2	0	2	1	0	0	2	0	−2	0	2	1	0	0
$h(-(k-n))$	0	0	0	0	0	1	2	3	→						
$y_1(n)$								6	4	−4	−4	4	7	4	1

$x_2(n)$	−2	−1	0	2	0	0	0	0	−2	−1	0	2	0	0	0
$h(-(k-n))$	0	0	0	0	0	1	2	3	→						
$y_2(n)$								0	−6	−7	−4	5	4	2	0

Overlapping each circular convolution result by $M - 1 = 2$ values and adding yields the output sequence as shown below:

n	0	1	2	3	4	5	6	7	8	9	10	11	12	13	...
$y_1(n)$	6	4	−4	−4	4	7	4	1							
$y_2(n)$							0	−6	−7	−4	5	4	2	0	
$y_3(n)$													X	X	...
$y(n)$	6	4	−4	−4	4	7	4	−5	−7	−4	5	4	X	X	...

This output sequence is seen to agree with that obtained in WE3.18.

*****

3.9 Correlation

Correlation is basically a process of comparing two data sequences to obtain a measure of similarity between them. Some typical application examples are voice recognition in audio signal processing which requires comparison of different speech waveforms; image classification in image processing which requires comparison of different image data; and object detection and location in sonar and radar systems which require comparison of the transmitted signal and the signal reflected from target objects.

The fundamental measure of the similarity between the two sequences $x(n)$ and $y(n)$ is the sum of the products of the corresponding pairs of data values, i.e. $\Sigma x(n)y(n)$. If there is some kind of proportionality relationship between $x(n)$ and $y(n)$ with positive/negative values generally occurring concurrently in both sequences, the sum of products will be a positive value indicating positive correlation between the two sequences. If there is some kind of inverse proportionality relationship between $x(n)$ and $y(n)$ with positive values in one sequence generally accompanied by negative values in the other sequence, the sum of products will be a negative value indicating negative correlation between the two sequences. If the two sequences are independent with positive values and negative values equally likely to occur in both, the sum of products will tend towards zero (due to self-cancelling of the product terms on summation) indicating no correlation between the two sequences.

To obtain the correct correlation value for two sequences, the two sequences need to be aligned. An in-phase relationship between the two sequences will result in a maximum correlation value, whilst an out-of-phase relationship will result in a minimum correlation value. In practice, the phase relationship between the two sequences to be correlated is normally unknown before the start of the correlation process. An example is the correlation of the transmitted signal and the delayed version of the transmitted signal reflected from the target object in sonar or radar systems. Consequently, all possible time delay intervals must be introduced into one of the sequences to reveal any similarity between the two sequences.

For two sequences $x(n)$ and $y(n)$, the cross-correlation function, $c_{xy}(p)$, is defined as

$$c_{xy}(p) = \lim_{N \to \infty} \frac{1}{N} \sum_{n=0}^{N-1} x(n)\, y(n-p) \qquad (3.42)$$

where $\pm p$ represents the number of sampling points by which $y(n)$ has been delayed/advanced in time with respect to $x(n)$, and $1/N$ is included as a normalisation scaling factor to ensure that the cross-correlation of two periodic sequences converge to the same result as more and more sample pairs from the two sequences are included in the cross-correlation operation.

When $y(n) = x(n)$ we have a special case, whereby the cross-correlation function becomes the autocorrelation function, and consequently replacing $y(n)$ by $x(n)$ in equation (3.42) gives the autocorrelation function, $c_{xx}(p)$, which is defined as

$$c_{xx}(p) = \lim_{N \to \infty} \frac{1}{N} \sum_{n=0}^{N-1} x(n)\, x(n-p) \qquad (3.43)$$

From equation (3.43) it is readily apparent that the maximum autocorrelation value occurs at $p = 0$ since two identical in-phase signals are being compared, and the autocorrelation value decreases as p increases.

❖ **WE 3.20**

Perform cross-correlation of the two sequences given in WE3.15, namely $x(n) = \{2, 0, 0, 1\}$ and $h(n) = \{4, 3, 2, 1\}$.

***Solution*:**

The computation of the cross-correlation values for the two sequences is illustrated in the following table:

n	−3	−2	−1	0	1	2	3	4	5	6	≥7		
$x(n)$	0	0	0	2	0	0	1	0	0	0	0	p	$c_{xh}(p)$
$h(n+3)$	4	3	2	1	0	0	0	0	0	0	0	−3	[0×4+0×3+0×2 +2×1]/4 = 0.5
$h(n+2)$	0	4	3	2	1	0	0	0	0	0	0	−2	[0×4+0×3+2×2 +0×1]/4 = 1
$h(n+1)$	0	0	4	3	2	1	0	0	0	0	0	−1	[0×4+2×3+0×2 +0×1]/4 = 1.5
$h(n)$	0	0	0	4	3	2	1	0	0	0	0	0	[2×4+0×3+0×2 +1×1]/4 = 2.25
$h(n-1)$	0	0	0	0	4	3	2	1	0	0	0	1	[0×4+0×3+1×2 +0×1]/4 = 0.5
$h(n-2)$	0	0	0	0	0	4	3	2	1	0	0	2	[0×4+1×3+0×2 +0×1]/4 = 0.75
$h(n-3)$	0	0	0	0	0	0	4	3	2	1	0	3	[1×4+0×3+0×2 +0×1]/4 = 1
$h(n-4)$	0	0	0	0	0	0	0	4	3	2	1	4	[0×4+0×3+0×2 +0×1]/4 = 0

Note: Compared with WE3.15, computation of the cross-correlation function is seen to be similar to computation of the convolution process except that $h(n)$ is not folded in the correlation process. This implies that a software program for computing convolution can be used to compute correlation by reversing the order of one of the sequences.

******

It is apparent from equation (3.43) that the magnitude of the autocorrelation function will have quite different values if all data values in the sequence are scaled by a constant factor. It is often desirable in practice to make the autocorrelation function values independent of the signal scaling by normalising the autocorrelation function with respect to its maximum value at zero phase. This normalisation results in an autocorrelation coefficient, ρ_{xx}, whose values always lie in a fixed range of ±1. That is

$$\rho_{xx}(p) = \frac{c_{xx}(p)}{c_{xx}(0)} \tag{3.44}$$

Similarly normalising the cross-correlation function results in a cross-correlation coefficient, ρ_{xy}, defined as

$$\rho_{xy}(p) = \frac{c_{xy}(p)}{\sqrt{c_{xx}(0)\ c_{yy}(0)}} \tag{3.45}$$

Note that ρ_{xy} lies in the fixed range of ±1, with +1, 0 and −1 indicating 100% positive correlation, no correlation and 100% negative correlation respectively. Given the fixed range (±1) of ρ_{xy} equation (3.45) implies that the cross-correlation coefficeint value must satisfy the condition

$$\left|c_{xy}(p)\right| \leq \sqrt{c_{xx}(0)\; c_{yy}(0)} \qquad (3.46)$$

❖ **WE 3.21**

Compute the cross-correlation coefficient values for the sequences given in WE.3.20.

Solution:

Applying equation (3.43), the respective autocorrelation coefficient values of $x(n)$ and $h(n)$ at zero phase are

$$c_{xx}(0) = \frac{1}{4}\sum_{n=0}^{3} x(n)^2 = \frac{1}{4}\left(2^2 + 0^2 + 0^2 + 1^2\right) = 1.25$$

$$c_{hh}(0) = \frac{1}{4}\sum_{n=0}^{3} h(n)^2 = \frac{1}{4}\left(4^2 + 3^2 + 2^2 + 1^2\right) = 7.5$$

Substituting the autocorrelation coefficient values obtained above and the cross-correlation coeffcient values obtained in WE3.20 into equation (3.45) yields the cross-correlation coefficient values:

p	−3	−2	−1	0	1	2	3
$c_{xh}(p)$	0.5	1	1.5	2.25	0.5	0.75	1
$\rho_{xh}(p)$	0.16	0.33	0.49	0.73	0.16	0.24	0.33

*****

3.9.1 Circular Correlation

Just like circular convolution discussed in Section 3.8, ***circular correlation*** is concerned with processing two periodic sequences having the same length. The cross-correlation of two sequences, equation (3.42), can be regarded as generating an averaged sum of products. If the two sequences are periodic with the same period N, then the averaged sum of products over one single period should be identical to that over the infinite interval and equation (3.42) becomes

$$c_{xy}(p) = \frac{1}{N}\sum_{n=0}^{N-1} x(n)\, y(n-p) \qquad \text{for } p = 0, 1, \ldots, (N-1) \qquad (3.47)$$

Equation (3.47) defines the circular correlation operation, and equation (3.42) is commonly referred to as the ***linear correlation*** operation.

❖ **WE 3.22**

Compute the circular correlation values for the sequences given in WE3.20.

Solution:

The circular correlation of the two sequences is summarised in the following table:

n	0	1	2	3	
$x(n)$	2	0	0	1	$c_{xy}(p)$
$h(n)$	4	3	2	1	$(2\times4+0\times3+0\times2+1\times1)/4=2.25$
$h(n-1)$	1	4	3	2	$(2\times1+0\times4+0\times3+1\times2)/4=1$
$h(n-2)$	2	1	4	3	$(2\times2+0\times1+0\times4+1\times3)/4=1.75$
$h(n-3)$	3	2	1	4	$(2\times3+0\times2+0\times1+1\times4)/4=2.5$

Note: Comparing WE3.15 with WE3.20 and this worked example, a number of similarities between convolution and correlation are apparent. For example, comparing linear convolution with linear correlation we note that both generate aperiodic sequences of length $2N-1$. Similarly comparing circular convolution with circular correlation we note that both generate periodic sequences of length N. Furthermore, linear correlation can be implemented by using circular correlation, if $M-1$ and $N-1$ zeros are respectively padded at the end of $x(n)$ with length N, and at the end of $h(n)$ with length M.

*****

3.9.2 DFT Property of Circular Correlation

The DFT property of circular correlation may be stated formally as

If $$c_{xy}(p) = \frac{1}{N}\sum_{n=0}^{N-1} x(n)\, y(n-p) \tag{3.48}$$

then $$Cxy_r = \frac{1}{N}(X_r\, Y_r^{*}) \tag{3.49}$$

where Cxy_r, X_r and Y_r are the DFTs of $c_{xy}(p)$, $x(n)$ and $y(n)$, respectively, and Y_r^* is the complex conjugate of Y_r.

❖ **WE 3.23**
Verify the values obtained in WE3.22 by applying the DFT property of circular correlation.

Solution:
In WE3.3, the DFT of {2, 0, 0, 1} was found to be {3, 2 + j, 1, 2 − j}, and in WE3.16, the DFT of {4, 3, 2, 1} was found to be {10, 2 − j2, 2, 2 + j2}. Hence

$$Cxy_r = \frac{1}{N}\left(X_r Y_r^*\right) = \frac{1}{4}\{3, 2+j, 1, 2-j\}\{10, 2+j2, 2, 2-j2\}$$
$$= \{7.5, 0.5+j1.5, 0.5, 0.5-j1.5\}$$

Using the butterfly diagram of the 4-point inverse DIF FFT shown in WE3.14, the IDFT values of Cxy_r are

$$c_{xy}(0) = a_0 + a_1 = \frac{1}{4}\left[Cxy_0 + Cxy_2\right] + \frac{1}{4}\left[Cxy_1 + Cxy_3\right]$$
$$= \frac{1}{4}[7.5 + 0.5] + \frac{1}{4}[(0.5 + j1.5) + (0.5 - j1.5)] = 2.25$$

$$c_{xy}(1) = b_0 + j\,b_1 = \frac{1}{4}\left[Cxy_0 - Cxy_2\right] + j\frac{1}{4}\left[Cxy_1 - Cxy_3\right]$$
$$= \frac{1}{4}[7.5 - 0.5] + j\frac{1}{4}[(0.5 + j1.5) - (0.5 - j1.5)] = 1$$

$$c_{xy}(2) = a_0 - a_1 = \frac{1}{4}\left[Cxy_0 + Cxy_2\right] - \frac{1}{4}\left[Cxy_1 + Cxy_3\right]$$
$$= \frac{1}{4}[7.5 + 0.5] - \frac{1}{4}[(0.5 + j1.5) + (0.5 - j1.5)] = 1.75$$

$$c_{xy}(3) = b_0 - j\,b_1 = \frac{1}{4}\left[Cxy_0 - Cxy_2\right] - j\frac{1}{4}\left[Cxy_1 - Cxy_3\right]$$
$$= \frac{1}{4}[7.5 - 0.5] - j\frac{1}{4}[(0.5 + j1.5) - (0.5 - j1.5)] = 2.5$$

The values are seen to agree with those obtained in WE3.22.

*****

In WE3.16 the DFT property of circular convolution was applied to speed up the computation of the linear convolution process. Similar speed advantages are gained if the DFT property of circular correlation is used to compute linear correlation of two relatively long sequences. When one of the data sequences to be correlated is long, the overlap-save and the overlap-add methods presented in Section 3.8.2 are applicable because the correlation operation differs from the convolution operation only in that one of the sequences is of reversed order.

3.10 Spectrum Analysis

Two general DSP applications of the FFT (DFT) were presented respectively in the previous two sections of this chapter. One was the FFT implementation of convolution, which is associated with signal filtering; the other was the FFT implementation of correlation, which is associated with signal detection. This section presents use of the FFT in spectrum analysis.

There are two important parameters to be considered in spectrum evaluation, namely, bandwidth and frequency resolution. The former sets the signal sampling frequency, and the latter sets the record length and the FFT length, as illustrated in the following worked example.

❖ WE 3.24

It is required to use the FFT to compute the spectrum of a voice signal with a bandwidth of 5 kHz. Determine the minimum record length if the frequency resolution is required to be at least 10 Hz.

Solution:

According to the sampling theorem introduced in Section 1.2.1, the sampling frequency must be at least twice the bandwidth of the signal in order to avoid aliasing errors. Hence the minimum sampling frequency is required to be

$$f_s \geq 2 \times \text{Bandwidth} \quad = 2 \times 5 \text{ kHz} = 10 \text{ kHz}$$

The relationship between the frequency resolution, the sampling frequency and the record length is given by equation (3.3). Hence the minimum number of samples required is

$$N \geq \frac{f_s}{f_o} = \frac{10000}{10} = 1000$$

Since N is required to be 2^y in the FFT, where y is a positive integer, the minimum record length is required to be $2^{10} = 1024$ samples in order to produce the required frequency resolution.

*****

Since the frequency resolution is determined by the number of samples included in the FFT, it can be increased by including more samples in the FFT. For short sequences, zeros can be padded to the end of the sequence to achieve higher frequency resolution, since it enables the FFT to use the zeros as additional samples to compute (interpolate) the spectrum at closer spaced frequency points. The effects of zero padding are illustrated in the following worked example.

❖ **WE 3.25**

For the rectangular pulse sequence defined in WE3.2, with $x(n) = 0.5$ V for $0 \le n \le 3$ and $x(n) = 0$ otherwise, compute the DFT for lengths of 8 and 16 respectively, and in each case plot the resulting magnitude spectrum. The sampling frequency is 10 kHz.

***Solution*:**

The 8-point DFT will have 4 zeros padded at the end of the rectangular sequence values. The first DFT output can be conveniently obtained by applying equation (3.16) to give

$$X_0 = \sum_{n=0}^{3} 0.5\, e^{n \times 0} = 2 \text{ V}$$

The next four DFT output values can be conveniently obtained by using the DTFT equation of the rectangular pulse obtained in WE3.2(a). Recalling that the DFT, equation (3.16), is derived from the DTFT, equation (3.15), by replacing the continuous frequency variable by a finite number of frequency points (see Section 3.4), it follows that replacing ω by $2\pi r/(NT)$ in the DTFT equation of the rectangular pulse obtained in WE3.2(a) yields

$$X_r = X(\mathrm{j}\,\omega)\Big|_{\omega = \frac{2\pi r}{NT}} = A\, e^{-\mathrm{j}\frac{\omega T\,(L-1)}{2}} \left.\frac{\sin\left(\frac{\omega TL}{2}\right)}{\sin\left(\frac{\omega T}{2}\right)}\right|_{\omega = \frac{2\pi r}{NT}}$$

$$= A\, e^{-\mathrm{j}\frac{(L-1)\pi r}{N}} \frac{\sin\left(\frac{L\pi r}{N}\right)}{\sin\left(\frac{\pi r}{N}\right)}$$

Substituting $A = 0.5$ V, $L = 4$, $N = 8$, and $r = 1$ to 4 into the above equation gives (0.5 – j1.207) V, 0 V, (0.5 – j0.207) V and 0 V for X_1 to X_4. Applying the DFT symmetry property, equation (3.29), gives X_5 to X_7 as (0.5 + j0.207) V, 0 V, (0.5 + j1.207) V respectively. The following table summarises these results and their magnitude values.

r	0	1	2	3	4	5	6	7
$f = rf_s/N$ (Hz)	0	1250	2500	3750	5000	6250	7500	8750
X_r (V)	2	0.5 –j1.207	0	0.5 –j0.207	0	0.5 +j0.207	0	0.5 +j1.207
$\lvert X_r \rvert$ (V)	2	1.306	0	0.541	0	0.541	0	1.306

To compute the 16-point DFT, 12 zeros are padded to the end of the rectangular pulse sequence values. Following the same method used above, the DFT outputs are summarised below:

r	0	1	2	3	4	5	6	7
$f=rf_s/N$ (Hz)	0	625	1250	1875	2500	3125	3750	4375
X_r (V)	2	1.507 −j1.007	0.5 −j1.207	−0.124 −j0.624	0	0.417 +j0.083	0.5 −j0.207	0.2 −j0.3
$\lvert X_r \rvert$ (V)	2	1.812	1.306	0.636	0	0.425	0.541	0.361

r	8	9	10	11	12	13	14	15
$f=rf_s/N$ (kHz)	5000	5625	6250	6875	7500	8125	8750	9375
X_r (V)	0	0.2 +j0.3	0.5 +j0.207	0.417 −j0.083	0	−0.124 +j0.624	0.5 +j1.207	1.507 +j1.007
$\lvert X_r \rvert$ (V)	0	0.361	0.541	0.425	0	0.636	1.306	1.812

The two magnitude spectra are shown in the following figure:

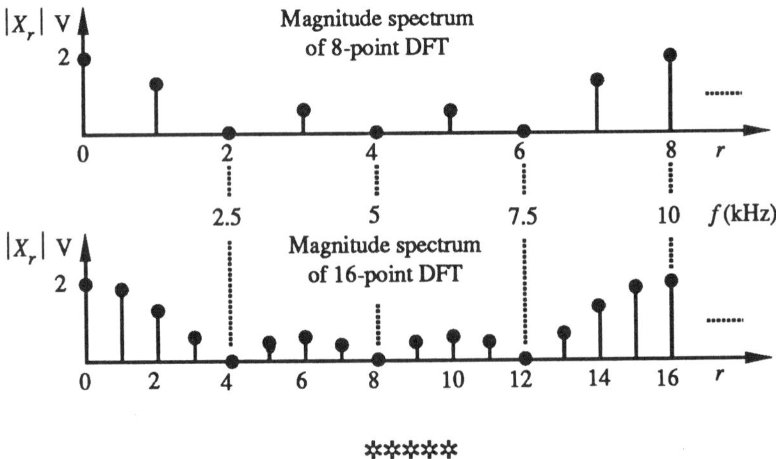

*****

3.10.1 Error Sources

In Section 3.4 the DFT was derived as an approximation of the DTFT in order to overcome two practical implementation problems, and consequently spectra produced by the DFT will contain two sources of error arising from the ***picket-fence effect*** and from ***spectral leakage***.

(a) *Picket-fence Effect*
The picket-fence effect is caused by the approximation of the continuous frequency spectrum of the DTFT using a finite number of frequency points. The spectrum is observed very much like looking through a picket-fence with the exact value of the spectrum known only at integer multiples of the frequency resolution. The peak of a particular frequency component in a signal could be hidden from view because it is located between two adjacent frequency points in the spectrum.

To reduce the picket-fence effect, the number of frequency points (frequency resolution) must be increased, since this enables more frequency components of a signal to coincide with the more closely spaced frequency points. This required increase in the number of frequency points can be achieved by including more data samples in the DFT or by employing the zero-padding interpolation technique discussed in the previous section.

(b) *Spectral Leakage*
Spectral leakage is a source of error caused by use of a window to truncate an infinitely long signal to a finite-length signal, as shown in Figure 3.2. If the window width is an integer multiple of periods of all of the frequency components of a discrete signal, then the periodic extension of the windowed sequence is identical to the original discrete signal and the DFT will produce a single spectral coefficient corresponding to each frequency component. If, however, the integer multiple of periods of a frequency component do not fit exactly into the window width, as shown in Figure 3.14, then the periodic extension of the windowed sequence differs from the original discrete signal with discontinuities occurring at the boundaries of the window, and this single frequency component will result in the DFT producing non-zero spectral coefficients at all frequencies. This phenomenon is known as spectral leakage and is illustrated in the following worked example.

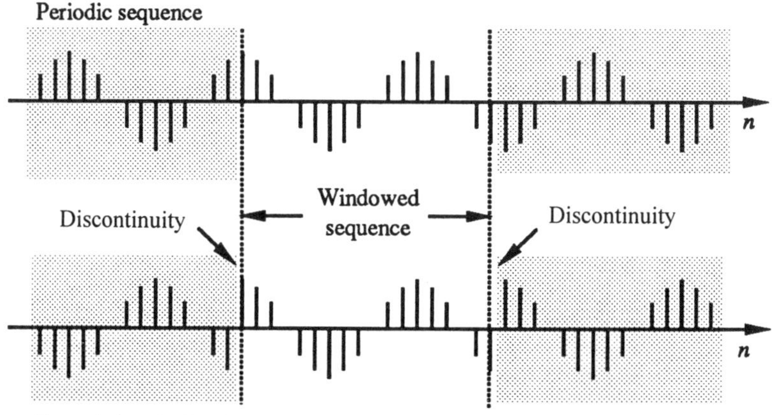

Figure 3.14 Window causing discontinuities

❖ **WE 3.26**

Evaluate and plot the magnitude spectrum of the 8-point DFT for the two signals: (a) $x(t) = \sin(2\pi 1000t)$ V and (b) $x(t) = \sin(2\pi 1300t)$ V. The sampling frequency is 8 kHz.

Solution:

(a) The discrete values of the windowed sequence are given by

$$x(n) = \sin(2\pi \times 1000 \times n / 8000) \qquad \text{for } n = 0, 1, \ldots 7$$

$$= \{0, 0.707, 1, 0.707, 0, -0.707, -1, -0.707\}$$

Taking the DFT of $x(n)$ by applying equation (3.16) gives

$$X_r = \sum_{n=0}^{7} x(n)\left\{\cos\left(\frac{2\pi rn}{8}\right) - j\sin\left(\frac{2\pi rn}{8}\right)\right\} \qquad \text{for } r = 0, 1, \ldots 7$$

$$= \{0, -j4, 0, 0, 0, 0, j4, 0\}$$

$$\therefore \quad |X_r| = \{0, 4, 0, 0, 0, 0, 4, 0\}$$

With the frequency resolution of $f_s/N = 8000/8 = 1$ kHz, the magnitude spectrum is:

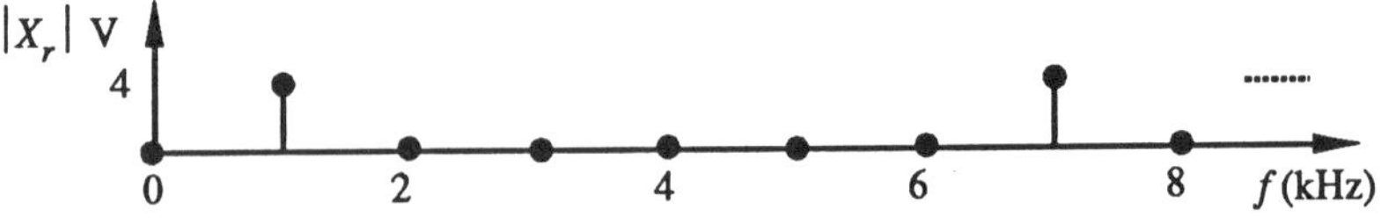

Note: This case corresponds to the period of the signal $x(n)$ being equal to the window width. No spectral leakage occurs because the spectral coefficients produced by the DFT are zero except at the signal frequency and its complementary frequencies.

(b) The discrete values of the windowed sequence are given by

$$x(n) = \sin(2\pi \times 1300 \times n / 8000) \qquad \text{for } n = 0, 1, \ldots 7$$

that is {0, 0.8526, 0.8910, 0.0785, –0.8090, –0.9239, –0.1564, 0.7604}.

Taking the DFT of $x(n)$ by applying equation (3.16) gives

$$X_r = \sum_{n=0}^{7} x(n)\left\{\cos\left(\frac{2\pi rn}{8}\right) - j\sin\left(\frac{2\pi rn}{8}\right)\right\} \qquad \text{for } r = 0, 1, \ldots 7$$

$$= \{0.6932, 2.5474 - j1.8214, -1.5436 + j0.9101, -0.9294 + j0.2735, -0.8421, -0.9294 - j0.2735, -1.5436 - j0.9101, 2.5474 + j1.8214\}$$

$$\therefore \ |X_r| = \{0.6932,\ 3.1316,\ 1.7919,\ 0.9688,\ 0.8421,\ 0.9688,\ 1.7919,\ 3.1316\}$$

With the frequency resolution of 1 kHz, the magnitude spectrum is:

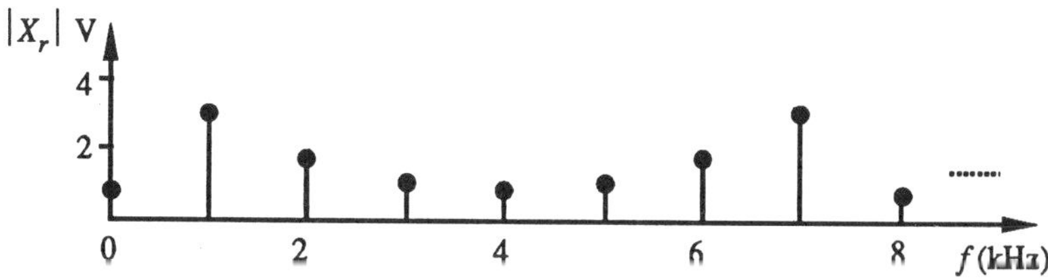

Note: This case corresponds to the period of the signal not equal to the window width. Spectral leakage occurs because all spectral coefficients produced by the DFT are non-zero.

*****

For a given window width, it is most likely that the period of more than one frequency component in a practical signal will not fit exactly into the window width, and each will produce a leakage spectrum. Since the total spectral leakage is the sum of all of the leakage spectra, spurious peaks may occur giving false indications of the frequency components of the signal, and small magnitude frequency components of the signal may never be detected.

3.10.2 Spectral Windows

The windowed sequence, $x_w(n)$, can be viewed as the product generated by multiplying the signal, $x(n)$ and a window function, $w(n)$. That is

$$x_w(n) = x(n) \times w(n) \tag{3.50}$$

The rectangular window function was used to produce the windowed sequence shown in Figure 3.14, that is

$$w(n) = \begin{cases} 1 & \text{for } 0 \le n \le N-1 \\ 0 & \text{otherwise} \end{cases} \tag{3.51}$$

Although the rectangular window is the simplest one to implement, it is the worst to use in spectrum analysis because its abrupt end may result in a large discontinuity in the periodically extended windowed sequence, thereby causing severe spectral leakage, as explained in Section 3.10.1. It is therefore better to use a gradually tapered window since it reduces the contribution of the samples near the boundaries of the window, and correspondingly reduces spectral leakage. Among various types of tapered windows which have been proposed for this purpose are cosine-based windows formed as linear combinations of sinusoidal sequences. Three members of this family are listed in Table 3.1:

Window functions	$w(n)$ for $0 \le n \le N-1$ (= 0 for other values of n)
Hamming	$w(n) = 0.54 - 0.46\cos\left(\frac{2\pi n}{N-1}\right)$
Hanning	$w(n) = 0.5 - 0.5\cos\left(\frac{2\pi n}{N-1}\right)$
Blackman	$w(n) = 0.42 - 0.5\cos\left(\frac{2\pi n}{N-1}\right) + 0.08\cos\left(\frac{4\pi n}{N-1}\right)$

Table 3.1 Cosine-based window functions

❖ **WE 3.27**

(a) Plot the 8-point Hamming window function.

(b) Repeat WE3.26(a) by applying the 8-point Hamming window to $x(t) = \sin(2\pi 1000t)$ V.

(c) Repeat WE3.26(b) by applying the 8-point Hamming window to $x(t) = \sin(2\pi 1300t)$ V.

(d) Describe the effect of the Hamming window on the spectrum.

Solution:

(a) With $N = 8$, the Hamming window is given by

$$w(n) = 0.54 - 0.46\cos\left(\frac{2\pi n}{8-1}\right) \qquad \text{for } n = 0, 1, \ldots 7$$

$$= \{0.0800,\ 0.2532,\ 0.6424,\ 0.9544,\ 0.9544,\ 0.6424,\ 0.2532,\ 0.0800\}$$

For comparison purposes, the 8-point Hamming window function is overlaid on the rectangular window function, as shown below:

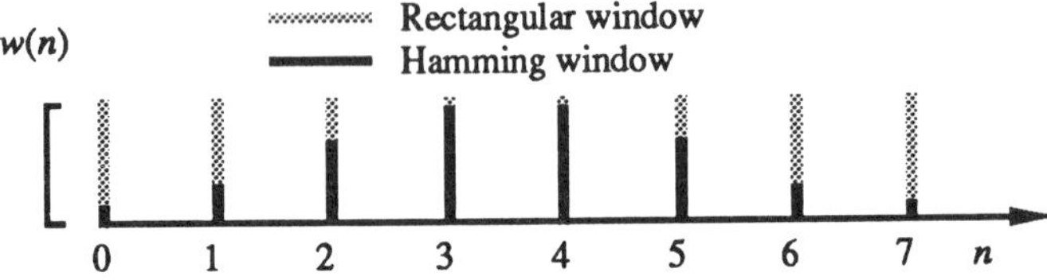

(b) Taking the DFT of the windowed sequence $x(n)w(n)$ by applying equation (3.16) gives

$$X_r = \sum_{n=0}^{7} x(n)\, w(n) \left\{ \cos\left(\frac{2\pi rn}{8}\right) - j\sin\left(\frac{2\pi rn}{8}\right) \right\} \quad \text{for } r = 0, 1, \ldots 7$$

The results are tabulated below:

n or r	0	1	2	3
$x(n)w(n)$	0	0.1790	0.6424	0.6749
X_r	0.7323	0.0694–j1.8606	–0.3892+j0.8935	0.0694–j0.0694
$\lvert X_r \rvert$	0.7323	1.8618	0.9746	0.0982

n or r	4	5	6	7
$x(n)w(n)$	0	–0.4542	–0.2532	–0.0566
X_r	0.046	0.0694+j0.0694	–0.3892–j0.8935	0.0694+j1.8606
$\lvert X_r \rvert$	0.0460	0.0982	0.9746	1.8618

For comparison purposes, the magnitude spectrum is overlaid on that obtained in WE3.26(a), as shown below:

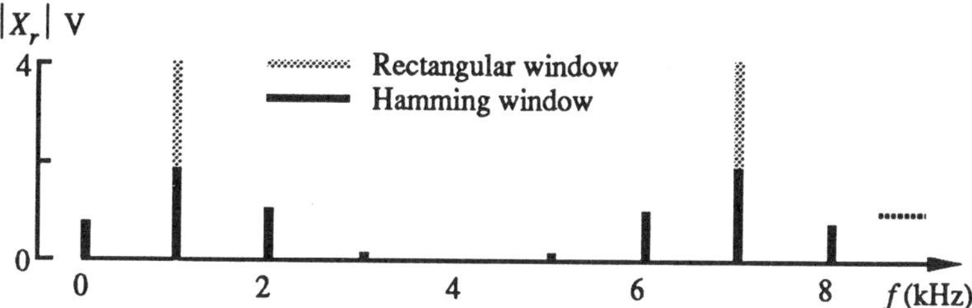

(c) Similarly for $x(t) = \sin(2\pi 1300t)$ V, the results are tabulated below:

n or r	0	1	2	3
$x(n)w(n)$	0	0.2159	0.5723	0.0749
X_r	–0.4813	1.3345–j1.1942	–1.3049+j0.5133	0.2098–j0.0297
$\lvert X_r \rvert$	0.4813	1.7908	1.4022	0.2119

n or r	4	5	6	7
$x(n)w(n)$	–0.7722	–0.5935	–0.0396	0.0608
X_r	0.024	0.2098–j0.0297	–1.3049–j0.5133	1.3345+j1.1942
$\lvert X_r \rvert$	0.0024	0.2119	1.4022	1.7908

For comparison purposes, the magnitude spectrum is overlaid on that obtained in WE3.26(b), as shown below:

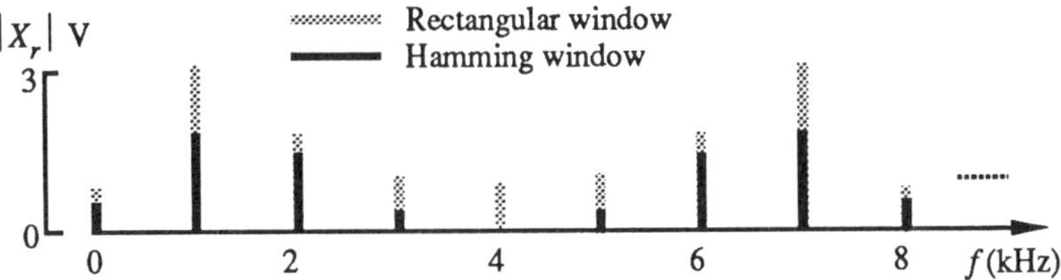

(d) In the time-domain, the original signal is distorted by the weighting introduced by the Hamming window function. In the frequency domain, the magnitude spectrum in (b), which corresponds to the case of the signal period equal to the window width, shows that use of the Hamming window function is worse than using the rectangular window function, because not only does it reduce the magnitude of the frequency component of the signal, but also spectral leakage occurs at those frequency points adjacent to the true frequency of the signal. The magnitude spectrum in (c), which corresponds to the case of the signal period not being equal to the window width, shows that use of the Hamming window function is better than using the rectangular window function, because it significantly reduces the spectral leakage at those frequency points which are not adjacent to the frequency of the signal.

*****

3.10.3 Power Density Spectrum

The ***power density spectrum***, or ***periodogram*** (originally introduced to determine 'hidden periodicities' in data), gives the distribution of the average power over various frequencies for a signal with indefinite length, and is defined as

$$P_x(r) = \frac{|X_r|^2}{N} \tag{3.52}$$

where X_r is the DFT of $x(n)$ and N is the window width. If $x(n)$ is a nonstationary or random signal, then the DFT of $x(n)$ for each window period will differ, and the average of a set of periodograms is used as an estimate of the power density spectrum. That is

$$\overline{P_x(r)} = \frac{1}{M} \sum_{m=0}^{M-1} P_{x(m)}(r) \tag{3.53}$$

where the estimated power density spectrum, $\overline{P_x(r)}$, is given as the average of the periodograms obtained from M windows.

❖ **WE 3.28**

Repeat WE1.5 by using the periodogram with a 4-point rectangular window.

Solution:

From WE1.5, the windowed sequence is given by {0.5V, 2V, –0.5V, –2}. Using the butterfly diagram of the 4-point DIT FFT in WE3.13, the DFT values of the sequence are

$$X_0 = E_0 + O_0 = [x(0) + x(2)] + [x(1) + x(3)]$$
$$= [0.5 + (-0.5)] + [2 + (-2)] = 0$$

$$X_1 = E_1 - j\,O_1 = [x(0) - x(2)] - j[x(1) - x(3)]$$
$$= [0.5 - (-0.5)] - j[2 - (-2)] = 1 - j\,4$$

$$X_2 = E_0 - O_0 = [x(0) + x(2)] - [x(1) + x(3)]$$
$$= [0.5 + (-0.5)] - [2 + (-2)] = 0$$

$$X_3 = E_1 + j\,O_1 = [x(0) - x(2)] + j[x(1) - x(3)]$$
$$= [0.5 - (-0.5)] + j[2 - (-2)] = 1 + j\,4$$

Applying equation (3.52) yields

$$P_x(r) = \left\{ \frac{|X_0|^2}{4}, \frac{|X_1|^2}{4}, \frac{|X_2|^2}{4}, \frac{|X_3|^2}{4} \right\}$$

$$= \{0, 4.25, 0, 4.25\}$$

Applying ***Parseval's relationship***, which states that the total energy of a sequence equals either the sum of squared values of its samples in the time-domain (equation (1.26)) or the sum of the terms of the power density spectrum in the frequency-domain, the energy of the windowed sequence is

$$E = \sum_{r=0}^{3} P_x(r)$$

$$= 0 + 4.25 + 0 + 4.25 = 8.5 \text{ Joules into } 1\,\Omega$$

and applying equation (1.25), the average power of the sequence is

$$P = \frac{E}{N} = \frac{8.5}{4} = 2.125 \text{ watts}$$

It is seen that the results are identical to those obtained in WE1.5.

*****

3.10.4 Joint Time-Frequency Analysis

As shown in Figure 3.2, the DFT of the windowed sequence provides only a snapshot of the frequency content of the sequence over a particular interval of time. If the sequence being analysed is long and nonstationary, a sliding window is required in order to track the variations of the frequency content of the sequence with respect to time, as shown in Figure 3.15. This method of joint time-frequency analysis is known as the **short-time Fourier transform** (STFT), and the resulting time-frequency description of the signal is known as the ***spectrogram***.

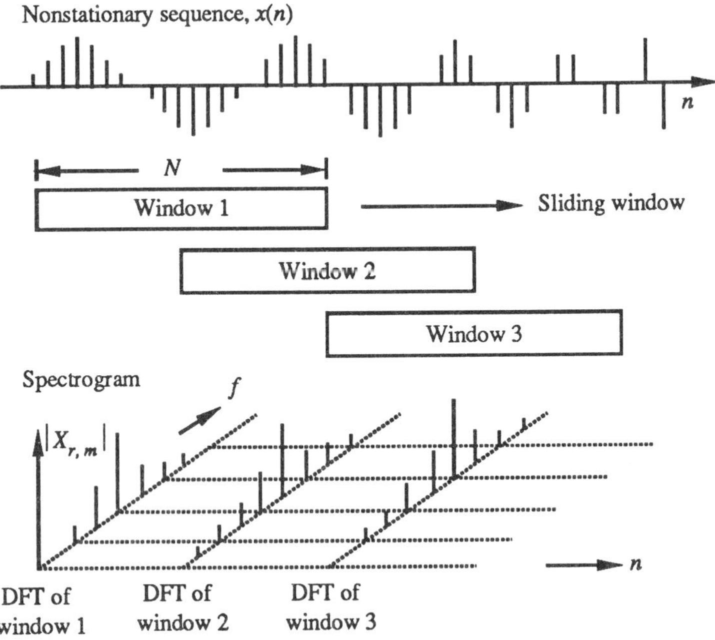

Figure 3.15 Joint time-frequency analysis

The expression for computing the DFT of each N-point windowed sequence can be written as

$$X_{r,\,m} = \sum_{n=m-N+1}^{m} x(n)\; w[n-(m-N+1)]\, e^{-j\frac{2\pi r}{N}n} \tag{3.54}$$

The summation limits in the above equation ensure that the last value of the sliding window coincides with a specified mth sample of $x(n)$, and the window index $[n-(m-N+1)$ ensures that the N-point window starts from $w(0)$ and ends at $w(N-1)$.

❖ **WE 3.29**

(a) A burst signal corresponds to a 250 Hz sinusoidal signal with an amplitude of 1V, continuously being switched on for 6 ms and off for an equal duration. If the sampling frequency is 1 kHz, the window type is Hamming, the window width is 8 points and the overlap of the sliding window is 4 points, plot the spectrogram for the sinusoidal burst signal.

(b) Design a DSP system capable of detecting the presence of the burst signal existing in the window period for at least 3 ms.

Solution:

(a) Consider one possible waveform of the burst signal and the sliding windows shown below:

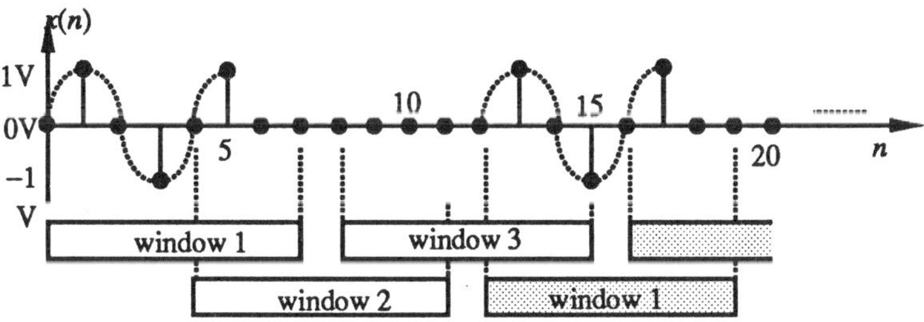

Using the values computed for the 8-point Hamming window in WE3.27(a) and applying equation (3.54), the results are:

Window 1								
n	0	1	2	3	4	5	6	7
$x(n)$	0	1	0	−1	0	1	0	0
$x(n)w(n)$	0	0.2532	0	−0.9544	0	0.6424	0	0
r	0	1	2	3	4	5	6	7
$X_{r,7}$	−0.0589	0.3997 +j0.9501	0 −j1.85	−0.3997 +j0.9501	0.0589	−0.3997 −j0.9501	0 +j1.85	0.3997 −j0.9501
$\lvert X_{r,7}\rvert$	0.0589	1.0307	1.85	1.0307	0.0589	1.0307	1.85	1.0307

Window 2								
n	4	5	6	7	8	9	10	11
$x(n)$	0	1	0	0	0	0	0	0
$x(n)w(n)$	0	0.2532	0	0	0	0	0	0
r	0	1	2	3	4	5	6	7
$X_{r,11}$	0.2532	0.179 −j0.179	0 −j0.2532	−0.179 −j0.179	−0.2532	−0.179 +j0.179	0 +j0.2532	0.179 +j0.179
$\lvert X_{r,11}\rvert$	0.2532	0.2532	0.2532	0.2532	0.2532	0.2532	0.2532	0.2532

Window 3								
n	8	9	10	11	12	13	14	15
$x(n)$	0	0	0	0	0	1	0	−1
$x(n)w(n)$	0	0	0	0	0	0.6464	0	−0.08
r	0	1	2	3	4	5	6	7
$X_{r,15}$	0.5624	−0.5108 +j0.3976	0 −j0.7224	0.5108 +j0.3976	−0.5624	0.5108 −j0.3976	0 +j0.7224	−0.5108 −j0.3976
$\lvert X_{r,15}\rvert$	0.5624	0.6473	0.7224	0.6473	0.5624	0.6473	0.7224	0.6473

The resolution on the frequency axis is $f_s/N = 1000/8 = 125$ Hz and the resolution on the time axis is the number of sliding window overlap points divided by f_s, which in this case is $4/f_s = 4$ ms. Using a set of shaded boxes, the spectrogram is shown below:

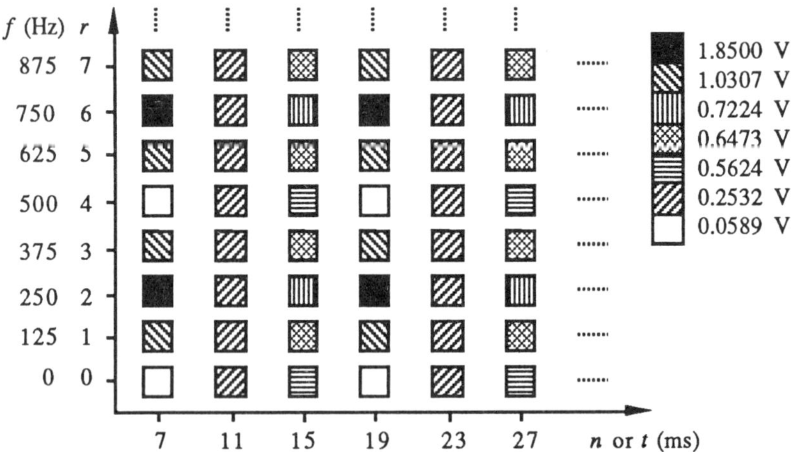

(b) From the spectrogram, the peak magnitude of 1.85 V occurring at 250 Hz and at 7 ms corresponds to the existence of the sinusoidal signal for 6 ms in window 1. The peak magnitude of 0.7224 V occurring at 250 Hz and at 15 ms corresponds to the existence of the sinusoidal signal for 3 ms in window 3. Since these peaks correspond to the values of $X_{r,m}$ computed for $r = 2$, the existence of the sinusoidal signal for at least 3 ms in a window can be detected by comparing $X_{2,m}$ with a threshold set to 0.7 V. Several forms of implementation are possible, one is to view the computation of $X_{2,m}$ as the convolution of the complex sequence $x(n)\,e^{-j2\pi 2n/8}$ with the real sequence $w(n)$. That is

$$X_{2,m} = \left[x(n)\,e^{-j\frac{\pi}{2}n}\right] * w(n)$$

$$= \left[x(n)\cos\left(\frac{\pi}{2}n\right)\right] * w(n) - j\left[x(n)\sin\left(\frac{\pi}{2}n\right)\right] * w(n)$$

With the $w(n)$ sequence implemented as the impulse response of a filter, the block diagram of the DSP system, based on the previous equation, capable of detecting the sinusoidal signal, is shown below:

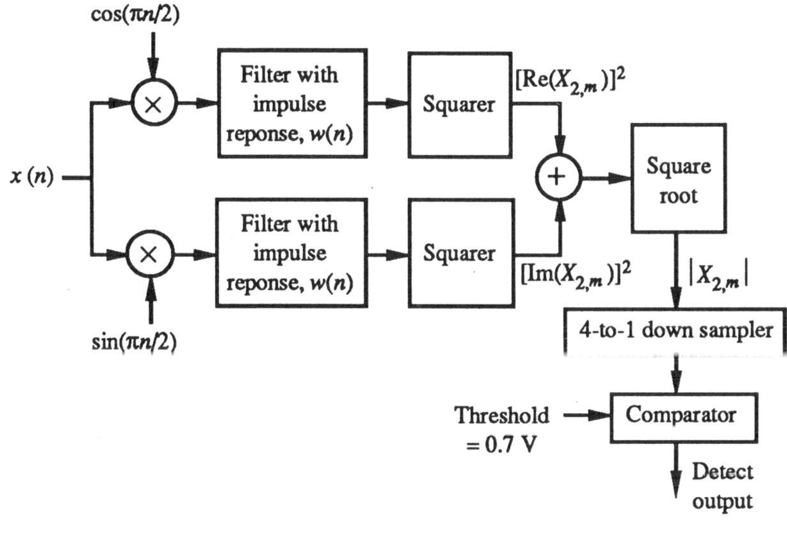

*****

3.11 Case Study: Electrocardiogram Data Compression

Aim:

The aim of this case study is to show how the DFT and the IDFT were used in an investigation to determine the possibility of achieving data compression of the electrocardiogram.

Problem:

The electrocardiogram (ecg) is a record of the electrical activity of the heart measured at the body's surface. The state of health of the heart can be monitored out of hospital using a portable signal acquisition and recording system. Cassette tape recorders have been used successfully to obtain ecg signal records, which can be subsequently transmitted over a low bandwidth telephone channel for analysis. The recording of the ecg waveform generally extends over a considerable time period, and in terms of reducing transmission time/storage requirements it is clearly advantageous to apply data compression to the electrocardiogram. However, it is clearly important that sufficient data be preserved to enable an adequate ecg waveform representation to be recovered from the compressed data.

For this case study the ecg signal was sampled over one heartbeat period to create the 64-sample waveform representation shown in Figure 3.16. The sample values are listed in Table 3.2. For transmission/storage each sample magnitude value is represented as an 8-bit binary number.

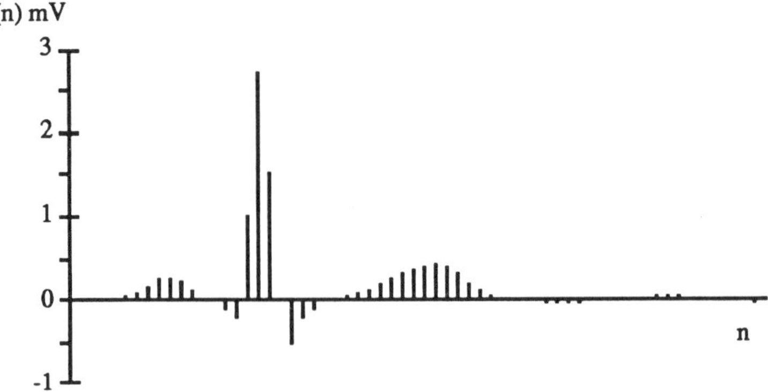

Figure 3.16 64-sample ecg waveform representation

n	0	1	2	3	4	5	6	7
$x(n)$ mV	0	0	0.01	0.01	0.02	0.05	0.09	0.15
n	8	9	10	11	12	13	14	15
$x(n)$ mV	0.23	0.25	0.21	0.1	0.01	−0.01	−0.1	−0.2
n	16	17	18	19	20	21	22	23
$x(n)$ mV	1	2.7	1.5	0	−0.5	−0.2	−0.08	−0.01
n	24	25	26	27	28	29	30	31
$x(n)$ mV	0.02	0.04	0.08	0.12	0.18	0.23	0.3	0.36
n	32	33	34	35	36	37	38	39
$x(n)$ mV	0.4	0.41	0.38	0.3	0.18	0.1	0.05	0.02
n	40	41	42	43	44	45	46	47
$x(n)$ mV	0.01	0	−0.01	−0.02	−0.03	−0.03	−0.02	−0.01
n	48	49	50	51	52	53	54	55
$x(n)$ mV	0	0.01	0.01	0.02	0.02	0.03	0.03	0.03
n	56	57	58	59	60	61	62	63
$x(n)$ mV	0.02	0.02	0.01	0.01	0	−0.01	−0.03	−0.01

Table 3.2 Sample values for 64-sample ecg waveform

Using the 64-sample ecg waveform data values given in Table 3.2, we will investigate (i) the achievable data compression ratio, and (ii) the fidelity of the reconstructed signal.

Method:

(a) Time-domain to Frequency-domain Conversion
The first step is to apply the DFT to the 64-sample ecg waveform data set to convert the time-domain representation to a frequency-domain representation, thereby yielding a set of spectral coefficients corresponding to the characteristic frequency components of the ecg waveform.

(b) Thresholding
The second step is to apply a threshold to the spectral coefficient values so that those less than the threshold value are set equal to zero, thereby removing their contribution to the reconstruction of the ecg waveform. In this case study various threshold settings are used to investigate the effect on the compression ratio and the fidelity of the reconstructed signal.

(c) Coding
The third step is to code the threshold spectral coefficients generated by the second step. A simple coding scheme is shown in Figure 3.17.

Header	Non-zero spectral coefficients				
33 bits	8 bits	8 bits	....	8 bits	8 bits
Binary pattern indicating positions of zero and non-zero spectral coefficients	Real part of first non-zero spectral coefficient	Imaginary part of first non-zero spectral coefficient		Real part of last non-zero spectral coefficient	Imaginary part of last non-zero spectral coefficient

Figure 3.17 Simple coding scheme

Each non-zero spectral coefficient is a complex number, with the magnitudes of its real and imaginary parts separately coded using 8-bit binary numbers. The coded non-zero spectral coefficients are preceded by a header section containing a binary word pattern with each bit indicating whether the corresponding spectral coefficient is zero or non-zero. In decoding, if the first binary bit is '1' it indicates that the first spectral coefficient is non-zero, and consequently the two 8-bit binary numbers immediately following the header section are taken as the real part and the imaginary part of the first spectral coefficient. If the second header bit is '0', indicating the second spectral coefficient is zero, the next header bit is considered. The number of bits in the header section equals the sum of the number of zero spectral coefficients and the number of non-zero spectral coefficients.

(d) Signal Reconstruction
The fourth step is to apply the IDFT to the coded spectral coefficients to reconstruct the ecg signal.

(e) Error Analysis
The final step is to make a critical quantitative comparison of the reconstructed signal and the original signal.

Execution of the Method:

(a) Time-domain to Frequency-domain Conversion
The DFT of the 64-sample ecg waveform is obtained using equation (3.18). Table 3.3 lists the spectral coefficient values and Figure 3.18 shows the corresponding magnitude/frequency spectrum of the ecg signal.

r	0	1	2	3	4	5	6	7
X_r	8.4500	−2.4399	−1.6731	−2.1798	4.9732	−3.4100	−3.4702	3.5425
		−j4.9057	−j0.2554	j3.8484	−j1.6766	−j3.7251	j3.1600	j4.2306
$\|X_r\|$ mV	8.4500	5.4790	1.6924	4.4228	5.2482	5.0501	4.6934	5.5179
r	8	9	10	11	12	13	14	15
X_r	3.9637	−4.2812	−2.3362	4.3195	0.6997	−3.8588	0.3679	3.2423
	−j4.4107	−j2.9470	j4.0973	j1.4858	−j4.2089	−j0.0781	j3.5864	−j0.6930
$\|X_r\|$ mV	5.9301	5.1975	4.7166	4.5679	4.2667	3.8596	3.6052	3.3155
r	16	17	18	19	20	21	22	23
X_r	−0.8700	−2.2619	0.9642	1.5079	−0.8214	−0.9347	0.5982	0.6033
	−j2.7200	j0.9229	j1.9062	−j0.9240	−j1.1369	j0.7200	j0.7988	−j0.4536
$\|X_r\|$ mV	2.8557	2.4429	2.1362	1.7685	1.4026	1.1798	0.9980	0.7548
r	24	25	26	27	28	29	30	31
X_r	−0.3637	−0.4431	0.3192	0.3928	−0.3715	−0.2815	0.4299	0.0825
	−j0.5107	j0.3585	j0.4191	−j0.3045	−j0.3645	j0.4333	j0.2221	−j0.4109
$\|X_r\|$ mV	0.6270	0.5699	0.5268	0.4970	0.5205	0.5167	0.4839	0.4191
r	32	33	34	35	36	37	38	39
X_r	−0.4700	0.0825	0.4299	−0.2815	−0.3715	0.3928	0.3192	−0.4431
		j0.4109	−j0.2221	−j0.4333	j0.3645	j0.3045	−j0.4191	−j0.3585
$\|X_r\|$ mV	0.4700	0.4191	0.4839	0.5167	0.5205	0.4970	0.5268	0.5699
r	40	41	42	43	44	45	46	47
X_r	−0.3637	0.6033	0.5982	−0.9347	−0.8214	1.5079	0.9642	−2.2619
	j0.5107	j0.4536	−j0.7988	−j0.7200	j1.1369	j0.9240	−j1.9062	−j0.9229
$\|X_r\|$ mV	0.6270	0.7548	0.9980	1.1798	1.4026	1.7685	2.1362	2.4429
r	48	49	50	51	52	53	54	55
X_r	−0.8700	3.2423	0.3679	−3.8588	0.6997	4.3195	−2.3362	−4.2812
	j2.7200	j0.6930	−j3.5864	j0.0781	j4.2089	−j1.4858	−j4.0973	j2.9470
$\|X_r\|$ mV	2.8557	3.3155	3.6052	3.8596	4.2667	4.5679	4.7166	5.1975
r	56	57	58	59	60	61	62	63
X_r	3.9637	3.5425	−3.4702	−3.4100	4.9732	−2.1798	−1.6731	−2.4399
	j4.4107	−j4.2306	−j3.1600	j3.7251	j1.6766	−j3.8484	j0.2554	j4.9057
$\|X_r\|$ mV	5.9301	5.5179	4.6934	5.0501	5.2482	4.4228	1.6924	5.4790

Table 3.3 Spectral coefficient values

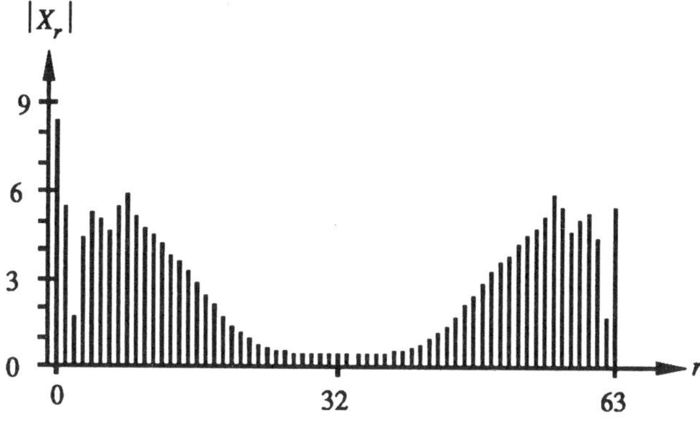

Figure 3.18 Magnitude/frequency spectrum of the ecg signal

The even symmetry of the resulting magnitude/frequency spectrum is readily seen in Figure 3.18, i.e. it is a mirror image about the frequency component at $r = 32$ (the real parts exhibit even symmetry, whereas the imaginary parts exhibit odd symmetry - see the DFT symmetry property on page 147). Consequently only thirty-three spectral coefficients need to be processed (coded) for transmission/storage. Furthermore, the frequency component at $r = 0$ corresponds to the d.c. component, which always has a zero imaginary part, and therefore a further saving of eight bits is achieved.

(b) Thresholding

Spectral coefficients having magnitude values less than the set threshold value are set equal to zero. Table 3.4 lists the results obtained for three settings of the threshold value.

r	0	1	2	3	4	5	6
X_r	8.4500	−2.4399 − j4.9057	−1.6731 − j0.2554	−2.1798 + j3.8484	4.9732 − j1.6766	−3.4100 − j3.7251	−3.4702 + j3.1600
$\|X_r\|$ mV	8.4500	5.4790	1.6924	4.4228	5.2482	5.0501	4.6934
r	7	8	9	10	11	12	13
X_r	3.5425 + j4.2306	3.9637 − j4.4107	−4.2812 − j2.9470	−2.3362 + j4.0973	4.3195 + j1.4858	0.6997 − j4.2089	−3.8588 − j0.0781
$\|X_r\|$ mV	5.5179	5.9301	5.1975	4.7166	4.5679	4.2667	3.8596
r	14	15	16	17	18	19	20
X_r	0.3679 j3.5864	3.2423 − j0.6930	− 0.8700 − j2.7200	−2.2619 + j0.9229	0.9642 j1.9062	1.5079 − j0.9240	0.88214 − j1.1369
$\|X_r\|$ mV	3.6052	3.3155	2.8557	2.4429	2.1362	1.7685	1.4026

r	21	22	23	24	25	26	27
X_r	−0.9347 + j0.7200	0	0	0	0	0	0
$\|X_r\|$ mV	1.1798	0	0	0	0	0	0

r	28	29	30	31	32
X_r	0	0	0	0	0
$\|X_r\|$ mV	0	0	0	0	0

Table 3.4(a) Results obtained for threshold value = 1

r	0	1	2	3	4	5	6
X_r	8.4500	−2.4399 − j4.9057	−1.6731 − j0.2554	−2.1798 + j3.8484	4.9732 − j1.6766	−3.4100 − j3.7251	−3.4702 + j3.1600
$\|X_r\|$ mV	8.4500	5.4790	1.6924	4.4228	5.2482	5.0501	4.6934

r	7	8	9	10	11	12	13
X_r	3.5425 + j4.2306	3.9637 − j4.4107	−4.2812 − j2.9470	−2.3362 + j4.0973	4.3195 + j1.4858	0.6997 − j4.2089	−3.8588 − j0.0781
$\|X_r\|$ mV	5.5179	5.9301	5.1975	4.7166	4.5679	4.2667	3.8596

r	14	15	16	17	18	19	20
X_r	0.3679 j3.5864	3.2423 − j0.6930	− 0.8700 − j2.7200	−2.2619 + j0.9229	0.9642 j1.9062	1.5079 − j0.9240	0
$\|X_r\|$ mV	3.6052	3.3155	2.8557	2.4429	2.1362	1.7685	0

r	21	22	23	24	25	26	27
X_r	0	0	0	0	0	0	0
$\|X_r\|$ mV	0	0	0	0	0	0	0

r	28	29	30	31	32
X_r	0	0	0	0	0
$\|X_r\|$ mV	0	0	0	0	0

Table 3.4(b) Results obtained for threshold value = 1.5

r	0	1	2	3	4	5	6
X_r	8.4500	−2.4399 − j4.9057	0	−2.1798 + j3.8484	4.9732 − j1.6766	−3.4100 − j3.7251	−3.4702 + j3.1600
$\|X_r\|$ mV	8.4500	5.4790	0	4.4228	5.2482	5.0501	4.6934

r	7	8	9	10	11	12	13
X_r	3.5425 + j4.2306	3.9637 − j4.4107	−4.2812 − j2.9470	−2.3362 + j4.0973	4.3195 + j1.4858	0.6997 − j4.2089	−3.8588 − j0.0781
$\|X_r\|$ mV	5.5179	5.9301	5.1975	4.7166	4.5679	4.2667	3.8596

r	14	15	16	17	18	19	20
X_r	0.3679 j3.5864	3.2423 − j0.6930	− 0.8700 − j2.7200	−2.2619 + j0.9229	0.9642 j1.9062	0	0
$\|X_r\|$ mV	3.6052	3.3155	2.8557	2.4429	2.1362	0	0
r	21	22	23	24	25	26	27
X_r	0	0	0	0	0	0	0
$\|X_r\|$ mV	0	0	0	0	0	0	0
r	28	29	30	31	32		
X_r	0	0	0	0	0		
$\|X_r\|$ mV	0	0	0	0	0		

Table 3.4(c) Results obtained for threshold value = 2

(c) Coding

Referring to the coding scheme shown in Figure 3.17, thirty-three bits are required in the header section to indicate whether the corresponding thirty-three coefficients are zero or non-zero. For the coding of non-zero spectral coefficients the use of 8-bit numbers gives $2^8 = 256$ quantisation levels. From Table 3.3 we see that the maximum positive and negative amplitudes to be quantised are 8.45 and −4.9057 respectively. If the full-scale value is conveniently set to ±9, then the full-scale range is 18, and correspondingly by equation (1.14) the quantisation interval for sign and magnitude coding is

$$Q = \frac{18}{2^8 - 2} \cong 0.\ 0709$$

Note: If the full-scale range is considered to be between −5 and 9 the quantisation interval will be correspondingly reduced, resulting in a smaller quantisation error. The quantisation error would also be reduced by using more bits to code the non-zero spectral coefficients, but this reduces the compression ratio.

Table 3.5 lists the quantised spectral coefficients for three threshold value settings.

r	0	1	2	3	4	5	6
X_r	8.4331	−2.4094 − j4.8898	−1.7008 − j0.2835	−2.1969 + j3.8268	4.9606 − j1.7008	−3.4016 − j3.7559	−3.4724 + j3.1890
r	7	8	9	10	11	12	13
X_r	3.5433 + j4.2520	3.9685 − j4.3937	−4.2520 − j2.9764	−2.3386 + j4.1102	4.3228 + j1.4882	0.7087 − j4.1811	−3.8268 − j0.0709
r	14	15	16	17	18	19	20
X_r	0.3543 +j3.6142	3.2598 − j0.7087	− 0.8504 − j2.6929	−2.2677 + j0.9213	0.9921 + j1.9134	1.4882 − j0.9213	0.8505 − j1.1339

r	21	22	23	24	25	26	27
X_r	–0.9213 + j0.7087	0	0	0	0	0	0
r	28	29	30	31	32		
X_r	0	0	0	0	0		

Table 3.5(a) Quantised spectral coefficients for threshold value = 1

r	0	1	2	3	4	5	6
X_r	8.4331	–2.4094 – j4.8898	–1.7008 – j0.2835	–2.1969 + j3.8268	4.9606 – j1.7008	–3.4016 – j3.7559	–3.4724 + j3.1890
r	7	8	9	10	11	12	13
X_r	3.5433 + j4.2520	3.9685 – j4.3937	–4.2520 – j2.9764	–2.3386 + j4.1102	4.3228 + j1.4882	0.7087 – j4.1811	–3.8268 – j0.0709
r	14	15	16	17	18	19	20
X_r	0.3543 +j3.6142	3.2598 – j0.7087	– 0.8504 – j2.6929	–2.2677 + j0.9213	0.9921 + j1.9134	1.4882 – j0.9213	0
r	21	22	23	24	25	26	27
X_r	0	0	0	0	0	0	0
r	28	29	30	31	32		
X_r	0	0	0	0	0		

Table 3.5(b) Quantised spectral coefficents for threshold value = 1.5

r	0	1	2	3	4	5	6
X_r	8.4331	–2.4094 – j4.8898	0	–2.1969 + j3.8268	4.9606 – j1.7008	–3.4016 – j3.7559	–3.4724 + j3.1890
r	7	8	9	10	11	12	13
X_r	3.5433 + j4.2520	3.9685 – j4.3937	–4.2520 – j2.9764	–2.3386 + j4.1102	4.3228 + j1.4882	0.7087 – j4.1811	–3.8268 – j0.0709
r	14	15	16	17	18	19	20
X_r	0.3543 +j3.6142	3.2598 – j0.7087	– 0.8504 – j2.6929	–2.2677 + j0.9213	0.9921 + j1.9134	0	0
r	21	22	23	24	25	26	27
X_r	0	0	0	0	0	0	0
r	28	29	30	31	32		
X_r	0	0	0	0	0		

Table 3.5(c) Quantised spectral coefficients for threshold value = 2

The total number of bits required to code the spectral coefficients, N_B, is

$$N_B = \{\text{Number of header bits} + 8 \text{ bits for d.c. value} + 16 \text{ bits} \times \text{Number of non-zero coefficients, excluding d.c. value}\}$$

Compared with the original requirement of eight bits per ecg waveform sample, the reductions in bits per sample (expressed as the compression ratio) are listed in Table 3.6.

Threshold value	Number of non-zero coefficients excluding d.c.	Total number of bits required for coding one period	Bits per sample	Compression ratio
1	21	377	5.89 (= 377/64)	1.36 (= 8/5.89)
1.5	19	345	5.39 (= 345/64)	1.48 (= 8/5.39)
2	17	313	4.89 (= 313/64)	1.64 (= 8/4.89)

Table 3.6 Reduction in bits per sample

(d) Signal Reconstruction
The reconstructed 64-sample ecg signal using the threshold value of 1.5 is shown in Figure 3.19.

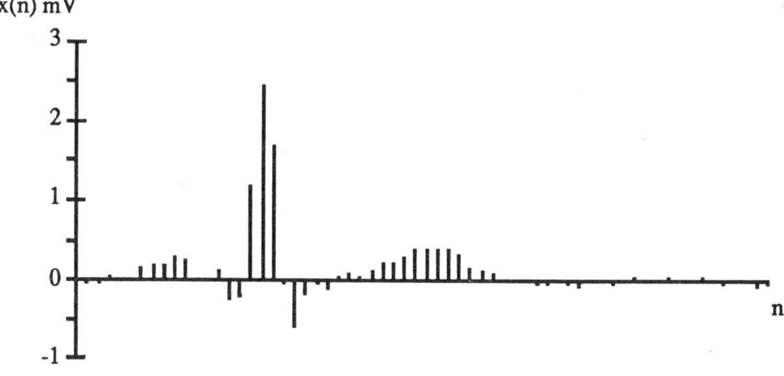

Figure 3.19 Reconstructed 64-sample ecg signal using threshold value of 1.5

Three sets of amplitude values, obtained by computing the IDFT (equation (3.19)) of the thresholded and quantised spectral coefficients, for the reconstruction of the ecg signal, are listed in Table 3.7.

Threshold value	1	1.5	2
n	$x(n)$	$x(n)$	$x(n)$
0	−0.0210	0.0343	0.0410
1	0.0183	−0.0187	0.0177
2	0.0097	−0.0184	0.0819
3	−0.0147	0.0499	0.0714
4	0.0467	0.0207	0.0077
5	0.0554	0.0090	0.0747
6	0.0609	0.1287	0.1600
7	0.1863	0.1765	0.1236
8	0.2308	0.1683	0.1719
9	0.2189	0.2829	0.3112
10	0.2532	0.2631	0.1946
11	0.0909	0.0165	−0.0445
12	−0.0439	0.0097	0.0198
13	0.0725	0.1027	0.0464
14	−0.1554	−0.2355	−0.3377
15	−0.2289	−0.1913	−0.2090
16	1.1350	1.1837	1.1593
17	2.5127	2.4340	2.3307
18	1.6622	1.6801	1.6363
19	−0.0858	−0.0228	−0.0103
20	−0.5014	−0.5719	−0.6351
21	−0.1652	−0.1680	−0.2234
22	−0.0996	−0.0284	0.0106
23	−0.0343	−0.0909	−0.0891
24	0.0579	0.0460	−0.0083
25	0.0155	0.0879	0.1344
26	0.0651	0.0263	0.0921
27	0.1508	0.1139	0.1017
28	0.1519	0.2188	0.2538
29	0.2286	0.2087	0.3121
30	0.3230	0.2767	0.3065
31	0.3421	0.3978	0.4106

Threshold value	1	1.5	2
n	$x(n)$	$x(n)$	$x(n)$
32	0.3953	0.3931	0.4927
33	0.4211	0.3722	0.4366
34	0.3585	0.3991	0.3902
35	0.2994	0.3110	0.3680
36	0.2010	0.1561	0.2319
37	0.0773	0.1017	0.0804
38	0.0508	0.0707	0.0637
39	0.0392	0.0038	0.0601
40	−0.0072	0.0023	−0.0191
41	0.0016	0.0234	−0.0430
42	0.0029	−0.0195	−0.0080
43	−0.0329	−0.0347	−0.0475
44	−0.0224	−0.0051	−0.1029
45	−0.0206	−0.0289	−0.0707
46	−0.0392	−0.0468	−0.0495
47	−0.0046	0.0030	−0.0870
48	0.0100	0.0144	−0.0675
49	−0.0066	−0.0137	−0.0112
50	0.0228	0.0175	−0.0301
51	0.0285	0.0418	−0.0492
52	0.0100	0.0096	0.0103
53	0.0420	0.0228	0.0338
54	0.0407	0.0572	−0.0062
55	0.0094	0.0208	0.0157
56	0.0329	0.0016	0.0637
57	0.0243	0.0376	0.0292
58	−0.0093	0.0170	0.0082
59	0.0197	−0.0195	0.0665
60	0.0074	0.0113	0.0641
61	−0.0408	0.0010	−0.0041
62	−0.0129	−0.0544	0.0208
63	−0.0035	−0.0141	0.0809

Table 3.7 Amplitude values of reconstructed 64-sample ecg signals

Comparing signal amplitude values in Tables 3.2 and 3.7, it is seen that the differences between the original ecg signal and its reconstructed version increase as the threshold value increases. This loss of fidelity is due to the reduction in the number of non-zero spectral coefficients used for signal reconstruction. Furthermore, the differences must also be attributed, in part, to quantising the spectral coefficients.

(e) Error Analysis

One way of quantitatively assessing the fidelity of the reconstructed signal is to compute the signal-to-noise ratio (SNR). Using the definition of signal power given in equation (1.24), the error (noise) signal power can be similarly defined as

$$P_{noise} = \frac{1}{N} \sum_{n=0}^{N-1} \left[x(n) - x_r(n) \right]^2 \qquad (3.55)$$

where $x(n)$ is the nth sample value of the original signal, and $x_r(n)$ is the nth sample value for the reconstructed signal.

It follows that the signal-to-noise ratio is

$$\text{SNR} = 10 \log_{10} \left[\frac{\sum_{n=0}^{N-1} x(n)^2}{\sum_{n=0}^{N-1} \left[x(n) - x_r(n) \right]^2} \right] \text{dB} \qquad (3.56)$$

Table 3.8 lists values of compression ratio and the corresponding SNR values for the three threshold values investigated.

Threshold value	1	1.5	2
Compression ratio	1.36	1.48	1.64
SNR (dB)	19.96	17.26	14.64

Table 3.8 Compression ratio and SNR values

***Concluding Remarks*:**

This case study demonstrates the classic situation of being able to achieve some degree of signal data compression at the expense of some loss of fidelity in the reconstructed signal. The end user will have to judge whether the reconstructed signal is adequate for its intended purpose. This can be done qualitatively by visual inspection of the resulting waveform, and/or quantitatively by, for example, considering the SNR value.

Problems

P3.1

The analogue signal $x(t) = 3\cos(2400\pi t) + 2\sin(4800\pi t)$ V is sampled at a frequency of 9.6 kHz.

(a) By inspection of the above signal definition sketch its magnitude/frequency and phase/frequency spectrum.

(b) By computing the Fourier series coefficients confirm the spectrum deduced in (a).

P3.2

(a) Compute the discrete-time Fourier transform of (i) the unit-impulse signal $\delta(n)$ and (ii) the unit-impulse signal delayed by 3 samples, $\delta(n-3)$.

(b) Sketch the magnitude/frequency and phase/frequency spectrum of each signal.

(c) Use the inverse discrete-time Fourier transform to confirm that each spectrum represents the corresponding given signal.

P3.3

The sinusoidal burst signal $x(t) = \sin(2500\pi t)$ V starts at time $t = 0$ and lasts for 0.6 ms, and is sampled 5000 times per second, with the first sample obtained at $t = 0$.

(a) Compute the discrete Fourier transform of the sampled-data sequence.

(b) Sketch the magnitude/frequency and phase/frequency spectrum of the burst signal.

(c) Show that the inverse discrete Fourier transform yields the original signal sample values.

P3.4

Two sampled-data signal sequences generated at a rate of 8000 samples per second are described by the following expressions:

(i) $(0.6)^n \times u(n)$ (ii) $(-0.6)^n \times u(n)$

(a) Using the z-transform of each sequence derive the discrete-time Fourier transform of each sequence.

(b) Using the discrete-time Fourier transforms derived in part (a) sketch the magnitude/frequency and phase/frequency spectrum of each sampled-data signal.

(c) For each sampled-data sequence compute its corresponding 8-point discrete Fourier transform.

(d) Using the discrete Fourier transforms derived in part (c) sketch the magnitude/frequency and phase/frequency spectrum of each sampled-data signal.

(e) Compare the frequency spectra obtained in parts (b) and (d).

P3.5

For the 8-sample sequence $x(n) = \{1, 2, 3, 5, 5, 3, 2, 1\}$ the first five DFT coefficients are $\{22, -7.5355 - j\,3.1213, 1 + j, -0.4645 - j\,1.1213, 0\}$.

(a) Determine the remaining three DFT coefficients.

(b) The given 8-sample sequence is used to form the following three sequences:

(i) $2x(n)$ (ii) $x(n-2)$ (iii) $2x(n) + x(n-2)$

Determine the DFT coefficients of each 8-sample sequence.

P3.6

(a) Draw the butterfly diagram of the 8-point decimation-in-time fast Fourier transform and use it to compute the FFT of the 8-sample sequence given in problem **P3.5.**

(b) Draw the butterfly diagram of the 8-point inverse decimation-in-time fast Fourier transform and use it to obtain the original eight sequence values.

P3.7

A 16-point DFT is implemented using the decimation-in-frequency FFT process.

(a) Using bit-reversed-order notation list the FFT inputs.

(b) Determine the number of computation stages required.

(c) Determine the number of additions/subtractions and the number of multiplications required at each stage.

(d) Compared with the direct form of DFT implementation determine the percentage reduction in the total number of additions/subtractions and the total number of multiplications achieved by employing the FFT process.

P3.8

An input sequence $x(n) = \{2, 1, 0, 1, 2\}$ is applied to a DSP system having an impulse sequence $h(n) = \{5, 3, 2, 1\}$. Determine the output sequence produced by:

(a) Linear convolution.

(b) Circular convolution.

(c) Indirect circular convolution based on the FFT and IFFT processes.

P3.9

A DSP system operating with a 2 kHz sampling frequency has an impulse response sequence defined as

$$h(n) = \begin{cases} e^{n} & 0 \le n \le 3 \\ 0 & \text{otherwise} \end{cases}$$

A 200 Hz squarewave input signal with an amplitude of ± 5V is applied to the input of the DSP system, determine the output sequence using:

(a) The overlap-save method.

(b) The overlap-add method.

Use an 8-point FFT in implementing both methods.

P3.10

Two periodic sampled-data signal sequences are defined as

$$x(n) = \{0, -1, 0, 1\} \qquad y(n) = \{1, 3, 2, 1\}$$

Determine:

(a) The cross-correlation sequence using the linear correlation operation.
(b) The cross-correlation sequence using the circular correlation operation.
(c) The cross-correlation sequence using the indirect circular correlation operation based on the DFT process.
(d) The auto-correlation of $x(n)$ using the linear correlation operation.
(e) The auto-correlation of $x(n)$ using the circular correlation operation.
(f) The auto-correlation of $x(n)$ using the indirect circular correlation operation based on the DFT process.
(g) The cross-correlation coefficients.
(h) The phase difference between the two sequences.

P3.11

A digital correlator implemented using an 8-point FFT is used to search through data sequences for the pattern $\{1, -2, 3, -1\}$. The input sequence applied to the correlator is $\{0, 2, -2, -3, -1, 2, -3, 1, 3, 3, 0, 1, -2, 0, 1\}$.

(a) Determine the output sequence obtained using:
   (i) The overlap-save method.
   (ii) The overlap-add method.
(b) Verify the results obtained in (a) using the linear correlation operation.
(c) Analyse the results obtained in (a) to determine whether pattern $\{1, -2, 3, -1\}$ has been found.

P3.12

A digital spectrum analyser based on the FFT process is used to analyse a 100 ms duration speech signal. The sampling frequency used is 20 kHz. Determine:

(a) The highest frequency which is allowed to be displayed in the spectrum without aliasing.
(b) The number of samples required to give a frequency resolution of 10 Hz.
(c) The number of zeros to be padded to make the length of the FFT an integer power of 2.
(d) The final frequency resolution.
(e) Which parameter could be modified to ensure correct representation of the 50 Hz frequency component.

P3.13

(a) Sketch the 8-point Blackman window function.

(b) Repeat WE3.26(a) by applying the 8-point Blackman window to the sampled version of signal $x(t) = \sin(2\pi \times 1000\, t)$ V. The first sample is obtained at $t = 0$.

(c) Repeat WE3.26(b) by applying the 8-point Blackman window to the sampled version of signal $x(t) = \sin(2\pi \times 1300\, t)$ V. The first sample is obtained at $t = 0$.

P3.14

For the two signals given in WE3.26, with the same sampling frequency:

(a) Calculate, using the signal sampled-data values, the energy per period and the average power for both signals.

(b) Using an 8-point rectangular window derive the periodogram for both signals.

(c) Using an 8-point Blackman window derive the periodogram for both signals.

(d) Calculate, using the results obtained in (b) and (c) respectively, the energy per period and the average power for both signals.

P3.15

A binary data pattern, continuously alternating between '1' and '0' with a bit duration of 1 ms, is applied to a frequency shift keying (FSK) modulator, which outputs a 1 kHz sinusoidal signal for the logic '0' input and a 2 kHz sinusoidal signal for the logic '1' input, as shown in the figure below. Tabulate the spectrogram magnitude values for the FSK modulator output when the sampling frequency is 8 kHz. Assume that an 8-point Hanning window is applied, and that the overlap of the sliding window is four points.

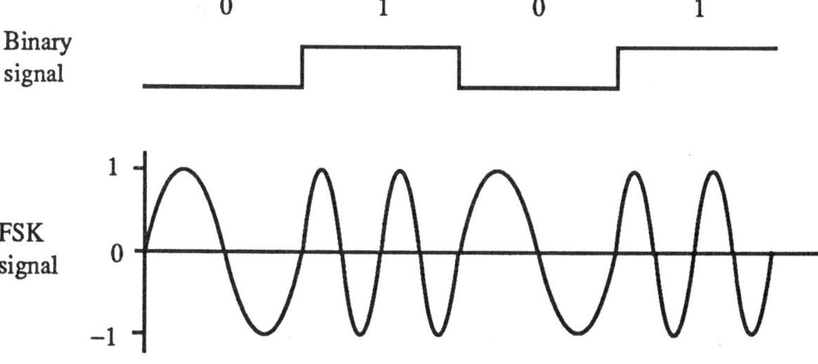

4 Digital Filters

4.1 Introduction

The description of the DSP system concept given in Section 1.1.1 (page 2) was conveyed using an example of a digital filter signal processing operation. It was explained that the in-band unwanted signal at 3 kHz should be removed (filtered out) to produce the wanted signal at 1 kHz. It will therefore be appreciated that a digital filter may be regarded as a DSP system that selectively modifies the frequency components of a signal according to specified processing requirements. Consequently the magnitude/frequency and phase/frequency characteristics of the digital filter must enable the required signal filtering operation to be achieved.

Digital filters can be designed and implemented either as recursive or non-recursive DSP systems. We therefore have the choice of using infinite impulse response (IIR) digital filters or finite impulse response (FIR) digital filters. A selection of popular and straightforward design methods for both types of digital filters are described and demonstrated in this chapter.

4.2 FIR Digital Filters

Non-recursive digital filters have a finite impulse response (FIR) sequence, and they are inherently stable. Furthermore, a digital filter with a symmetrical impulse response has a linear phase/frequency characteristic, and therefore in this case there is no signal phase distortion imposed by the filter.

Compared with an IIR filter, an FIR counterpart will generally use more memory and arithmetic for its implementation. For many applications the advantages significantly outweigh the disadvantages, and consequently FIR filters are often used in practice.

4.2.1 The Moving Averager Digital Filter

The output signal sample value of a moving averager digital filter is the arithmetic average of the current input sample value and one or more delayed input sample values. This averaging action is a lowpass filtering process, and its action smooths fluctuations in the filter input signal. However, it should be noted that there is a characteristic *start up transient* before the smoothing action becomes effective. For an N-term moving averager, the start up transient exists over the period $t = 0$ to $t = NT$ (T is the sampling period), which is the duration of its impulse response sequence.

We assume that the moving averager FIR filter coefficients are all equal to unity. The impulse response sequence of the corresponding N-term moving averager is therefore

$$g(i) = \Big\{ \underbrace{\frac{1}{N}, \frac{1}{N}, \dots, \frac{1}{N}}_{\leftarrow N-\text{terms} \rightarrow}, 0, 0, \dots \Big\}$$

The transfer function of this N-term moving averager is

$$G(z) = \frac{1}{N}\left[1 + z^{-1} + z^{-2} + \dots + z^{-(N-1)}\right]$$

Expressing $G(z)$ in *closed form* we obtain

$$G(z) = \frac{1}{N}\left[\frac{1 - z^{-N}}{1 - z^{-1}}\right]$$

The corresponding FIR filter frequency response function is

$$G\left(e^{j\omega T}\right) = \frac{1}{N}\left[\frac{1 - e^{-j\omega NT}}{1 - e^{-j\omega T}}\right] \tag{4.1}$$

The magnitude/frequency characteristics for three unity-coefficient moving averagers are shown in Figure 4.1. It may be noted that in each case the first null occurs at a frequency $\omega = 2\pi/(NT)$, which applies in general to N-term moving averagers having equal-value filter coefficients. Therefore for a filter with a known sampling frequency, the design of a moving averager simply involves specifying the frequency value for the first null, which in turn determines the number of terms used in implementing the averaging process.

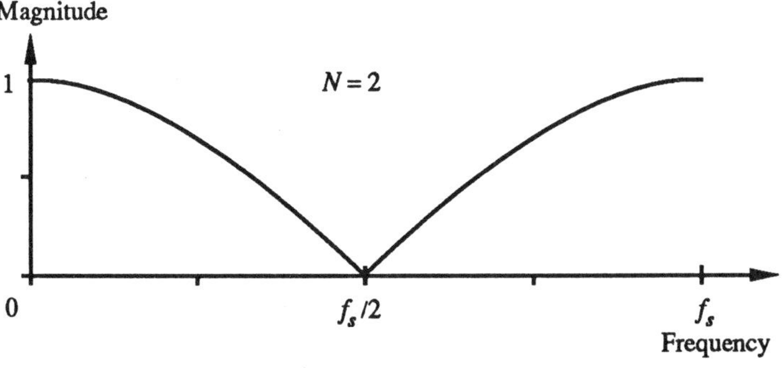

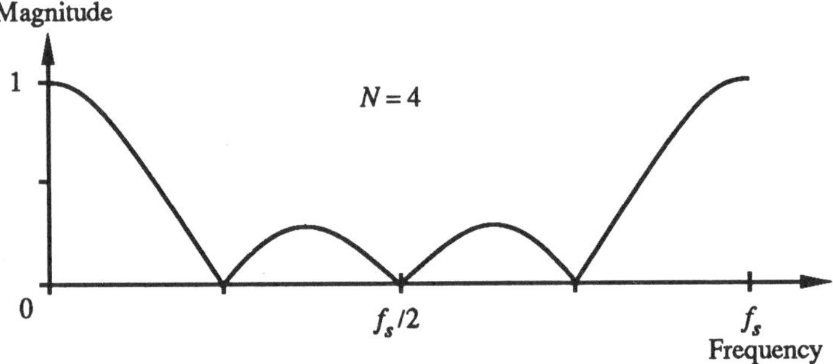

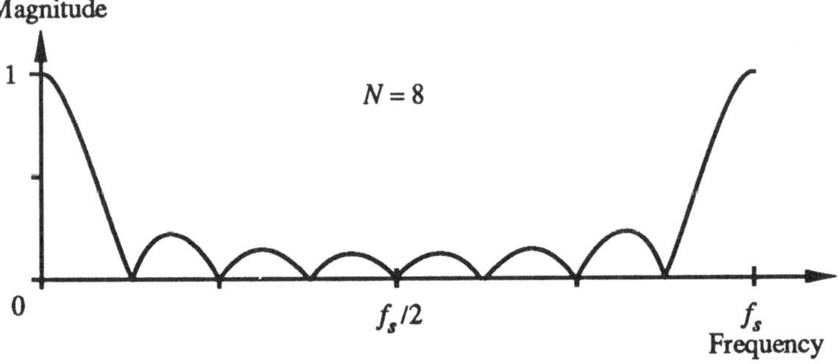

Figure 4.1 Magnitude/frequency characteristics for three moving averagers

❖ **WE 4.1**

A digital filter based on an N-term moving averager is to be used such that the first null occurs at a frequency of 4 kHz, determine the signal flow graph of the filter. The sampling frequency is 12 kHz. Plot the magnitude/frequency characteristic of the filter.

Solution:

$$\omega = \frac{2\pi}{NT} \qquad \therefore N = \frac{f_s}{f} = \frac{12000}{4000} = 3$$

The linear difference equation for the required three-term moving averager is

$$y(n) = \frac{x(n) + x(n-1) + x(n-2)}{3}$$

The signal flow graph of this digital filter is shown below:

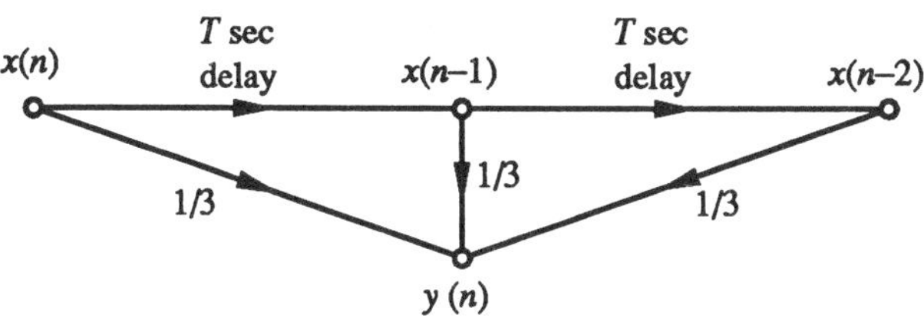

The magnitude/frequency characteristic of the 3-term moving average is shown below:

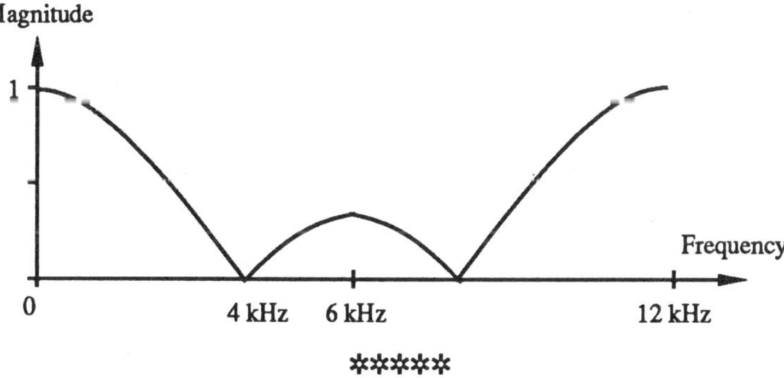

*****

4.2.2 Frequency Sampling Design Method

A digital filter with a finite impulse response sequence, $g(i)$, also has an equivalent N-point discrete Fourier transform (DFT), $G(k)$, where $G(k)$ is a sampled version of the continuous frequency response of a specified ideal filter. For this case we have

$$G(k) = G\left(e^{j\omega T}\right)\Big|_{\omega = \frac{2\pi k}{N}} \qquad k = 0, 1, 2, \ldots, (N-1) \tag{4.2}$$

where $G(e^{j\omega T})$ is the continuous frequency response of the specified ideal filter. Equation (4.2) implies that to approximate the ideal continuous frequency response, frequency samples have to be obtained at a set of N points uniformly spaced on the circumference of the unit-circle in the z-plane. The z-transform of $g(i)$, for $i = 0, 1, 2, \ldots, (N-1)$, is

$$G(z) = \sum_{i=0}^{N-1} g(i)\, z^{-i} \tag{4.3}$$

The inverse discrete Fourier transform (IDFT) relationship between $g(i)$ and $G(k)$ is

$$g(i) = \frac{1}{N} \sum_{k=0}^{N-1} G(k) e^{j\frac{2\pi ik}{N}} \tag{4.4}$$

Substituting equation (4.4) in (4.3) yields

$$G(z) = \sum_{i=0}^{N-1} \left\{ \frac{1}{N} \sum_{k=0}^{N-1} G(k) e^{j\frac{2\pi ik}{N}} \right\} z^{-i}$$

$$= \sum_{k=0}^{N-1} \frac{G(k)}{N} \sum_{i=0}^{N-1} e^{j\frac{2\pi ik}{N}} z^{-i}$$

$$\therefore \quad G(z) = \sum_{k=0}^{N-1} \left[\frac{G(k)}{N} \right] \left[\frac{1 - z^{-N}}{1 - e^{j\frac{2\pi k}{N}} z^{-1}} \right] \tag{4.5}$$

Thus to obtain the transfer function of the FIR digital filter we simply let $G(k)$ be a uniformly spaced N-point representation of the ideal frequency response, with the value of N chosen to ensure that the resulting filter frequency response is acceptable. Clearly the greater the value of N, the smaller the differences between the derived and ideal filter frequency response characteristics.

❖ **WE 4.2**

Design an FIR filter based on the 8-point sampling of the ideal frequency response shown below:

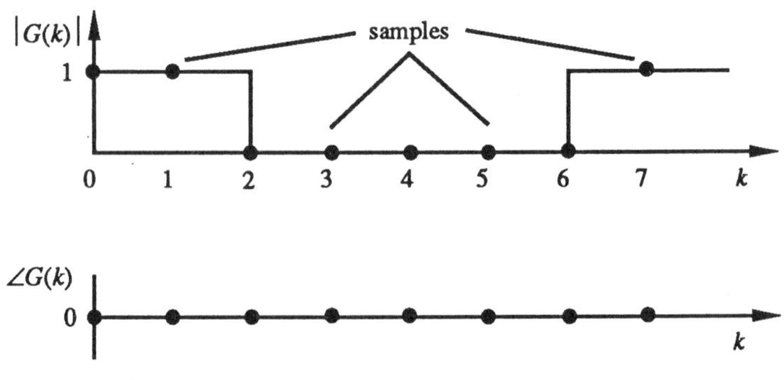

***Solution*:**
In this case $N = 8$, and substituting this value in equation (4.5) gives

$$G(z) = \sum_{k=0}^{7}\left[\frac{G(k)}{8}\right]\left[\frac{1 - z^{-8}}{1 - e^{j\frac{\pi k}{4}} z^{-1}}\right]$$

$$= \frac{1 - z^{-8}}{8} \sum_{k=0}^{7}\left[\frac{G(k)}{1 - e^{j\frac{\pi k}{4}} z^{-1}}\right]$$

but $G(0) = G(1) = G(7) = 1$ and $G(2) = G(3) = G(3) = G(4) = G(5) = G(6) = 0$

$$\therefore G(z) = \frac{1 - z^{-8}}{8}\left[\frac{1}{1 - z^{-1}} + \frac{1}{1 - c^{j\frac{\pi}{4}} z^{-1}} + \frac{1}{1 - e^{j\frac{7\pi}{4}} z^{-1}}\right]$$

$$= \frac{1 - z^{-8}}{8}\left[\frac{1}{1 - z^{-1}} + \frac{1}{1 - \left(\frac{1}{\sqrt{2}} + j\frac{1}{\sqrt{2}}\right) z^{-1}} + \frac{1}{1 - \left(\frac{1}{\sqrt{2}} - j\frac{1}{\sqrt{2}}\right) z^{-1}}\right]$$

$$= \frac{z^8 - 1}{8z^8}\left[\frac{z}{z - 1} + \frac{z}{z - \left(\frac{1}{\sqrt{2}} + j\frac{1}{\sqrt{2}}\right)} + \frac{z}{z - \left(\frac{1}{\sqrt{2}} - j\frac{1}{\sqrt{2}}\right)}\right]$$

$$= \frac{z^8 - 1}{8z^8}\left[\frac{3z^3 - 2\left(1 + \sqrt{2}\right) z^2 + \left(1 + \sqrt{2}\right) z}{(z - 1)\left(z - \left(\frac{1}{\sqrt{2}} + j\frac{1}{\sqrt{2}}\right)\right)\left(z - \left(\frac{1}{\sqrt{2}} - j\frac{1}{\sqrt{2}}\right)\right)}\right]$$

but
$$z^8 - 1 = \left(z + \frac{1}{\sqrt{2}} + j\frac{1}{\sqrt{2}}\right)\left(z + \frac{1}{\sqrt{2}} - j\frac{1}{\sqrt{2}}\right)(z + 1)(z - 1)$$
$$\times\left(z - \frac{1}{\sqrt{2}} + j\frac{1}{\sqrt{2}}\right)\left(z - \frac{1}{\sqrt{2}} - j\frac{1}{\sqrt{2}}\right)(z + j)(z - j)$$

$$\therefore G(z) = \frac{1}{8z^8}\left[(3z^3 - 2(1+\sqrt{2})z^2 + (1+\sqrt{2})z)\left(z + \frac{1}{\sqrt{2}} + j\frac{1}{\sqrt{2}}\right)\right.$$

$$\left. \times \left(z + \frac{1}{\sqrt{2}} - j\frac{1}{\sqrt{2}}\right)(z+1)(z+j)(z-j)\right]$$

$$G(z) = 0.375 + 0.302\,z^{-1} + 0.125\,z^{-2} - 0.052\,z^{-3} - 0125\,z^{-4}$$
$$- 0.052\,z^{-5} + 0.125\,z^{-6} + 0.302\,z^{-7}$$

The linear difference equation of this filter is

$$y(n) = 0.375\,x(n) + 0.302\,x(n-1) + 0.125\,x(n-2)$$
$$- 0.052\,x(n-3) - 0.125\,x(n-4) - 0.052\,x(n-5)$$
$$+ 0.125\,x(n-6) + 0.302\,x(n-7)$$

The signal flow graph for this filter is shown below:

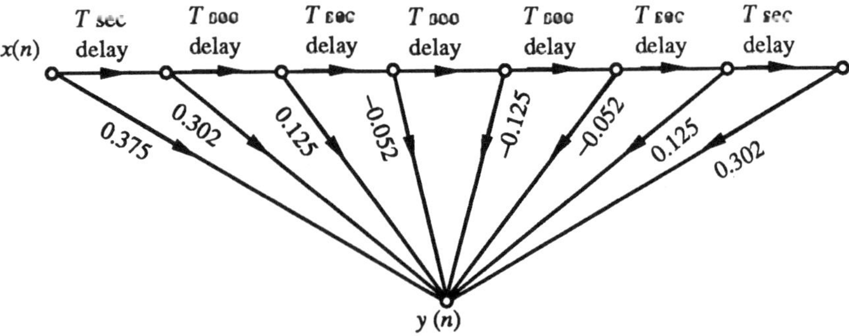

Note that the coefficients of this FIR filter can be calculated directly using equation (4.4).

*****

4.2.3 The Window Method

This design method is basically a frequency sampling technique involving four main steps. The design process is:

(i) The desired ideal frequency response is specified.

(ii) The specified frequency response is sampled at regular intervals along the frequency axis, and the corresponding impulse response sequence is computed.

(iii) The impulse response sequence is modified by a window function sequence (a cosine-like sequence).

(iv) The transfer function of the FIR filter is derived from the modified impulse response sequence.

Steps (i) and (ii) are identical to the method described in Section 4.2.2. Step (iii) is included to minimise the *oscillations* (observed as ripples and overshoots in the magnitude/frequency characteristics) known as Gibb's phenomenon caused by abruptly truncating the infinite impulse response sequence of the ideal filter to create a finite impulse response sequence of N values.

The application of the window function results in a gradual tapering of the impulse response such that the middle value, $g(0)$, of the corresponding symmetrical windowed response is undisturbed, whereas the values become increasingly less significant as the response series moves out from the middle. Consequently the unwanted overshoot at sharp transitions in the ideal (specified response characteristic) is significantly reduced, see Figure 4.2.

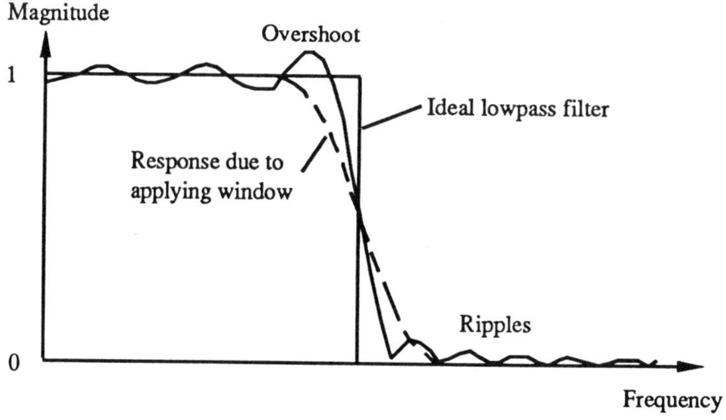

Figure 4.2 Reduction of overshoots

Three window functions commonly used in this method for the design of FIR filters are: (a) Hamming window, which is defined by $w(r) = 0.54+0.46\cos(r\pi/I)$; (b) Hanning window, which is defined by $w(r) = 0.5+0.5\cos(r\pi/I)$; (c) Blackman window, which is defined by $w(r) = 0.42+0.5\cos(r\pi/I)+0.08\sin(2r\pi/I)$. For each of these window functions I is taken to be the number of terms to be included on both sides of $g(0)$, and r is an integer index corresponding with the sampling points.

The following worked example illustrates this design method.

❖ **WE 4.3**

Using the window method design an FIR filter based on the 16-point sampling of the ideal frequency response shown below:

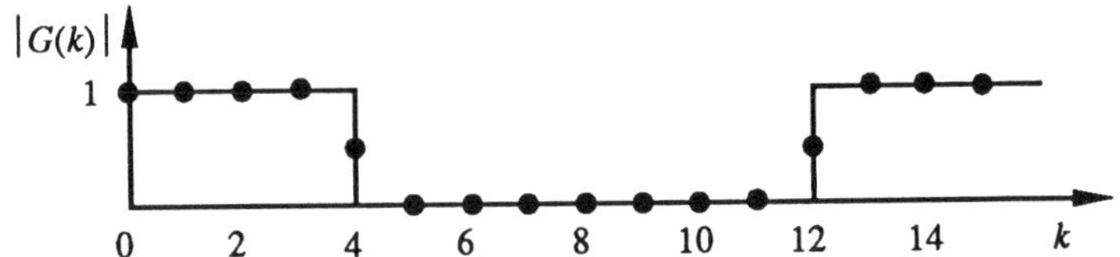

Use a Hamming window and let $I = 4$.

Solution:

Step 1: In this case the number of samples, N, is sixteen, and the corresponding sample values ($G(k)$ values) are

$$\{1, 1, 1, 1, 0.5, 0, 0, 0, 0, 0, 0, 0, 0.5, 1, 1, 1\}$$

Step 2: The corresponding sixteen coefficients of this FIR filter can be calculated directly using equation (4.4), i.e.

$$g(i) = \frac{1}{16} \sum_{k=0}^{15} G(k)\, e^{j\frac{\pi i k}{8}} \qquad \text{for } i = 0, 1, \ldots, 15$$

However, in this case $I = 4$ (the number of terms to be included on either side of $g(0)$) so we need only compute $g(i)$ values for $i = 0, 1, 2, 3$ and 4.

$$\therefore g(i) = \frac{1}{16}\left[\left(1 \times e^{j0}\right) + \left(1 \times e^{j\frac{\pi i}{8}}\right) + \left(1 \times e^{j\frac{\pi i}{4}}\right) + \left(1 \times e^{j\frac{3\pi i}{8}}\right)\right.$$

$$+ \left(0.5 \times e^{j\frac{\pi i}{2}}\right) + \left(0.5 \times e^{j\frac{3\pi i}{2}}\right) + \left(1 \times e^{j\frac{13\pi i}{8}}\right)$$

$$\left. + \left(1 \times e^{j\frac{7\pi i}{4}}\right) + \left(1 \times e^{j\frac{15\pi i}{8}}\right)\right]$$

Therefore the computed impulse response values are

$$\{0.5, 0.314, 0, -0.094, 0\}$$

Step 3: For the Hamming window with $I = 4$

$$w(r) = 0.54 + 0.46 \cos\left(\frac{r\pi}{4}\right)$$

and we need only compute $w(r)$ for $r = 0, 1, 2, 3$, and 4 to correspond with the computed $g(i)$ values. Therefore the computed window values are

$$\{1, 0.865, 0.54, 0.215, 0.08\}$$

The modification of the $g(i)$ impulse response values by the $w(r)$ window values is achieved by forming the product $g(i) \times w(r)$, resulting in the sequence

$$\{0.5, 0.272, 0, -0.0202, 0\}$$

For a linear phase characteristic the modified impulse response sequence must be symmetrical about $g(0)$, i.e.

$$\{0, -0.0202, 0, 0.272, 0.5, 0.272, 0, -0.0202, 0\}$$

Step 4: The apparent transfer function, $G_A(z)$, of the FIR filter is the z-transform of the symmetrical modified impulse response sequence, i.e.

$$G_A(z) = -0.0202\ z^3 + 0.272\ z^1 + 0.5\,z^0 + 0.272\ z^{-1} - 0.0202\ z^{-3}$$

However, from a practical implementation point of view, z raised to a positive power is impractical, thus in this design example it is necessary to introduce the appropriate z^{-3} time delay to obtain the realisable transfer function, $G(z)$, i.e.

$$G(z) = G_A(z) \times z^{-3}$$

$$\therefore G(z) = -0.0202 + 0.272\ z^{-2} + 0.5\,z^{-3} + 0.272\ z^{-4} - 0.0202\ z^{-6}$$

The frequency response characteristics of this filter are shown below:

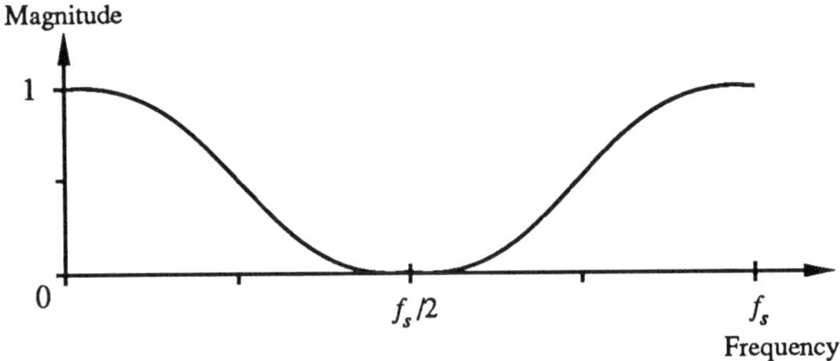

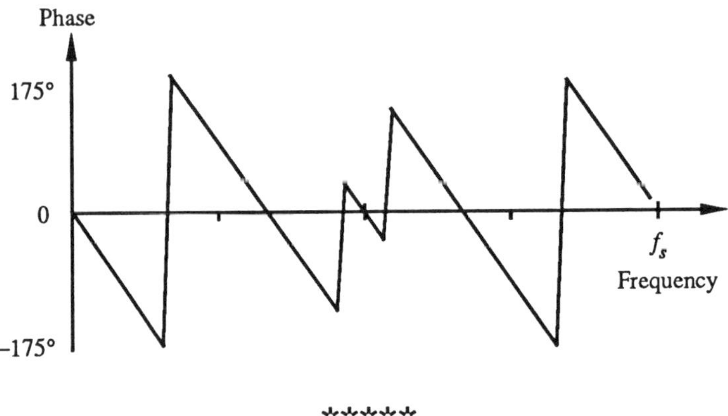

*****

The following comments concerning the design method used in the above worked example should be noted:

(a) Stopband attenuation can be improved by increasing the window width (increase of I), or by using a different type of window, or by changing both.

(b) An FIR digital filter with transfer function $G(z)$ has a linear phase characteristic, $\angle G(e^{j\omega T})$, which is a straight line relationship with a slope denoted by $-\phi$. The phase characteristic of $G(z) \times z^{-n}$ is also governed by a straight line relationship, but with a slope equal to $-(\phi + n)$. Consequently, making the filter realisable by shifting the symmetrical modified impulse response sequence along the time axis has no effect on the magnitude/frequency characteristic, however it does change a zero phase ($\phi = 0$) filter to a linear phase filter (a straight line relationship with a slope equal to $-n$).

(c) It is desirable that N is an integral power of 2 so that it will be compatible with the Fast Fourier Transform (FFT) - a technique used to expedite the evaluation of the IDFT. Also N must be at least equal to the width of the window ($N \geq I + 1$). In many practical designs N is chosen so that the interval between sampling points is a fraction (typically ≤ 0.1) of the widths of the transition bands in the final filter design.

4.2.4 The Comb Filter

The comb filter is basically a form of notch filter having nulls in its magnitude/frequency characteristic, which occur at periodic intervals along the frequency axis, see Figure 4.3. It is obvious from inspection of Figure 4.3 why this form of repetitive notch characteristic is said to be attributable to a *comb* filter. A typical application of a comb filter is for elimination (rejection) of harmonically related signal components.

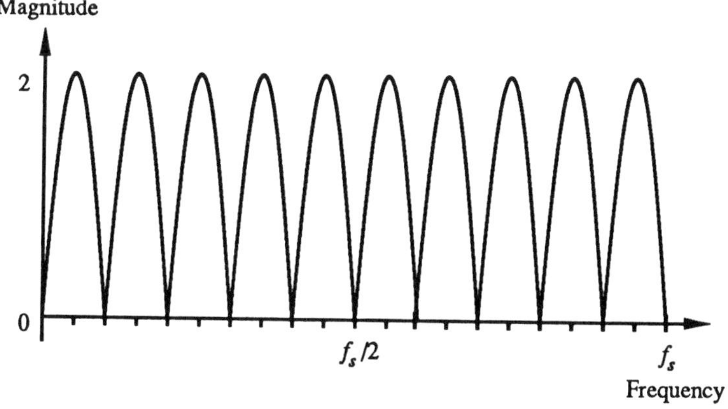

Figure 4.3 10th-order comb filter magnitude/frequency characteristic

It will be instructive to consider the simple (2nd-order) comb filter z-plane representation shown in Figure 4.4:

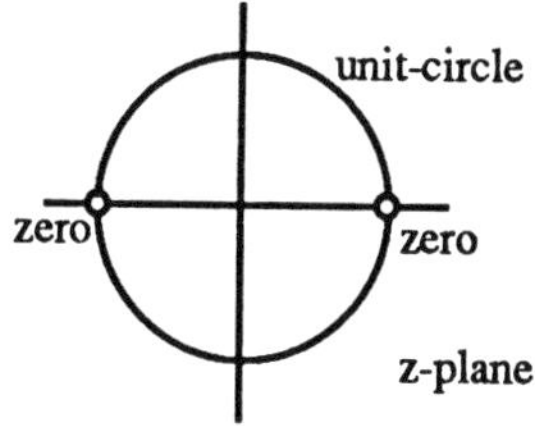

Figure 4.4 z-plane representation of 2nd-order comb filter (non-realisable form)

From inspection of Figure 4.4 the filter transfer function is

$$G(z) = (z+1)(z-1) = z^2 - 1 = \frac{Y(z)}{X(z)}$$

$$\therefore \quad Y(z) = X(z)\,z^2 - X(z)$$

The corresponding linear difference equation is

$$y(n) = x(n+2) - x(n)$$

The $x(n+2)$ term means that a sample value must exist 2 sampling instants before time $t = 0$, which correspondingly means that the above linear difference equation is impossible to realise. To overcome this difficulty we introduce a double pole at $z = 0$, see Figure 4.5:

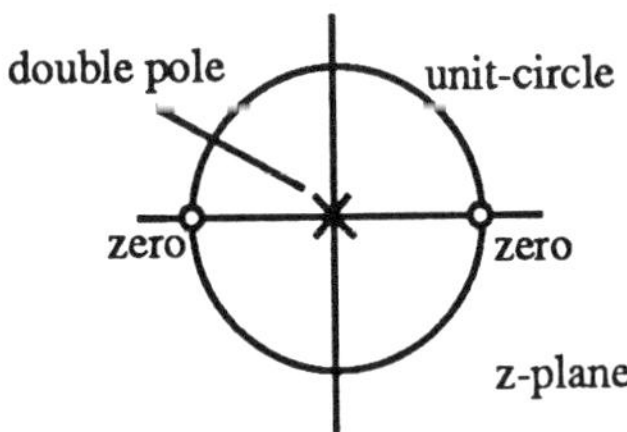

Figure 4.5 Double pole added to make comb filter realisable

The resulting transfer function is

$$G(z) = \frac{z^2 - 1}{z^2} = 1 - z^{-2} = \frac{Y(z)}{X(z)}$$

The corresponding linear difference equation is

$$y(n) = x(n) - x(n-2)$$

Recall that the transfer function of an FIR filter may be expressed as

$$G(z) = A_0 + A_1 z^{-1} + A_2 z^{-2} + A_3 z^{-3} + \ldots$$

For $G(z) = 1 - z^{-2}$, $A_0 = 1$ and $A_2 = -1$ and all other coefficients are zero. The corresponding frequency response is shown in Figure 4.6.

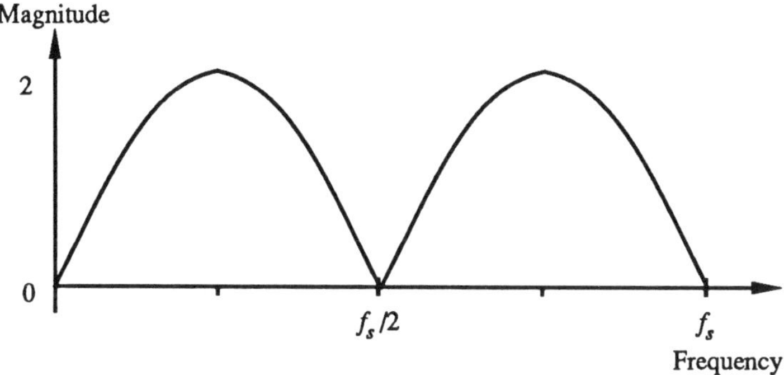

Figure 4.6 Frequency response characteristic of 2nd-order comb filter

A kth-order comb filter has k nulls (and k peaks) in the frequency range 0 to f_s Hz (see Figures 4.3 and 4.6). These are produced by k equally spaced zeros placed on the circumference of the unit-circle in the z-plane. Placement of a kth-order pole at the origin of the unit-circle is required to make the comb filter realisable. The corresponding transfer function of the comb filter is

$$G(z) = 1 - z^{-k} \tag{4.6}$$

Therefore the linear difference equation of the kth-order comb filter is

$$y(n) = x(n) - x(n-k) \tag{4.7}$$

❖ **WE 4.4**

Given that the transfer function of a comb filter is $G(z) = 1 - z^{-3}$, (i) draw the pole/zero diagram of the filter, (ii) verify that the pole/zero representation corresponds to the given transfer function, and (iii) plot the filter's magnitude/frequency characteristic.

Solution:

(i) The filter pole/zero diagram is

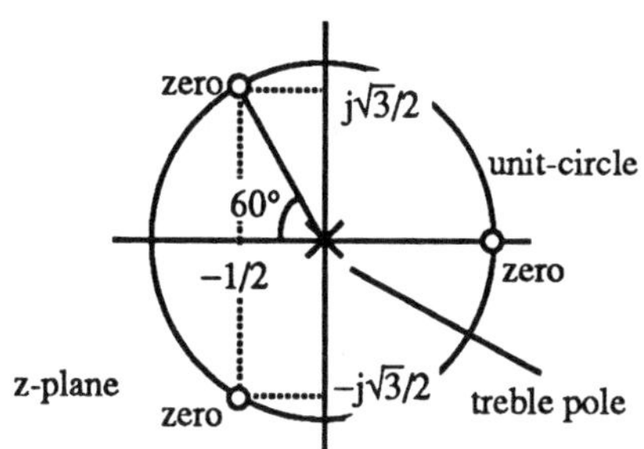

(ii) Using the pole/zero diagram the transfer function may be written as

$$G(z) = \frac{(z-1)\left(z+\frac{1}{2}-j\frac{\sqrt{3}}{2}\right)\left(z+\frac{1}{2}+j\frac{\sqrt{3}}{2}\right)}{z^3}$$

$$= \frac{(z-1)(z^2+z+1)}{z^3} = \frac{z^3-1}{z^3}$$

$\therefore \quad G(z) = 1 - z^{-3}$

(iii) The filter's magnitude/frequency response characteristic is shown below:

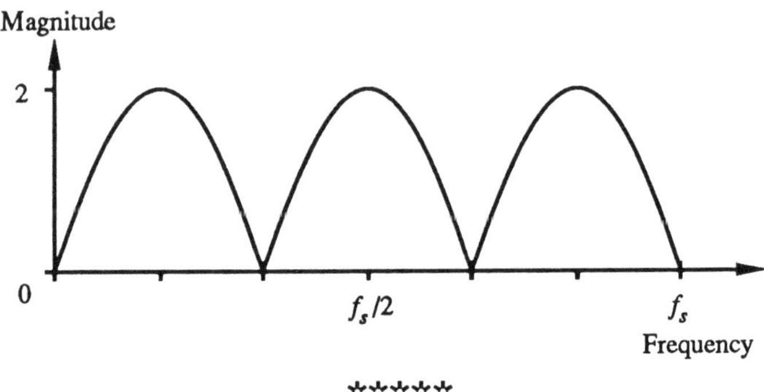

*****

4.3 IIR Digital Filters

Infinite impulse response (IIR) digital filters are ***recursive*** in form (defined by equation (2.23) and shown in block diagram form in Figure 2.2), and one simple approach based on the placement of poles and zeros in the z-plane was used in the case study presented in Section 2.7 to design an IIR notch filter. There are two other main approaches to the design of IIR filters. One method is the ***indirect approach,*** which transforms a prototype analogue filter transfer function, $G(s)$, to an equivalent digital filter transfer function, $G(z)$. In this context, the s to z mappings used in this chapter are: (a) the standard z-transform (impulse invariant), (b) the bilinear z-transform, and (c) the matched z-transform. The other method is the ***direct approach*** to the derivation of $G(z)$, which is applicable to the design of frequency sampling filters and filters based on squared magnitude functions.

4.3.1 Designs Based on Prototype Analogue Filters

The main steps involved in this design method are:

Analogue filter specification

⇓

(1) derive a realisable transfer function $G(s)$

⇓

(2) z-transform $G(s)$ to $G(z)$

Step (1) involves the design of the prototype analogue filter, and since Butterworth and Chebyshev analogue filters are commonly used for this purpose, the design of both types will be described.

4.3.1.1 Butterworth Normalised Lowpass Filter

The magnitude-squared response of a Butterworth normalised lowpass filter of order n is defined as

$$|G(j\,\omega)|^2 = \frac{1}{1+\left(\frac{\omega}{\omega_c}\right)^{2n}}, \text{ where } \omega_c \text{ is the radian cut-off frequency.}$$

$$\text{Attenuation } (-X\text{ dB}) = 10\log_{10}|G(j\,\omega)|^2$$

$$= 10\log_{10}1 - 10\log_{10}\left[1+\left(\frac{\omega}{\omega_c}\right)^{2n}\right]$$

$$\therefore \quad X\text{ dB} = 10\log_{10}\left[1+\left(\frac{\omega}{\omega_c}\right)^{2n}\right] \tag{4.8}$$

Thus if X dB attenuation is specified at a particular stopband frequency, ω, and if ω_c is given, then the order of filter complexity, n, may be calculated.

Once the value of n is known, then the positions of the s-plane Butterworth poles may be determined. For $1 \le n \le 6$, the pole locations for the case when $\omega_c = 1$ may be obtained from Table 4.1.

$n=1$	$n=2$	$n=3$	$n=4$	$n=5$	$n=6$
−1.0000000	−0.7071068	−1.0000000	−0.3826834	−1.0000000	−0.2588190
	±j0.7071068		±j0.9238795		±j0.9659258
		−0.5000000	−0.9238795	−0.3090170	−0.7071068
		±j0.8660254	±j0.3826834	±j0.9510565	±j0.7071068
				−0.8090170	−0.9659258
				±j0.5877852	±j0.2588190

Table 4.1

In general, if the angle of the kth pole is denoted by ϕ_k, where $k = 0, 1, 2, \ldots, (2n-1)$, and located on the circumference of the unit-circle in the s-plane, then

$$\phi_k = \left.\frac{k\pi}{n}\right|_{n\ \text{odd}} \quad \text{or} \quad \phi_k = \left.\frac{\left(k+\frac{1}{2}\right)\pi}{n}\right|_{n\ \text{even}}$$

However, only the poles in the left-hand half of the s-plane are used in deriving $G(s)$ (to preserve stability). Having determined the pole locations, the transfer function, $G(s)$, may be written down in the form

$$G(s) = \frac{1}{(s+p_1)(s+p_2)(s+p_3)\ldots(s+p_n)}$$

$$\therefore \quad G(s) = \frac{1}{a_n s^n + a_{n-1} s^{n-1} + \ldots + a_1 s + a_0} \tag{4.9}$$

For $1 \le n \le 6$, the denominator polynomial coefficients of the normalised Butterworth filter may be obtained from Table 4.2:

n	a_1	a_2	a_3	a_4	a_5	a_6
1	1.0000000					
2	1.4142136	1.0000000			$a_0 = 1$ for all n	
3	2.0000000	2.0000000	1.0000000			
4	2.6131259	3.4142136	2.6131259	1.0000000		
5	3.2360680	5.2360680	5.2360680	3.2360680	1.0000000	
6	3.8637033	7.4641016	9.1416202	7.4641016	3.8637033	1.0000000

Table 4.2

A normalised transfer function is converted to one with the required frequency characteristic via a technique known as **frequency denormalisation**. Referring to Table 4.3, ω_c is the desired radian cutoff frequency of the lowpass or highpass denormalised filter; ω_{cl} is the desired radian lower transition frequency of the bandstop or bandpass denormalised filter; ω_{cu} is the desired radian upper transition frequency of the bandstop or bandpass denormalised filter.

To transform from normalised lowpass to	Substitute for s in $G(s)$
Lowpass	$\dfrac{s}{\omega_c}$
Highpass	$\dfrac{\omega_c}{s}$
Bandstop	$\dfrac{s(\omega_{cu}-\omega_{cl})}{s^2+\omega_{cu}\omega_{cl}}$
Bandpass	$\dfrac{s^2+\omega_{cu}\omega_{cl}}{s(\omega_{cu}-\omega_{cl})}$

Table 4.3

❖ **WE 4.5**

Derive the transfer function for a Butterworth highpass filter with a magnitude/frequency response of (i) –3 dB attenuation at a frequency of 2 kHz, and (ii) at least –15 dB attenuation at a frequency of 1 kHz.

***Solution*:**

Firstly, the design is based on a normalised Butterworth lowpass prototype, and therefore the above specification must be translated to the corresponding lowpass case. That is, since the highpass filter stopband attenuation (–15 dB) is specified at a frequency (1 kHz) equal to half the cut-off frequency value, then this frequency ratio (1:2) is reversed in the translation to the lowpass prototype (2:1). Thus the magnitude/frequency response of the lowpass prototype becomes (i) –3 dB attenuation at a frequency of 1 kHz, and (ii) –15 dB attenuation at a frequency of 2 kHz.

The next step is to determine the required order of filter complexity.

Substituting the specified values in equation (4.8) gives

$$15 = 10 \log_{10}\left[1 + \left(\frac{2}{1}\right)^{2n}\right]$$

$$n = \frac{\log_{10}\{(\text{antilog}_{10} 1.5) - 1\}}{2 \log_{10} 2} \cong 2.47$$

$\therefore$ use $n = 3$

Now using Table 4.2 the transfer function of the required 3rd-order normalised Butterworth lowpass filter is determined as:

$$G(s)_N = \frac{1}{s^3 + 2s^2 + 2s + 1}$$

This transfer function is now denormalised (denoted by subscript *DN*) using the transform given in Table 4.3, i.e. $s \to \omega_c / s$, as follows:

$$\therefore \quad G(s)_{DN} = \frac{1}{\left(\frac{\omega_c}{s}\right)^3 + 2\left(\frac{\omega_c}{s}\right)^2 + 2\left(\frac{\omega_c}{s}\right) + 1}$$

$$\text{i.e.} \quad G(s)_{DN} = \frac{s^3}{s^3 + 2\omega_c s^2 + 2\omega_c^2 s + \omega_c^3}$$

but $\omega_c = 2\pi f_c = 2\pi \times 2 \times 10^3 = 4\pi \times 10^3$ rad/s

$$\therefore \quad G(s)_{DN} = \frac{s^3}{s^3 + 8\pi \times 10^3 s^2 + 32\pi^2 \times 10^6 s + 64\pi^3 \times 10^9}$$

The magnitude/frequency response may be checked as follows:

$$G(\mathrm{j}\,\omega)_{DN} = \frac{-\mathrm{j}\,\omega^3}{-\mathrm{j}\,\omega^3 - 8\pi \times 10^3 \omega^2 + \mathrm{j}\,32\pi^2 \times 10^6 \omega + 64\pi^3 \times 10^9}$$

$$= \frac{\omega^3}{\left(\omega^3 - 32\pi^2 \times 10^6 \omega\right) + \mathrm{j}\left(64\pi^3 \times 10^9 - 8\pi \times 10^3 \omega^2\right)}$$

but $\omega = 2\pi f$, and if f is expressed in kHz it follows that $G(\mathrm{j}\omega)_{DN}$ is

$$G(\mathrm{j}\,\omega)_{DN} = \frac{8\pi^3 10^9 f^3}{\left(8\pi^3 10^9 f^3\right) - \left(64\pi^3 10^9 f\right) + \mathrm{j}\left(64\pi^3 10^9 - 32\pi^3 10^9 f^2\right)}$$

$$= \frac{f^3}{\left(f^3 - 8f\right) + \mathrm{j}\left(8 - 4f^2\right)}$$

$$\therefore \quad \left|G(j\omega)_{DN}\right| = \frac{f^3}{\sqrt{f^6 + 64}}$$

The corresponding magnitude/frequency characteristic is shown in Figure 4.7:

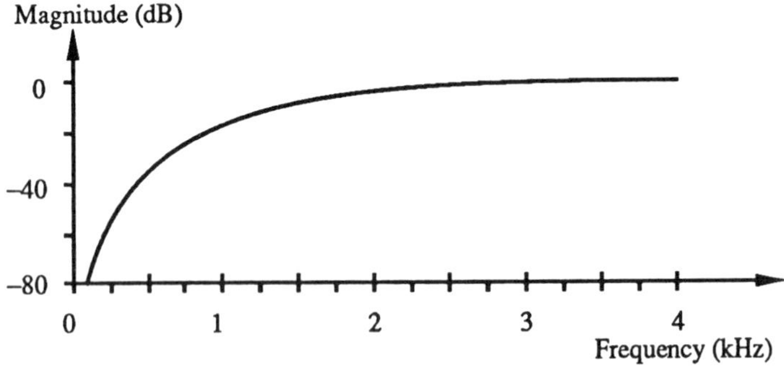

Figure 4.7 Magnitude/frequency characteristic

*****

4.3.1.2 Chebyshev Normalised Lowpass Filter

The magnitude-squared response of a Chebyshev normalised lowpass filter of order n is defined as

$$|G(j\,\omega)|^2 = \frac{1}{1+\varepsilon^2\left[C_n\left(\frac{\omega}{\omega_c}\right)\right]^2}$$

where ω_c is the cutoff frequency, ε is the ripple factor (which is real and <1), and $C_n\,(\omega/\omega_c)$ is an nth-order Chebyshev cosine polynomial.

Taking $\omega_c = 1$ (the usual value for the normalised frequency scale), then the Chebyshev cosine polynomial is defined as

$$C_n(\omega) = \begin{cases} \cos\left(n\cos^{-1}\omega\right)\Big|_{\omega\le 1} \\ \cosh\left(n\cosh^{-1}\omega\right)\Big|_{\omega > 1} \end{cases}$$

when $n = 0$ we have $C_0(\omega) = 1$, and when $n = 1$ we have $C_1(\omega) = \omega$. Higher order polynomials may be determined using the relationship

$$C_n(\omega) = 2\omega C_{n-1}(\omega) - C_{n-2}(\omega)$$

In the stopband a frequency, ω_{sb}, exists whereby the condition $\varepsilon^2[C_n(\omega)]^2 >> 1$ is satisfied, and then we may deduce that

$$|G(j\,\omega)| \cong \left.\frac{1}{\varepsilon\times C_n(\omega)}\right|_{\omega\ge\omega_{sb}}$$

$$\text{Attenuation}\quad(-X\,\mathrm{dB}) = 20\log_{10}|G(j\,\omega)|$$

$$= 20\log_{10}\left[\varepsilon\times C_n(\omega)\right]^{-1}$$

$$\therefore\quad X\,\mathrm{dB} = 20\log_{10}\varepsilon + 20\log_{10}C_n(\omega)$$

For large values of ω (in the stopband) $C_n(\omega) \cong 2^{n-1}\times\omega^n$.

$$\therefore \quad X\,\mathrm{dB} \cong 20\ \log_{10} \varepsilon + 20\ \log_{10}\left(2^{n-1} \times \omega^{n}\right)$$

$$= 20\ \log_{10} \varepsilon + \left[(n-1) \times 20\ \log_{10} 2\right] + 20\, n \log_{10} \omega$$

$$\text{i. e.} \quad X\,\mathrm{dB} \cong 20\ \log_{10} \varepsilon + 6(n-1) + 20\, n \log_{10} \omega \tag{4.10}$$

Thus if the maximum passband ripple is specified, the corresponding value of ε may be calculated, and if X dB is specified at a particular stopband frequency, ω, then the order of filter complexity, n, may be calculated.

Once the value of n is known, then the positions of the s-plane Chebyshev poles may be determined. A straightforward way of achieving this is to firstly determine the position of the nth-order Butterworth poles, and then translate them to corresponding nth-order Chebyshev poles. This is possible because there is a geometrical relationship between the Butterworth pole positions and the Chebyshev pole positions in the s-plane.

A design parameter is defined as $A = \frac{1}{n} \sinh^{-1}\left(\frac{1}{\varepsilon}\right)$ and is used as follows.

$$\mathrm{Re}\ [\mathrm{Chebyshev}]_{P2} = \mathrm{Re}\ [\mathrm{Butterworth}]_{P1} \times \tanh A \tag{4.11}$$

$$\mathrm{Im}\ [\mathrm{Chebyshev}]_{P2} = \mathrm{Im}\ [\mathrm{Butterworth}]_{P1} \tag{4.12}$$

$$[\mathrm{Chebyshev}]_{P3} = [\mathrm{Chebyshev}]_{P2} \times \cosh A \tag{4.13}$$

The translational relationships defined by equations (4.11), (4.12) and (4.13) are illustrated in Figure 4.8. The translation P1 to P2 corresponds to using equations (4.11) and (4.12); the translation from P2 to P3 is achieved using equation (4.13). The result is an overall translation of the normalised Butterworth lowpass filter pole at P1 to a normalised Chebyshev lowpass filter pole at P3.

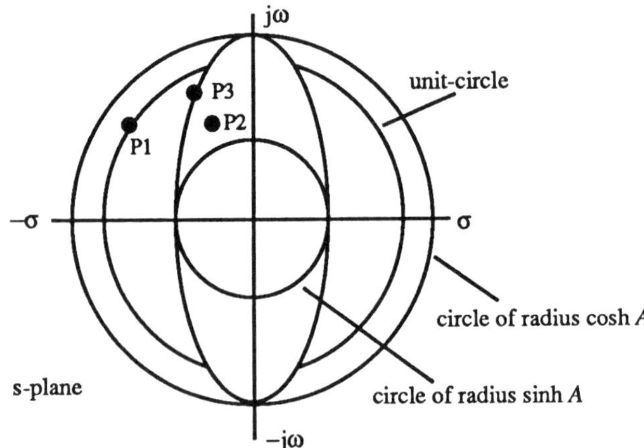

Figure 4.8 Translation of Butterworth pole position (P1) to Chebyshev pole postion (P3)

❖ WE 4.6

Derive the transfer function of a denormalised Chebyshev lowpass filter with a magnitude/frequency response conforming to (i) 0.5 dB passband ripple, (ii) stopband attenuation of at least 20 dB at 10 kHz, and (iii) a cutoff frequency equal to 2 kHz.

Solution:

At $\omega = 1,\quad \left|G(j\,1)\right| = -0.5\ \mathrm{dB} = 20\ \log_{10} \dfrac{1}{\sqrt{1+\varepsilon^2}}$

$$\therefore\quad -0.5 = 20\ \log_{10} 1 - 20\ \log_{10} \sqrt{1+\varepsilon^2}$$

$$\text{i.e.}\quad 0.5 = 10\ \log_{10}\left(1+\varepsilon^2\right)$$

$$\therefore\quad \varepsilon = \sqrt{10^{0.05} - 1} = 0.3493$$

Substituting this value and the specified values in equation (4.10) gives

$$20 = 20\ \log_{10} 0.3493 + 6(n-1) + 20\,n\ \log_{10} 5$$

$$\therefore\quad n \cong 1.76, \qquad \text{i.e.}\quad \text{use}\ n = 2$$

$$A = \frac{1}{2}\sinh^{-1}\left(\frac{1}{0.3493}\right) = 0.8871$$

$$\therefore\quad \tanh A = 0.71 \quad \text{and} \quad \cosh A = 1.42$$

Butterworth poles for $n = 2$:

$$k = 0, 1, 2 \text{ and } 3, \quad \therefore \phi_0 = \frac{\pi}{4}, \phi_1 = \frac{3\pi}{4}, \phi_2 = \frac{5\pi}{4} \text{ and } \phi_3 = \frac{7\pi}{4}$$

These normalised Butterworth lowpass filter pole positions are shown in Figure 4.9.

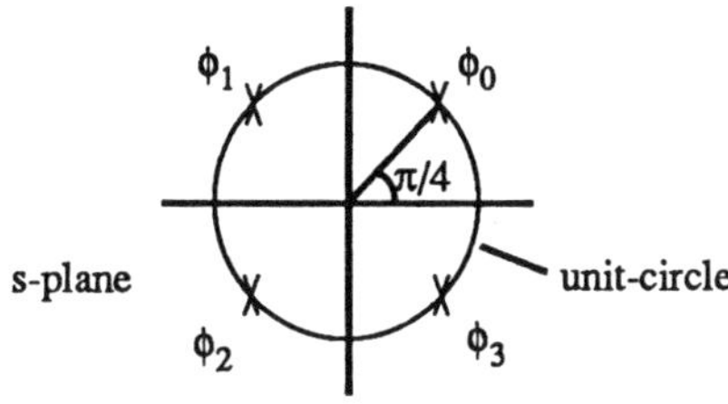

Figure 4.9 Butterworth pole positions for $n = 2$

For a stable transfer function we only use ϕ_1 and ϕ_2:

$$\phi_1 \text{ is located at } -\frac{1}{\sqrt{2}} + \mathrm{j}\,\frac{1}{\sqrt{2}}, \text{ and}$$

$$\phi_2 \text{ is located at } -\frac{1}{\sqrt{2}} - \mathrm{j}\,\frac{1}{\sqrt{2}}$$

$$\text{Re [Chebyshev]}_{P2} = -\frac{1}{\sqrt{2}} \times 0.71 \cong -\frac{1}{2}$$

$$\text{Im [Chebyshev]}_{P2} = \pm\,\mathrm{j}\,\frac{1}{\sqrt{2}}$$

$$\text{Re [Chebyshev]}_{P3} = -\frac{1}{2} \times 1.42 \cong -\frac{1}{\sqrt{2}}$$

$$\text{Im [Chebyshev]}_{P3} = \pm\,\mathrm{j}\,\frac{1}{\sqrt{2}} \times 1.42 \cong \pm\,\mathrm{j}$$

$$\therefore \quad G(s)_N = \frac{1}{\left(s + \frac{1}{\sqrt{2}} + \mathrm{j}\right)\left(s + \frac{1}{\sqrt{2}} - \mathrm{j}\right)} = \frac{1}{s^2 + \sqrt{2}\,s + \frac{3}{2}}$$

Denormalising by $s \rightarrow s/\omega_c$ gives

$$G(s)_{DN} = \frac{1}{\frac{s^2}{\omega_c^{\,2}} + \frac{\sqrt{2}\,s}{\omega_c} + \frac{3}{2}} = \frac{\omega_c^{\,2}}{s^2 + \sqrt{2}\,\omega_c\,s + \frac{3}{2}\,\omega_c^{\,2}}$$

$$\text{but } \omega_c = 2\,\pi\,f_c = 2\pi \times 2 \times 10^3 = 4\,\pi \times 10^3 \text{ rad/s}$$

$$\therefore \quad G(s)_{DN} = \frac{16\,\pi^2 \times 10^6}{s^2 + 4\sqrt{2}\,\pi \times 10^3 s + 24\,\pi^2 \times 10^6} \tag{4.14}$$

The magnitude/frequency characteristic may be checked as follows:

$$G(\mathrm{j}\,\omega)_{DN} = \frac{16\,\pi^2 \times 10^6}{\left(24\,\pi^2 \times 10^6 - \omega^2\right) + \mathrm{j}\left(4\sqrt{2}\,\pi \times 10^3 \omega\right)}$$

where $\omega = 2\,\pi f$, and if f is expressed in kHz we may write

$$G(j\,\omega)_{DN} = \frac{16\,\pi^2 10^6}{\left(24\,\pi^2 10^6 - 4\,\pi^2 10^6 f^2\right) + j\left(4\sqrt{2}\,\pi\,10^3 \times 2\pi\,10^3 f\right)}$$

$$= \frac{4}{\left(6 - f^2\right) + j\left(2\sqrt{2}\,f\right)}$$

$$\therefore \quad \left|G(j\,\omega)_{DN}\right| = \frac{4}{\sqrt{f^4 - 4\,f^2 + 36}}$$

at $f = 0,\ \left|G(j\,0)_{DN}\right| = 0.6667$

However, the specification requires $|G(j0)_{DN}| = 0.944$ (– 0.5 dB), consequently it is necessary to introduce a gain term, k, into the transfer function to achieve this.

$$\therefore \quad k = \frac{0.944}{0.6667} = 1.416$$

$$\therefore \quad \left|G(j\,\omega)_{DN}\right| = \frac{4 \times 1.416}{\sqrt{f^4 - 4\,f^2 + 36}}$$

The corresponding magnitude/frequency characteristic is shown in Figure 4.10, and it is seen that the derived transfer function has the desired magnitude/frequency characteristic.

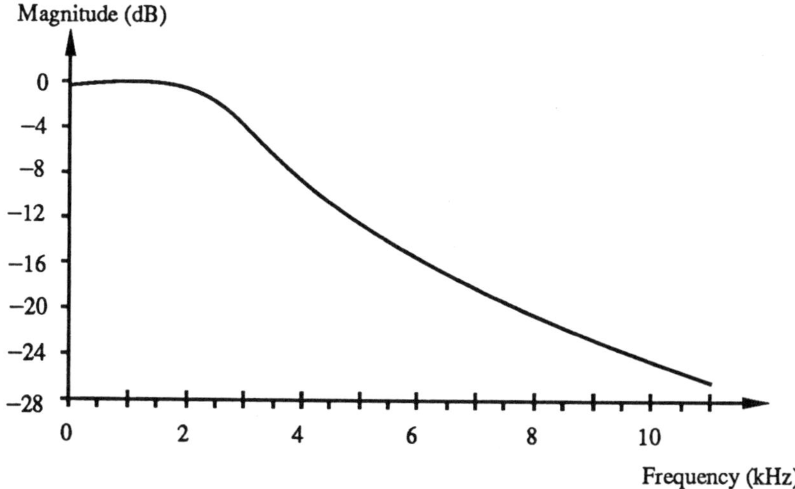

Figure 4.10 Chebyshev filter magnitude/frequency characteristic

Having derived the required $G(s)_{DN}$, the corresponding $G(z)$ may be determined using one of the s-plane to z-plane transformation methods described in the following sections of this chapter.

*****

4.3.2 Impulse-Invariant Design Method

The prototype filter, with transfer function $G(s)_{DN}$ has an impulse response, $g(t)$, defined by $\mathbf{L}^{-1}[G(s)_{DN}]$, and if we consider $G(s)_{DN}$ to have m simple poles, then it follows that

$$g(t) = \mathbf{L}^{-1}\left[\sum_{i=1}^{m} \frac{c_i}{s+p_i}\right] = \sum_{i=1}^{m} c_i \, e^{-p_i t}$$

For the impulse-invariant design method the digital filter is required, at the sampling instants, to have impulse response values equal to the prototype filter's impulse response, i.e. $g(n) = g(t)$ for $t = nT$, where T is the sampling period, therefore

$$g(n) = \sum_{i=1}^{m} c_i \, e^{-p_i nT} \tag{4.15}$$

Obtaining the standard z-transform of equation (4.15) and multiplying the result by T yields

$$G_T(z) = T \times G(z) = T \times \sum_{i=1}^{m} c_i \left[\frac{z}{z - e^{-p_i T}}\right] \tag{4.16}$$

Multiplying the standard z-transform, $G(z)$, by T ensures that the frequency spectra of the sampled signal, $x^*(t)$, are amplitude scaled to adequately represent the amplitudes of frequency components in the original baseband spectrum of $x(t)$. This was discussed in detail in Section 2.4.2.

❖ **WE 4.7**

Apply the impulse-invariant design method to the Chebyshev lowpass filter defined by equation (4.14).

Solution:

Equation (4.14) may be re-written in the form

$$G(s)_{DN} = 4\pi \times 10^3 \left[\frac{4\pi \times 10^3}{\left(s + 2\sqrt{2}\pi \times 10^3\right)^2 + \left(4\pi \times 10^3\right)^2}\right] \tag{4.17}$$

We may now apply the standard z-transform to equation (4.17) to obtain the corresponding $G(z)$. The z-transform used (Table 2.2) in this case is

$$\frac{\beta}{(s+\alpha)^2+\beta^2} \rightarrow \frac{z\,e^{-\alpha T}\sin\beta T}{z^2-2z\,e^{-\alpha T}\cos\beta T+e^{-2\alpha T}}$$

Therefore the transfer function of the equivalent impulse-invariant digital filter is

$$G_T(z) = G(z) \times T$$

$$= T\left[\frac{4\pi 10^3 z\,e^{-2\sqrt{2}\,\pi 10^3 T}\sin 4\pi 10^3 T}{z^2-2z\,e^{-2\sqrt{2}\,\pi 10^3 T}\cos 4\pi 10^3 T+e^{-4\sqrt{2}\,\pi 10^3 T}}\right] \quad (4.18)$$

*****

4.3.3 *Bilinear z-Transform Design Method*

This is a commonly used design method which is described in section 2.5 and illustrated in WE2.26. The main steps involved in the IIR filter design using this method are:

(a) Derive a realisable normalised transfer function $G(s)$ of a prototype filter having the specified frequency response characteristic (e.g. as illustrated in WE4.5).

(b) Calculate the pre-warped frequency value(s), $\omega_a = (2/T)[\tan(\omega_d T/2)]$, and using the appropriate transform in Table 4.3 derive the pre-warped denormalised transfer function $G(s)_{PWDN}$.

(c) Derive $G(z)$ by substituting $(2/T)[(z-1)/(z+1)]$ for s in $G(s)_{PWDN}$.

The following worked example illustrates the above steps.

❖ **WE 4.8**

Derive the transfer function $G(z)$ of an IIR digital filter having a magnitude/frequency characteristic equivalent to that of the Butterworth highpass filter specified in WE4.5. The sampling frequency is 8 kHz. Plot the magnitude/frequency characteristic to confirm that the specification is satisfied.

Solution:

From WE4.5 we know that

$$G(s)_{DN} = \frac{s^3}{s^3+2\omega_c s^2+2\omega_c^2 s+\omega_c^3}$$

The radian cutoff frequency of the digital filter is

$$\omega_{cd} = 2\pi \times 2000 = 4000\,\pi \text{ radians per second}$$

$$f_s = 8000 \text{ Hz}, \quad \text{therefore} \quad T = 125\mu\, s$$

The pre-warped value is

$$\omega_{ca} = \frac{2 \times 10^6}{125}\left[\tan\left(\frac{4000\,\pi \times 125 \times 10^{-6}}{2}\right)\right]$$

$$= 16000 \text{ radians per second}$$

Substituting this value in $G(s)_{DN}$ yields

$$G(s)_{PWDN} = \frac{s^3}{s^3 + 32000\, s^2 + 2(16000)^2 s + (16000)^3}$$

For the bilinear z-transform s is replaced with

$$\frac{2 \times 10^6}{125}\left[\frac{z-1}{z+1}\right] = 16000\left[\frac{z-1}{z+1}\right]$$

that is

$$G(z) = \frac{\dfrac{(16000)^3 (z-1)^3}{(z+1)^3}}{\left\{\dfrac{(16000)^3 (z-1)^3}{(z+1)^3} + \dfrac{32000(16000)^2 (z-1)^2}{(z+1)^2} + \dfrac{2(16000)^2\, 16000(z-1)}{(z+1)} + (16000)^3\right\}}$$

$$= \frac{(z-1)^3}{(z-1)^3 + 2(z-1)^2 (z+1) + 2(z-1)(z+1)^2 + (z+1)^3}$$

$$\therefore \quad G(z) = \frac{1 - 3z^{-1} + 3z^{-2} - z^{-3}}{6 + 2z^{-2}} = \frac{0.167 - 0.5\,z^{-1} + 0.5\,z^{-2} - 0.167\,z^{-}}{1 + 0.333z^{-2}}$$

The magnitude/frequency characteristic of this IIR filter is shown below:

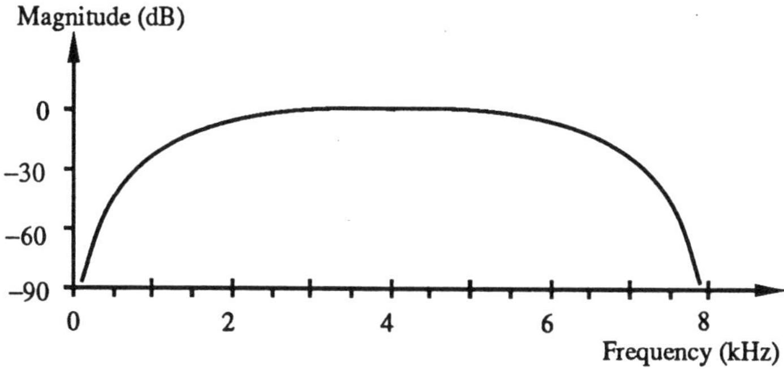

It is seen that the derived IIR digital filter has the specified highpass filter characteristic.

*****

4.3.4 Matched z-Transform Design Method

The matched z-transform method directly maps the s-plane poles and zeros of $G(s)$ to corresponding poles and zeros in the z-plane.

Real s-plane poles/zeros are mapped using the following relationship

$$(s+\alpha) \rightarrow (1 - e^{-\alpha T} z^{-1})$$

Complex s-plane poles/zeros are mapped using

$$(s+\alpha)^2 + \beta^2 \rightarrow [1 - (2\,e^{-\alpha T} \cos \beta T)\, z^{-1} + e^{-2\alpha T} z^{-2}]$$

❖ **WE 4.9**

Using the matched z-transform design method derive the transfer function $G(z)$ for the Chebyshev prototype filter defined in equation (4.17).

***Solution*:**

The transfer function of the second-order Chebyshev filter defined by equation (4.17) simply transforms to

$$G(z) = 4\pi\, 10^3 \left[\frac{4\pi\, 10^3\, z^2}{z^2 - 2\, z\, e^{-2\sqrt{2}\,\pi 10^3 T} \cos 4\pi 10^3 T + e^{-4\sqrt{2}\,\pi 10^3 T}} \right]$$

This particular transfer function may be usefully compared to that derived for the impulse-invariant design method, see equation (4.18). The poles are identical, but the multiplication factor is different and the order of complexity of zeros is increased by one.

*****

4.3.5 (sin *x*)/*x* *Digital Correction Filter*

It was explained in Section 1.3 that D/A amplitude distortion can be reduced by using a (sin *x*)/*x* digital correction filter placed before the D/A converter. A practical first-order (sin *x*)/*x* correction filter has a digital transfer function of the form

$$G_T(z) = G(z) \times T = \frac{\alpha z}{z + \beta} \times T = \frac{Y(z)}{X(z)} \tag{4.19}$$

The corresponding frequency response function is

$$G_T(e^{j\omega T}) = \frac{\alpha e^{j\omega T}}{e^{j\omega T} + \beta} \times T$$

$$= \frac{\alpha(\cos \omega T + j \sin \omega T)}{(\cos \omega T + j\sin \omega T) + \beta} \times T$$

and the magnitude/frequency characteristic is

$$\left| G_T(e^{j\omega T}) \right| = \frac{\alpha}{\sqrt{1 + 2\beta \cos \omega T + \beta^2}} \times T \tag{4.20}$$

The (sin *x*)/*x* correction filter should have a magnitude/frequency characteristic which is the inverse of the magnitude/frequency characteristic of the D/A zero-order hold linear filter, as shown in Figure 4.11.

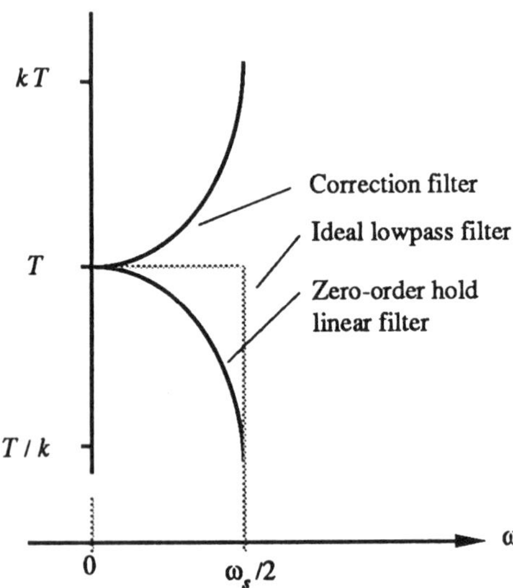

Figure 4.11 Correction filter magnitude/frequency characteristic

The gain term α and the pole location $z = -\beta$ can be evaluated by considering the required performance of the correction fiter at two specified frequencies, namely at $\omega = 0$ and at $\omega = \omega_s/2$. Considering each case in turn gives:

(i) For $\omega = 0$:

$$\left|G_T\left(e^{j\omega T}\right)\right| = \frac{\alpha}{1+\beta} \times T$$

and it may be seen from Figure 4.11 that at this frequency value the magnitude frequency response function is required to have a value of T, i.e.

$$\alpha = 1 + \beta \tag{4.21}$$

(ii) For $\omega = \omega_s/2$:

$$\left|G_T\left(e^{j\omega T}\right)\right| = \frac{\alpha}{1-\beta} \times T$$

and it may be seen from Figure 4.11 that at this frequency value this magnitude frequency response function is required to have a value of kT, i.e.

$$\alpha = k(1-\beta) \tag{4.22}$$

From equations (4.21) and (4.22) it follows that

$$1+\beta = k(1-\beta)$$

$$\therefore \beta = \frac{k-1}{k+1} \tag{4.23}$$

Using equation (1.18) it can be verified that the value of k is $\pi/2$ when $\omega = \omega_s/2$, and correspondingly using equations (4.23) and (4.21) respectively yields

$$\beta = \frac{\frac{\pi}{2} - 1}{\frac{\pi}{2} + 1} = 0.222$$

$$\alpha = 1 + \beta = 1.222$$

Therefore substituting these values in equation (4.19) the digital transfer function of the correction filter is

$$G_T(z) = \frac{1.222\ z}{z + 0.222} \times T$$

and the corresponding magnitude/frequency characteristic is

$$\left|G_T\left(e^{j\omega T}\right)\right| = \frac{1.222}{\sqrt{1 + 0.444\cos\omega T + (0.222)^2}} \times T \qquad (4.24)$$

The magnitude/frequency characteristic of this correction filter is shown in Figure 4.12.

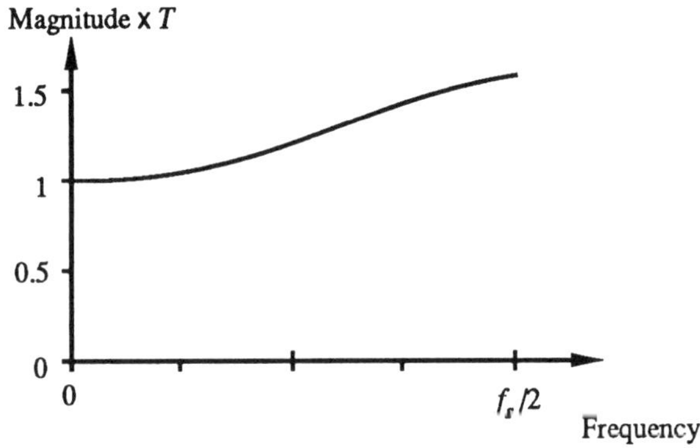

Figure 4.12 Correction filter magnitude/frequency characteristic

❖ WE 4.10

For an input signal containing two sinusoidal components at 500Hz and 750 Hz each having a respective amplitude value of 0.5 V and 0.1 V, the D/A converter produces amplitude attenutaion such that the amplitudes are correspondingly reduced to 0.4716 V and 0.09003 V (these values can be verified using equation (1.18)). The amplitude attenuation is to be compensated by a (sin x)/x digital correction filter placed before the D/A converter. Determine the amplitude value of each sinusoidal component at the output of the D/A converter. The sampling frequency is 8 kHz.

***Solution*:**

The sampling period $T = 1/8000 = 125 \times 10^{-6}$ s. There are two sinusoidal components under consideration. Using equation (4.24) the gain introduced by the correction filter is

(i) $f = 1500$ Hz:

$$\left|G_T\left(e^{j\omega T}\right)\right| = \frac{1.222 \times T}{\sqrt{1 + 0.444\cos\left(2\pi \times 1500 \times 125 \times 10^{-6}\right) + (0.222)^2}}$$

$$= 1.1067 \times T$$

(ii) $f = 2000$ Hz:

$$\left|G_T\left(e^{j\omega T}\right)\right| = \frac{1.222 \times T}{\sqrt{1 + 0.444\cos\left(2\pi \times 2000 \times 125 \times 10^{-6}\right) + (0.222)^2}}$$

$$= 1.193 \times T$$

Since $|G_T(e^{j\omega T})| = T$ corresponds to zero attenuation, the output values produced by the correction filter corresponding to the 1.5 kHz and 2 kHz sinusoidal components are, respectively, $0.4716 \times 1.1067 = 0.522$ V and $0.0900 \times 1.193 = 0.1074$ V.

Note that some degree of correction has been achieved using the filter since the component amplitude values 0.522 V and 0.1074 V are, respectively, closer to the ideal values 0.5 V and 0.1 V (the uncorrected amplitude values are 0.4716 V and 0.0900 V).

*****

4.4 Quantisation and Rounding Problems

All operations in digital filters are performed with discrete value representations, and consequently they are characteristically approximate procedures. If the approximations are too coarse or of a particular form, the errors involved can lead to inaccuracies which seriously impair the performance of the DSP system. The main sources of error are:

(i) Quantisation due to resolving the input sequence, $x(n)$, into a set of discrete levels (see Section 1.2).

(ii) Quantisation due to limits in the precision available to represent filter coefficient values. This source of error may be particularly significant when fixed-point DSP processors are used to implement the filter. However, this is not generally a problem when 32-bit (or greater) floating-point processors are used.

(iii) Arithmetic operations involving number rounding/truncation, or the rounding of computation results.

A basic understanding of these sources of error enables a DSP system designer to estimate the minimum number of bits required to form a word length in the filter implementation. This knowledge allows the designer to make informed decisions concerning trade-offs between hardware costs and DSP system performance.

4.4.1 Quantisation of the Input Signal

The continuous input signal is sampled using an A/D converter and produces a set of fixed-point binary number representations corresponding to the set of input samples (see Section 1.2). The probability density function corresponding to A/D round-off quantisation errors is generally assumed to be uniform (any error value has an equal chance of being anywhere in the range –Q/2 to +Q/2, where Q is the quantisation interval). Referring to equations (1.7) and (1.11), and assuming a normalised full-sacle voltage range, the mean-square error (variance or quantisation noise power) is

$$\sigma_q^2 = \frac{Q^2}{12} = \frac{1}{12\left(2^b - 1\right)^2} \qquad (4.25)$$

By modelling the quantisation error introduced by the A/D converter as an additive noise input source, $e(n)$, the input to the digital filter is

$$x(n)\big|_Q = x(n) + e(n) \qquad (4.26)$$

However, in practice, if the amplitude of the input signal exceeds the dynamic range of the A/D converter, the signal amplitude should be reduced to eliminate clipping. To accommodate this, the model of the quantisation process includes a scaling factor, F, such that

$$x(n)\big|_Q = F\,x(n) + e(n) \qquad (4.27)$$

where F lies in the range 0 to 1. In this case, and assuming that the quantisation errors are due to rounding, the signal-to-noise ratio is

$$\text{SNR} = 10\log_{10}\left[\frac{F^2\sigma_n^2}{\sigma_q^2}\right]\ \text{dB} \qquad (4.28)$$

where $F^2\sigma_n^2$ is the variance (average signal power) of $F\,x(n)$. As a *rule-of-thumb*, for negligible clipping, F is generally set equal to $1/(5\sigma_n)$, and for this case it follows that

$$\text{SNR} = 10\log_{10}\left[\frac{1}{25\,\sigma_q^2}\right]\ \text{dB} \qquad (4.29)$$

For $2^b >> 1$, substituting equation (4.25) in equation (4.29) gives

$$\text{SNR} \cong (6n - 3.2)\,\text{dB} \tag{4.30}$$

From equation (4.30) it is seen that the signal-to-noise ratio increases by 6 dB for each additional bit added to the A/D converter word length.

The noise power at the filter output due to quantisation of the input signal produced by the A/D converter can be determined using Parseval's theorem for discrete systems, that is

$$(\sigma_0)^2 = \frac{Q^2}{12} \times \frac{1}{j2\pi} \oint G(z)\, G^*(z) \frac{dz}{z} = \frac{Q^2}{12} \sum_{n=0}^{\infty} [g(n)]^2 \tag{4.31}$$

The significance of equation (4.31) is demonstrated in the following worked example.

❖ **WE 4.11**

Suppose that a digital filter has the transfer finction, $G(z) = z/(z - \alpha)$, where $|\alpha| < 1$. Show that the pole location (filter structure) has a significant influence on the noise power at the filter output due to quantisation of the input signal.

Solution:

The impulse response sequence $g(n)$ may be determined using the z-transform relationship $z/(z - \alpha) \Leftrightarrow \alpha^n$, and therefore using equation (4.31) we obtain

$$(\sigma_0)^2 = \frac{Q^2}{12} \sum_{n=0}^{\infty} [\alpha^n]^2 = \frac{Q^2}{12} (1 + \alpha^2 + \alpha^4 + \alpha^6 + \cdots) = \frac{Q^2}{12} \times \frac{1}{(1 - \alpha^2)}$$

It follows that as $\alpha^2 \to 1$ then $\sigma_0{}^2 \to \infty$, and as $\alpha^2 \to 0$ then $\sigma_0{}^2 \to Q^2/12$. Thus it is seen that the pole location has a significant influence on the noise power at the filter output due to quantisation of the input signal.

*****

4.4.2 Effect of Finite Word Length on Stability and Frequency Response

If one or more poles of a digital filter are located close to the circumference of the unit-circle in the z-plane, making $G(z)$ marginally stable, it is desirable to investigate how a small change in one of the transfer function denominator coefficients, b_j $(0 \le j \le q)$ (equation (2.22), page 88), may result in one or more poles moving outside the unit-circle, rendering the filter unstable.

If one of the filter coefficients, b_k, is changed to a new value equal to $b_k + \Delta b_k$ the transfer function denominator characteristic equation becomes

$$1 + \sum_{j=1}^{q} b_j z^{-j} + \Delta b_k z^{-k} = 0 \tag{4.32}$$

Assuming a stable $G(z)$, and that the sampling frequency is relatively high, then all poles will be inside the unit-circle close to $z = 1$, therefore we seek the value of Δb_k which takes a pole outside the unit-circle. Substituting this condition of $z = 1$ in equation (4.32) gives

$$\left|\Delta b_k\right| = 1 + \sum_{j=1}^{q} b_j \tag{4.33}$$

By comparing $|\Delta b_k|$ with the largest b_j coefficient the required number representation resolution may be determined, and thereby yielding the required minimum word length.

Based on the assumption that coefficient values are truncated rather than rounded, an alternative method of determining the processor word length to maintain stability for an Nth-order digital filter having distinct poles located in the z-plane at $(\cos \omega_k T - \mathrm{j} \sin \omega_k T)$, where $k = 1, 2, 3, \ldots, N$, is

$$n = \text{smallest integer exceeding} - \log_2 \left\{ \left[\frac{5\sqrt{N}}{2^{N+2}} \right] \prod_{k=1}^{N} \left| \omega_k T \right| \right\} \tag{4.34}$$

❖ **WE 4.12**

A digital filter designed by the impulse-invariant method, which is based on a prototype 2nd-order Butterworth lowpass filter with a cutoff frequency of 1 radian/second and a sampling frequency of 30.2 radians/second, has the transfer function $G(z) = z/(26.8\,z^2 - 45.6\,z + 20)$. Calculate the minimum word length to maintain stability, assuming that filter coefficients are (i) rounded, and (ii) truncated.

Solution:

(i) Consider the given transfer function:

$$G(z) = z/(26.8\,z^2 - 45.6\,z + 20) \cong 0.04\,z/(z^2 - 1.7\,z + 0.746)$$

Using equation (4.33) we obtain $|\Delta b_k| = 1 - 1.7 + 0.746 = 0.046$, and the corresponding quantisation interval is $2 \times |\Delta b_k| = 2 \times 0.046 = 0.092$. Now comparing this value with the largest coefficient value we obtain

$$\frac{1.7}{0.092} \leq 2^{(n-1)}$$

Thus the minimum word length to maintain stability is six ($n = 6$).

Note: If coefficients are truncated rather than rounded the calculated value of n obtained using the above method is increased by one, i.e. in this example n would be increased to equal seven (see part (ii) below).

(ii) Consider the given 2nd-order ($N = 2$) transfer function:

$$G(z) \cong 0.04\, z / (z^2 - 1.7\, z + 0.746)$$

$$= 0.04\, z / [(z - 0.85 + j\, 0.153)(z - 0.85 - j\, 0.153)]$$

since the poles are a complex conjugate pair, then

$$|\omega_1 T| = |\omega_2 T| = \tan^{-1}\left(\frac{0.153}{0.85}\right) = 0.178 \text{ radians}$$

Substituting $|\omega_1 T| = |\omega_2 T| = 0.178$ radians and $N = 2$ in equation (4.34) we obtain

$$n = \text{smallest integer exceeding } \left\{-\log_2\left[\frac{5\sqrt{2}}{2^{2+2}}\right](0.178)^2\right\}$$

$$= \text{smallest integer exceeding } \{-\log_2 (0.014)\}$$

that is, $2^n \geq \dfrac{1}{0.014} = 71.43, \quad \therefore n = 7.$

*****

As a *rule-of-thumb* the required frequency response precision is generally achieved by adding three or four bits to the word length value calculated for maintaining stability. However, it should be understood that these word length calculations are simple estimates only, and consequently, if possible, a few extra bits should be added to minimise rounding or truncation effects. Clearly there will be cost implications in using processors with longer word lengths, but these have to be weighed against the need to build adequate safety margins in the filter design to ensure that stability and specified performance is achieved when the filter is used in practice to process signals.

4.4.3 Arithmetic Errors

Arithmetic errors can arise when arithmetic-logic-unit (ALU) operations are performed. For example, the multiplication of two n-bit binary numbers produces a $2n$-bit product, which can be truncated to its n most significant bits for storage and further arithmetic. Another example is that of adding two n-bit fixed-point binary numbers which produces a result exceeding n bits, thereby creating a number *overflow* condition. When such quantities are used in successive or subsequent calculations the effect is cumulative, and large overall errors can build up. Consequently arithmetic errors, together with other sources of error, may lead to stability problems, unacceptable inaccuracy, limit cycle oscillations, or the deadband effect.

Limit cycle oscillations and the deadband effect correspond respectively to the phenomenon of a filter generating an oscillatory or fixed non-zero output, even when the filter input is zero-valued. The following worked example demonstrates the significance of arithmetic rounding when the input signal is zero-valued (which would be the case when a digital filter is placed in a telephone signal path and the speaker is pausing between words).

❖ **WE 4.13**

(a) An IIR digital filter has the transfer function $G(z) = z/(z - 0.93) = Y(z)/X(z)$. Assuming that (i) the input signal is zero-valued, (ii) the initial condition is $y(-1) = 11$, and (iii) computed $y(n)$ results are rounded to the nearest integer value (integer number resolution), show that under these stated conditions the filter output exhibits the deadband effect.

(b) Assuming (i) that the sign of the b_1 coefficient in the given transfer function is changed, (ii) the filter input is the impulse signal $\{12, 0, 0, \ldots\}$, (iii) the initial condition is $y(-1) = 0$, and (iv) computed $y(n)$ results are rounded to the nearest integer value, show that the filter output exhibits limit cycle oscillations.

Solution:

(a) The linear difference equation of the filter is

$$y(n) = x(n) + 0.93\, y(n-1)$$

but since the input signal is zero-valued it reduces to

$$y(n) = 0.93\, y(n-1)$$

This yields the following computations:

$$y(0) = 0.93\ y(-1) = 0.93 \times 11 = 10.23 \to 10$$

$$y(1) = 0.93\ y(0) \quad = 0.93 \times 10 = 9.3 \to 9$$

$$y(2) = 0.93\ y(1) \quad = 0.93 \times 9 = 8.37 \to 8$$

$$y(3) = 0.93\ y(2) \quad = 0.93 \times 8 = 7.44 \to 7$$

$$y(4) = 0.93\ y(3) \quad = 0.93 \times 7 = 6.51 \to 7$$

$$y(5) = 0.93\ y(4) \quad = 0.93 \times 7 = 6.51 \to 7$$

It is seen that the filter ouput reaches a steady value of 7. This is the deadband effect.

Any initial value in the range $-R \le y(-1) \le R$, where $R = 0.5/(1-|b_1|)$ rounded down to the nearest integer value, will produce a steady ouput value $y(n) = y(-1)$. If, however, $y(-1)$ is outside the range $-R \le y(-1) \le R$, the steady ouput value is equal to R if $y(-1)$ is positive, or alternatively the steady ouput value is equal to $-R$ if $y(-1)$ is negative.

(b) The linear difference equation of the filter is

$$y(n) = x(n) - 0.93\ y(n-1)$$

This yields the following computations:

$$y(0) = x(0) - 0.93\ y(-1) = 12 - 0.93 \times 0 = 12 \to 12$$

$$y(1) = -0.93\ y(0) \quad = -0.93 \times 12 = -11.16 \to -11$$

$$y(2) = -0.93\ y(1) \quad = -0.93 \times (-11) = 10.23 \to 10$$

$$y(3) = -0.93\ y(2) \quad = -0.93 \times 10 = -9.3 \to -9$$

$$y(4) = -0.93\ y(3) \quad = -0.93 \times (-9) = 8.37 \to 8$$

$$y(5) = -0.93\ y(4) \quad = -0.93 \times 8 = -7.44 \to -7$$

$$y(6) = -0.93\ y(5) \quad = -0.93 \times (-7) = -6.51 \to 7$$

$$y(7) = -0.93\ y(6) \quad = -0.93 \times 7 = -6.51 \to -7$$

$$y(8) = -0.93\ y(7) \quad = -0.93 \times (-7) = 6.51 \to 7$$

It is seen that the filter's impulse response ouput is an oscillatory signal, namely the limit cycle output, with a frequency equal to half the sampling frequency, and with a peak amplitude of ± 7.

*****

WE4.13 shows that fixed-point word length arithmetic rounding errors cannot be assumed to be uncorrelated random variables. Fortunately, modern microprocessors are available with instruction sets containing suitable arithmetic processes for DSP applications, existing in fixed-point or floating-point forms, and therefore many of the potential error difficulties arising from arithmetic operations are easily handled by careful program design.

4.5 Case Study: Digital Filters for FSK Modem

Frequency shift keying (FSK) is a modulation scheme whereby the carrier frequency is switched (keyed) between two frequencies such that one frequency represents binary '0' and the other frequency represents binary '1'.

Aim:

The aim of this case study is to describe how digital filters may be designed and used in the implementation of the FSK demodulator part of a modem (***mo***dulator-***dem***odulator).

Background:

It is sometimes appropriate, and relatively inexpensive, for computers to communicate with each other via the Public Switched Telephone Network (PSTN); the data communication being enabled using a pair of modems. One modem is located at the sending end of the telephone link, the other is placed at the receiving end. One modem standard specified by CCITT (Consultative Committee on International Telegraphy and Telephony) is V.21, which is a full-duplex splitband FSK communication system operating at 300 baud, with the transmitter and receiver sharing the available channel bandwidth, as shown in Figure 4.13. Consequently for the full-duplex system both modems are capable of simultaneously transmitting and receiving the computer data.

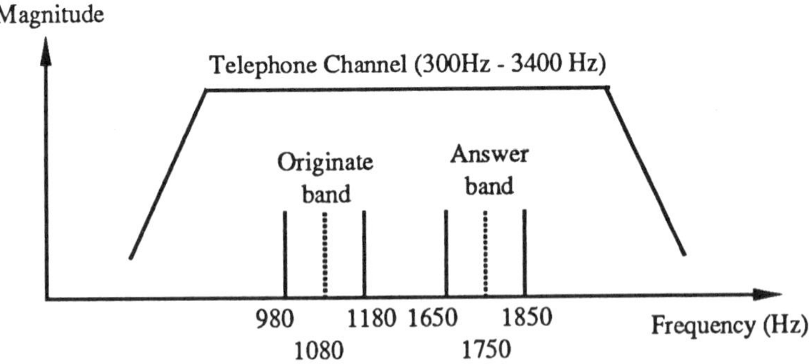

Figure 4.13 V.21 modem frequency bands

The modem uses two bandpass filters to separate the telephone channel into the 'originate' and 'answer' bands. In each band the centre component is the tone signal carrier frequency, the lower frequency component corresponds to a binary state of '1' in the transmitted symbol data word, and the upper frequency component corresponds to a binary state of '0' in the transmitted symbol data word, see Figure 4.14.

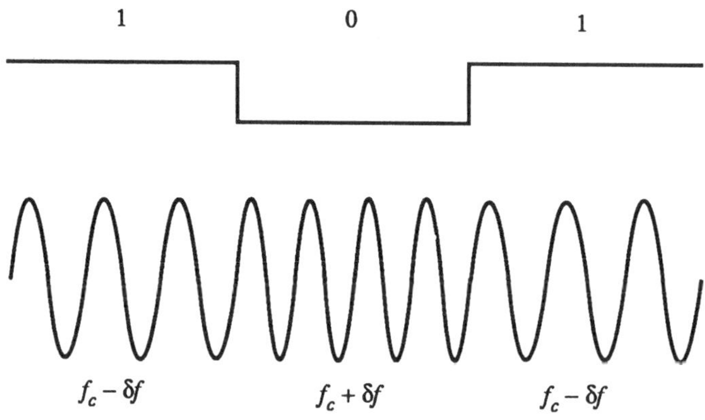

Figure 4.14 FSK signal

The FSK signal has to be demodulated by the receiver section of the modem to recover the binary data stream. This case study describes the design of digital filters suitable for demodulating the FSK signal existing in the originate band.

FSK Demodulator:

The scheme used in this case study to demodulate the FSK signal is shown in block diagram form in Figure 4.15. It simply consists of the multiplication of the received FSK signal with a delay version of it, followed by a lowpass filter.

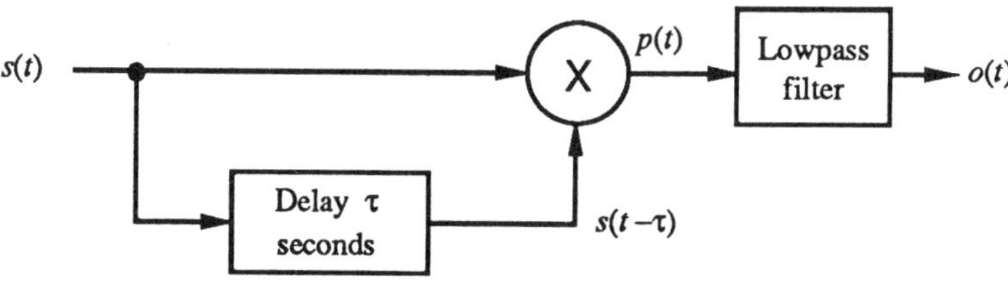

Figure 4.15 FSK Demodulator: front-end tone signal delay

We will assume that the received tone signal, $s(t)$, is of the form

$$s(t) = \cos\ (\omega_c\ \pm \delta\ \omega)\, t = \cos\ \alpha\, t = \cos\ A \tag{4.35}$$

After a dealy of τ seconds the received signal becomes

$$s(t-\tau) = \cos[(\omega_c \pm \delta\omega)(t-\tau)] = \cos[\alpha(t-\tau)] = \cos B \qquad (4.36)$$

The received tone signal is multiplied by the delayed version of itself to form the signal denoted as $p(t)$ in Figure 4.15, that is

$$\begin{aligned} p(t) &= \cos A \times \cos B \\ &= \frac{1}{2}[\cos(A+B) + \cos(A-B)] \end{aligned}$$

Noting that $A + B = \alpha t + \alpha(t-\tau) = 2\alpha t - \alpha\tau$, and

$$A - B = \alpha t - \alpha(t-\tau) = \alpha\tau$$

then

$$p(t) = \frac{1}{2}\{\cos[2(\omega_c \pm \delta\omega)t - (\omega_c \pm \delta\omega)\tau] + \cos[(\omega_c \pm \delta\omega)\tau]\} \qquad (4.37)$$

The lowpass filter following the multiplier removes the double frequency component: $\cos[2(\omega_c \pm \delta\omega)t - (\omega_c \pm \delta\omega)\tau]$, and outputs two constant values, one for each tone signal frequency.

Design of Digital Lowpass Filter:

For the lowpass filter, it is appropriate to use a second order ($n = 2$) IIR digital filter based on a Butterworth prototype filter. In the design of this digital filter a cutoff frequency of 500 Hz is used, and the sampling frequency is taken to be 9.6 kHz.

Using equation (4.9), Table 4.2 and Table 4.3, we obtain the transfer function of the denormalised Butterworth prototype filter:

$$G(s)_{DN} = \frac{(\omega_c)^2}{s^2 + \sqrt{2}\,\omega_c\, s + (\omega_c)^2}$$

Firstly we prewarp the specified digital filter cutoff frequency using

$$\omega_{ca} = \frac{2}{T}\tan\left(\frac{\omega_{cd}\, T}{2}\right) = \lambda \tan\mu$$

to obtain the transfer function of the prewarped denormalised Butterworth prototype filter:

$$G(s)_{PWDN} = \frac{1}{\left(\frac{s}{\lambda\tan\mu}\right)^2 + \sqrt{2}\left(\frac{s}{\lambda\tan\mu}\right) + 1} \qquad (4.38)$$

Using the bilinear z-transform we derive the transfer function of the digital filter. The substitutions to be made in equation (4.38) are:

$$s \to \lambda \frac{(z-1)}{(z+1)} \qquad \text{and} \qquad s^2 \to \lambda^2 \frac{(z-1)^2}{(z+1)^2}$$

Therefore the transfer function of the IIR digital filter is

$$G(z) = \frac{1}{\dfrac{(z-1)^2}{(z+1)^2 \tan^2 \mu} + \dfrac{\sqrt{2}\,(z-1)}{(z+1)\tan \mu} + 1}$$

$$= \frac{\tan^2 \mu \,(z+1)^2}{(z-1)^2 + \sqrt{2} \tan \mu \,(z-1)(z+1) + \tan^2 \mu \,(z+1)^2}$$

$$\tan \mu = \tan \frac{\omega_{cd} T}{2} = \tan \frac{2\pi \times 500}{2 \times 9.6 \times 1000} = 0.1651$$

therefore

$$G(z) = \frac{(0.1651)^2 (z+1)^2}{(z-1)^2 + \sqrt{2}\,(0.1651)(z-1)(z+1) + (0.1651)^2 (z+1)^2}$$

which simplifies to

$$G(z) = \frac{0.0216 z^2 + 0.0432 z + 0.0216}{z^2 - 1.5432 z + 0.6296}$$

***Design of Digital Delay Filter*:**

If we let $\omega_c \tau = \pi / 2$, then considering equation (4.37) the digital lowpass filter output will be

$$\frac{1}{2} \cos\left(\frac{\pi}{2} \pm \delta \omega \tau\right)$$

$$= \frac{1}{2}\left(\cos \frac{\pi}{2} \cos \delta \omega \tau \pm \sin \frac{\pi}{2} \sin \delta \omega \tau\right)$$

$$= \pm \frac{1}{2} \sin \delta \omega \tau$$

When a binary state of '0' is transmitted (tone frequency = 1180 Hz) the incremental frequency, $\delta\omega$, is positive and the filter output is equal to $+0.5 \sin \delta\omega\tau$, but when a binary state of '1' is transmitted (tone frequency = 980 Hz) then $\delta\omega$ is negative and the filter output is equal to $-0.5 \sin \delta\omega\tau$. That is, the sign of the filter output indicates the state ('1' or '0') of the received bit.

From the requirement that $\omega_c\tau = \pi/2$, then it follows that the signal dealy period, τ, must be equal to $1/(4 \times f_C)$. We know that the tone signal carrier frequency, f_C, is 1080 Hz, therefore $\tau = 1/(4 \times 1080)$ seconds = 231.48 μs. The sampling frequency is 9.6 kHz, so the sampling period, T, is equal to 1/(9600) seconds, i.e. $T = 104.17$ μs. Therefore the number of sample periods needed to cover the required signal delay period is 231.48/104.17 = 2.2222. Thus we see that it is necessary to create a $0.2222 \times T$ delay following a $2T$ delay. The fractional part of the delay can be achieved using the single-zero FIR digital filter represented in signal flowgraph form in Figure 4.16.

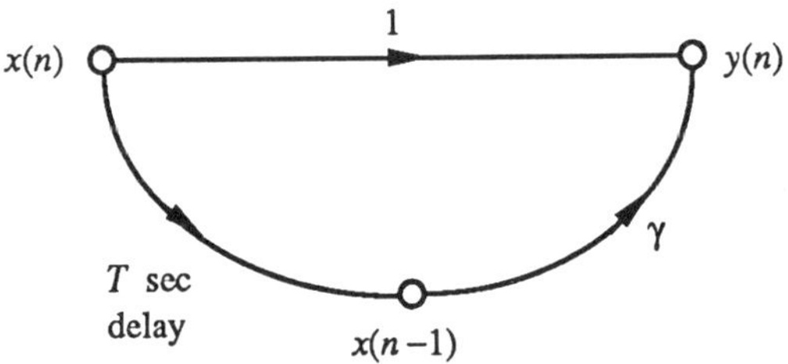

Figure 4.16 Single-zero FIR digital filter

The transfer function of this single-zero FIR digital filter is

$$G(z) = \frac{Y(z)}{X(z)} = 1 + \gamma z^{-1}$$

and its frequency response function is

$$G\left(e^{j\omega T}\right) = 1 + \gamma e^{-j\omega T} = (1 + \gamma \cos \omega T) - j(\gamma \sin \omega T)$$

Therefore the phase/frequency response is

$$\phi(\omega T) = \tan^{-1}\left(\frac{-\gamma \sin \omega T}{1 + \gamma \cos \omega T}\right)$$

The group delay (the average time delay introduced by the filter on each frequency component of the input signal) is, by definition, given by the negative of the slope of the phase/frequency response. Therefore

$$\tau = \frac{-\mathrm{d}\,\phi(\omega T)}{\mathrm{d}(\omega T)} = \frac{-\mathrm{d}}{\mathrm{d}(\omega T)}\left[\tan^{-1}\left(\frac{-\gamma \sin \omega T}{1+\gamma \cos \omega T}\right)\right]$$

Note: $$\frac{\mathrm{d}}{\mathrm{d}x}[\tan^{-1}(F)] = \frac{1}{1+F^2} \times \frac{\mathrm{d}F}{\mathrm{d}x}$$

therefore

$$\tau = \frac{-1}{1+\left(\dfrac{-\gamma \sin \omega T}{1+\gamma \cos \omega T}\right)^2} \times \frac{\mathrm{d}}{\mathrm{d}(\omega T)}\left(\frac{-\gamma \sin \omega T}{1+\gamma \cos \omega T}\right)$$

$$= \frac{-(1+\gamma \cos \omega T)^2}{(1+\gamma^2+2\gamma \cos \omega T)} \times \frac{\mathrm{d}}{\mathrm{d}(\omega T)}\left(\frac{-\gamma \sin \omega T}{1+\gamma \cos \omega T}\right) \qquad (4.39)$$

Consider $y = \dfrac{U}{V}$ then $$\frac{\mathrm{d}y}{\mathrm{d}x} = \frac{V\dfrac{\mathrm{d}U}{\mathrm{d}x} - U\dfrac{\mathrm{d}V}{\mathrm{d}x}}{V^2}$$

Applying the above to equation (4.39) we obtain

$$U = -\gamma \sin \omega T; \quad \frac{\mathrm{d}U}{\mathrm{d}\omega T} = -\gamma \cos \omega T$$

$$V = 1+\gamma \cos \omega T; \quad \frac{\mathrm{d}V}{\mathrm{d}\omega T} = -\gamma \sin \omega T$$

$$\frac{\mathrm{d}}{\mathrm{d}(\omega T)}\left(\frac{-\gamma \sin \omega T}{1+\gamma \cos \omega T}\right)$$

$$= \frac{(1+\gamma \cos \omega T)(-\gamma \cos \omega T) - (-\gamma \sin \omega T)(-\gamma \sin \omega T)}{(1+\gamma \cos \omega T)^2}$$

$$= \frac{-\gamma \cos \omega T - \gamma^2}{(1+\gamma \cos \omega T)^2}$$

$$\therefore \quad \tau = \frac{-(1+\gamma\cos\ \omega T)^2}{(1+\gamma^2+2\gamma\cos\ \omega T)} \times \frac{-\gamma\cos\ \omega T - \gamma^2}{(1+\gamma\cos\ \omega T)^2}$$

$$= \frac{\gamma^2+\gamma\cos\ \omega T}{1+\gamma^2+2\gamma\cos\ \omega T} \tag{4.40}$$

Rearranging equation (4.40) gives the following quadratic equation

$$(1-\tau)\gamma^2+[(1-2\tau)\cos\omega T]\gamma-\tau=0 \tag{4.41}$$

Since this FIR filter is required to introduce a delay to the input signal with frequency components centred about the carrier frequency of 1080 Hz, and since the delay τ is expressed as a fraction of the sampling period, i.e. $\tau = 0.2222$, it follows that

$$1-\tau = 1-0.2222 = 0.7778$$

$$1-2\tau = 1-(2 \times 0.2222) = 0.5556$$

$$\cos\omega T = \cos(2\pi \times 1080 \times 104.167 \times 10^{-6}) = 0.7604$$

Solving the quadratic equation (4.41) using the above values gives

$\gamma = 0.3279$ or $\gamma = -0.8711$

Using the positive root, the transfer function of the FIR digital filter is

$$G(z) = 1 + 0.3279\ z^{-1}$$

Performance Evaluation:

The designed IIR and FIR filters were used in the FSK demodulator simulation model shown in Figure 4.17.

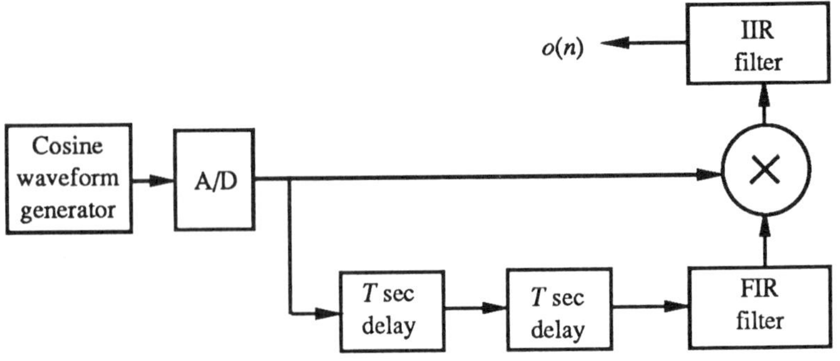

Figure 4.17 FSK demodulator simulation model

Using a squarewave test signal to produce a corresponding FSK waveform consisting of tones (sinusoidal signals with maximum amplitude of 1 V) alternating between 980 Hz and 1180 Hz, sampled at a rate of 9600 samples per second, gives the resulting IIR filter output sequence shown in Figure 4.18. Note that after an initial transient, the output sequence resembles the input square wave in digitised form. The amplitude variations in the IIR filter output sequence can be eliminated by subsequent amplification (say using a gain of 50), followed by threshoding (to limit the amplifier output amplitude to say ±0.5 V) and then applying a d.c. shift by adding 0.5 V to each value produced by the limiter, to yield the desired 0 V to 1 V squarewave signal.

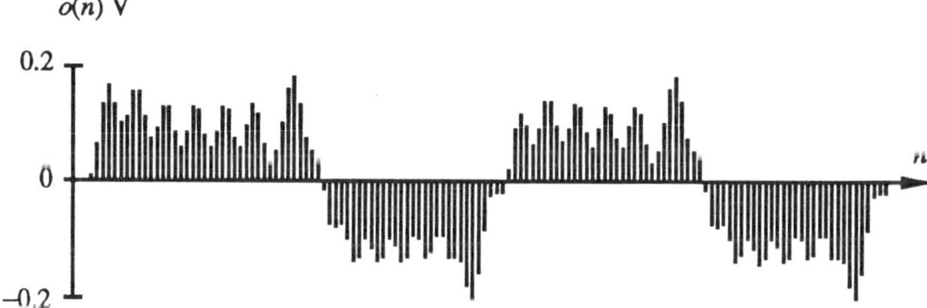

Figure 4.18 IIR filter output sequence corresponding to FSK test signal

Problems

P4.1

A digital filter based on an N-term moving averager is to be used such that the first null occurs at a frequency of 50 Hz, determine the linear difference equation of the filter. The sampling frequency is 400 Hz.

P4.2

Design an FIR filter based on the 8-point sampling of the ideal frequency response shown below:

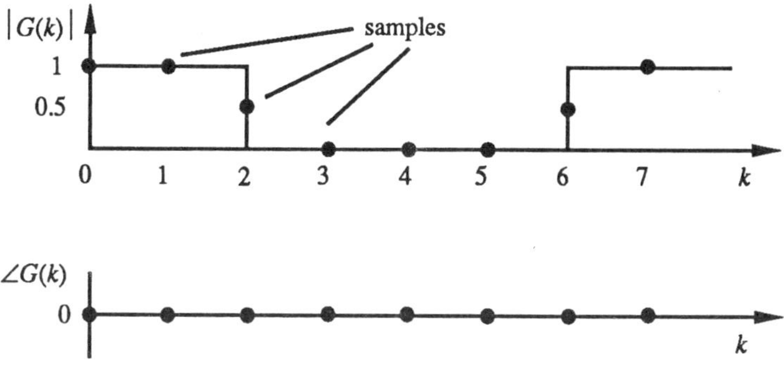

P4.3

Using the window method design an FIR filter based on the 16-point sampling of the ideal frequency response shown below. Use a Blackman window and let $I = 5$.

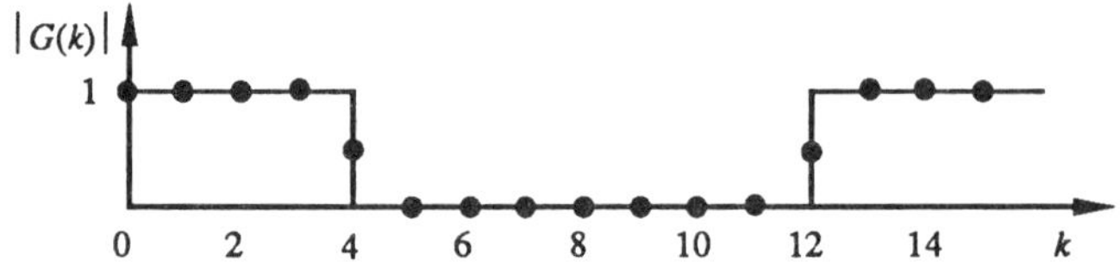

P4.4

A 6th-order comb filter has the transfer function $G(z) = 1 - z^{-6}$ plot its pole/zero representation in the z-plane. If the sampling frequency is 10 kHz, at what frequency does the first peak in the magnitude/frequency characteristic occur?

P4.5

Using the bilinear z-transform design method derive the IIR digital filter transfer function for each of the specifications listed below:

(i)	Prototype:	Butterworth normalised 2nd-order lowpass filter.
	IIR filter:	Lowpass filter with a cutoff frequency = 2 kHz. Sampling frequency = 8 kHz.
(ii)	Prototype:	Butterworth normalised 2nd-order lowpass filter.
	IIR filter:	Highpass filter with a cutoff frequency = 2 kHz. Sampling frequency = 8 kHz.
(iii)	Prototype:	Butterworth normalised 2nd-order lowpass filter.
	IIR filter:	Bandpass filter with a lower cutoff frequency = 1.9 kHz, and upper cutoff frequency = 2.1 kHz. Sampling frequency = 8 kHz.
(iv)	Prototype:	Butterworth normalised 2nd-order lowpass filter.
	IIR filter:	Bandstop filter with a lower cutoff frequency = 1.9 kHz, and upper cutoff frequency = 2.1 kHz. Sampling frequency = 8 kHz.
(v)	Prototype:	Chebyshev normalised 2nd-order lowpass filter with 0.25 dB passband ripple.
	IIR filter:	Lowpass filter with a cutoff frequency = 2 kHz. Sampling frequency = 8 kHz.
(vi)	Prototype:	Chebyshev normalised 2nd-order lowpass filter with 0.25 dB passband ripple.
	IIR filter:	Highpass filter with a cutoff frequency = 2 kHz. Sampling frequency = 8 kHz.

P4.6

A (sin x)/x digital correction filter, operating with a sampling frequency of 6 kHz, is placed before a D/A converter. Determine the signal amplitude values for each sinusoidal signal component at the output of the D/A converter when the correction filter input signal contains sinusoidal signal components at 500 Hz and 750 Hz, each having respective amplitude values of 0.5 V and 0.1 V.

P4.7

A digital filter has the transfer function $G(z) = z/(z + 0.2)$, calculate the average output noise power into 1 Ω due to quantisation of the input signal when the quantisation interval is 0.1 mV.

P4.8

A digital filter has the transfer function $G(z) = 0.3\,z/(z^2 - 1.5z + 0.6)$, calculate the minimum word length for stability to be maintained, assuming that (i) filter coefficients are rounded, and (ii) filter coefficients are truncated.

P4.9

An IIR digital filter has the transfer function $G(z) = z/(z - 0.97)$, assuming that (i) the input signal is zero-valued, (ii) the initial condition is $y(-1) = 20$, and (iii) computed $y(n)$ results are rounded to the nearest integer value (integer number resolution), show that under these stated conditions the filter output exhibits the deadband effect.

5 Practical Implementation Considerations

5.1 Introduction

The numerous worked examples and the case studies contained in this book clearly demonstrate that digital signal processing operations are governed by discrete-time representations of algorithmic processes. For example, we have seen that the characteristic performance of a digital filter is determined by its linear difference equation. The practical implementation of *real-time* digital signal processing operations is generally achieved using one of two practical options, namely (a) using dedicated hardware, such as an application specific integrated-circuit (ASIC) or a bit-slice processor, or (b) using a programmable integrated-circuit (microprocessor or digital signal processor chip). If the processing operations are not required as real-time implementations, then it is often appropriate to perform the DSP computations using a general-purpose personal computer (PC). For example, a number of proprietary software packages have been produced to enable model definitions and simulation of DSP systems.

However, in an age of rapidly changing digital hardware and software technology it is beneficial for students to be introduced to the fundamental principles involved in manipulating and implementing real-time processing operations using programmable devices. It is true that much of the information used to achieve the practical implementation of a DSP operation will be device specific (instruction set, processor architecture, etc), but it has been found generally that a considerable amount of the basic knowledge and experience gained by students engaged in hands-on hardware and software implementation activities, can be transferred to new design situations when different DSP hardware/software is encountered. For this reason the material presented in this chapter concentrates mainly on describing the fundamental principles involved in implementing linear difference equations.

5.2 Implementation Using Microprocessors

For ease of implementation we may assume that the DSP system has a transfer function $G(z)$ consisting of cascaded first-order/second-order sections. For example, a 4th-order digital filter may be formed by cascading two 2nd-order sections, whereas a 5th-order digital filter may be formed by cascading two 2nd-order sections and a 1st-order section.

Consider the general 2nd-order transfer function:

$$G(z) = \frac{A_0 + A_1 z^{-1} + A_2 z^{-2}}{1 + B_1 z^{-1} + B_2 z^{-2}}$$

The general 1st-order transfer function is derived from the general 2nd-order transfer function by setting coefficients A_2 and B_2 equal to zero. Therefore we note that 1st and 2nd-order sections act as basic building blocks and play an important role in the implementation of DSP systems. It is the corresponding DSP system linear difference equations that must be defined when the computation aspects of the implementation are considered. The general 1st-order/2nd-order section may be implemented using the following linear difference equation:

$$y(n) = A_0 x(n) + A_1 x(n-1) + A_2 x(n-2) - B_1 y(n-1) - B_2 y(n-2) \tag{5.1}$$

The programming of the microprocessor can be considered when the processes to handle the data and instructions have been correctly organised. The structuring of the program into a set of logical steps is commonly facilitated using a flowchart (an example is shown in Figure 3.3, page 139).

Considering the linear difference equation of the general 1st-order/2nd-order section (equation (5.1)) we may summarise the processes involved in its implementation using the flowchart shown in Figure 5.1

A relatively simple form of implementation may be obtained using a general purpose 8-bit microprocessor, as described in the following section of this chapter.

5.2.1 M6802 Microprocessor-based Digital Signal Processor

Figure 5.2 shows the block diagram of a basic microprocessor system. It consists of three basic parts, namely, the microprocessor, the memory and the input/output (I/O) interface. The microprocessor, generally based on a von Neumann-type architecture, repetitively fetches and executes instructions of a program. The memory can be divided into two forms. The read-only memory (ROM) is a *non-volatile store* which is used to hold the sequence of program instructions. Erasable programmable read-only memory (EPROM) is often used for prototype system designs. The random access memory (RAM), which is a *volatile* read-write store, holds the results of arithmetic and/or logical operations, or it holds variable data derived via the input/output (I/O) interface. In a DSP system the I/O interface enables the A/D and D/A converters to be connected to the microprocessor unit (MPU).

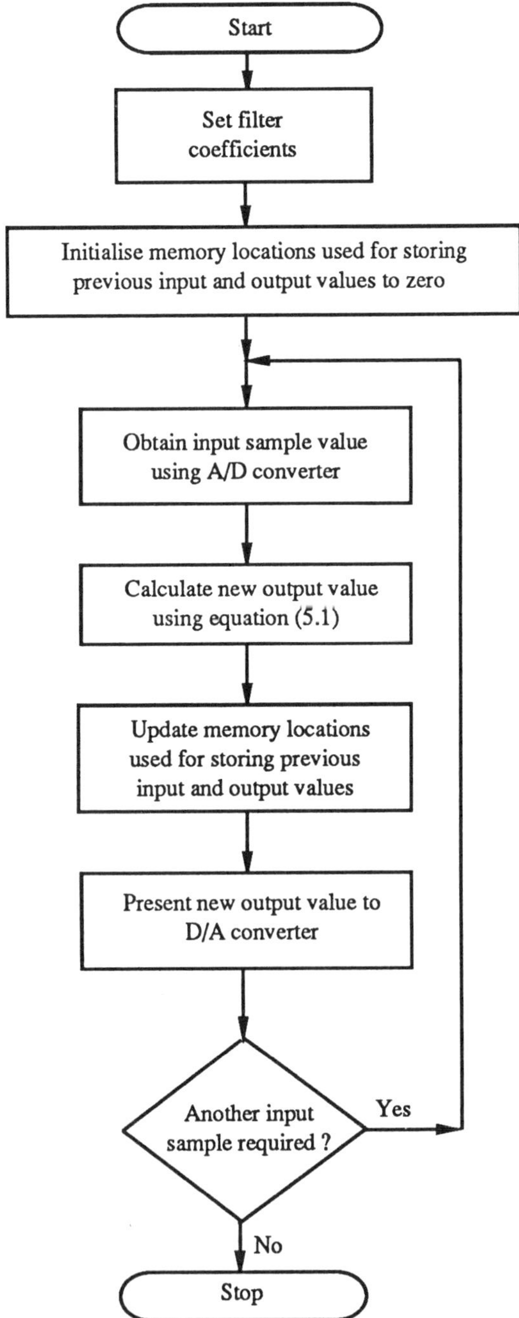

Figure 5.1 Flowchart for implementation of equation (5.1)

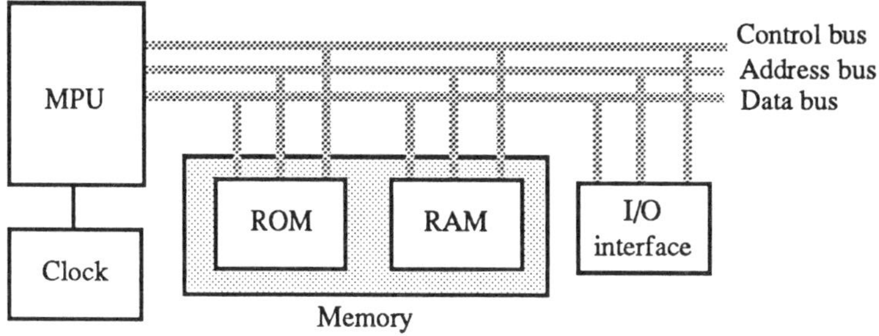

Figure 5.2 Block diagram of a basic microprocessor system

The address bus is uni-directional and carries the address code sent by the microprocessor to select a particular memory location or a particular I/O interface. The data bus is bi-directional and carries instruction/data words sent between the microprocessor and the memory or the I/O interface. The control bus generally has one set of lines to carry status signals generated by the I/O interface (such as interrupt request signals) and one set of lines to carry status/control signals generated by the microprocessor (such as the memory read / $\overline{\text{write}}$ signal).

The microprocessor word length is important because it can significantly influence the accuracy of data representation, the processor speed, memory requirements, and costs. Clearly these factors cannot be ignored when considering the possibility of using a microprocessor to implement a DSP system.

A word is often (and conveniently) divided into 8-bit lengths, commonly referred to as *bytes* (i.e. one byte represents 8 bits). In the following description each memory location is assumed to store one byte. To enable these bytes to be accessed (via memory read or write operations) each store location has a unique address; a single byte can address any one of 256 memory locations, whereas a double-byte can address any one of 65536 memory locations. The byte stored in a particular memory location is either data (e.g. the sampled-data input value or a constant value), or it is an instruction operation code (*op-code*), or part of a multiple-byte instruction.

The representation of the 8-bit memory contents and/or the 16-bit memory address codes, frequently involves using the hexadecimal (radix 16) code. Each 4-bit binary number is represented by a single hexadecimal character, as shown in Table 5.1. A byte is represented by two hexadecimal characters. For example, the two's complement binary number 01111110 may be converted to hexadecimal as follows:

binary:	0111	1110
hexadecimal	7	E

that is $(01111110)_2 = (7\,E)_{16} = (+\,126)_{10}$

Similarly $(11111010)_2 = (FA)_{16} = (-6)_{10}$

Decimal	Binary	Hexadecimal
0	0000	0
1	0001	1
2	0010	2
3	0011	3
4	0100	4
5	0101	5
6	0110	6
7	0111	7
8	1000	8
9	1001	9
10	1010	A
11	1011	B
12	1100	C
13	1101	D
14	1110	E
15	1111	F

Table 5.1 Code conversion table

Hexadecimal memory address 28CA expressed in binary form is

2	8	C	A
0010	1000	1100	1010

that is $(28\,CA)_{16} = (0010100011001010)_2 = (10442)_{10}$

The binary codes that define the microprocessor's data, instructions and memory addresses may therefore be written using their equivalent hexadecimal representation.

A microprocessor-based system is not able to perform any useful operation without having a suitable program written for it. If a program is written using binary number representation, it is said to be a machine language program; whereas if a program is written using mnemonics specific to the microprocessor being used, it is an assembly language program. However, an assembly language program must be converted to an equivalent machine language version before it can be executed by the microprocessor. This conversion process is achieved using a special-purpose assembler program.

A program instruction may be one, two or three bytes in length. A one-byte instruction would consist of the operation code (*op-code*) only. For example, the Motorola M6802 microprocessor has two accumulator registers, A and B, and instruction op-code $(16)_{16}$, corresponding to TAB in the assembly language, when *fetched and executed*, will cause the microprocessor to copy the contents of accumulator A into accumulator B, with the contents of accumulator A remaining unchanged. Thus we see that the op-code instructs the microprocessor in what it must do. A two-byte instruction consists of the one-byte op-code followed by a one-byte *operand*, the operand being the memory address of the data used by the instruction. The one-byte operand forms a numerical memory address in the range $(0 \text{ to } 255)_{10} = (0 \text{ to } FF)_{16}$. A two-byte instruction is referred to as a *direct addressing mode* instruction. For example, op-code $(DB)_{16}$ followed by operand $(6E)_{16}$, corresponding to ADDB $6E in the assembly language (where the $ prefix denotes a hexadecimal number), causes the microprocessor to add the contents of the specified memory location $(6E)_{16}$ to the contents of accumulator B, the result being placed in accumulator B and the contents of the specified memory location remaining unchanged. A three-byte instruction consists of the one-byte op-code followed by a two-byte operand. The second byte contains the most significant (highest) 8 bits of the memory address, and the third byte contains the least significant (lowest) 8 bits of the memory address. Therefore by using a 16-bit address the range of accessible memory locations is $(0 \text{ to } 65536)_{10} = (0 \text{ to } FFFF)_{16}$. Consequently a three-byte instruction is referred to as an *extended addressing mode* instruction. For example, op-code $(FB)_{16}$ followed by operand $(6E00)_{16}$, corresponding to ADDB $6E00 in the assembly language, causes the microprocessor to add the contents of the specified extended addressed memory location $(6E00)_{16}$ to the contents of accumulator B, the result being placed in accumulator B and the contents of the specified memory location remaining unchanged.

Another form of two-byte instruction is available, known as an *immediate addressing mode* instruction. In this case the op-code is followed immediately by the actual value of the operand. For example, op-code $(CB)_{16}$ followed by $(6E)_{16}$, corresponding to ADDB #$6E in the assembly language (where the # prefix denotes an immediate addressing mode instruction), causes the microprocessor to add the value $(6E)_{16}$ to the contents of accumulator B, the result being placed in accumulator B.

It is now appropriate to consider the basic internal registers of the M6802 microprocessor, as shown in Figure 5.3:

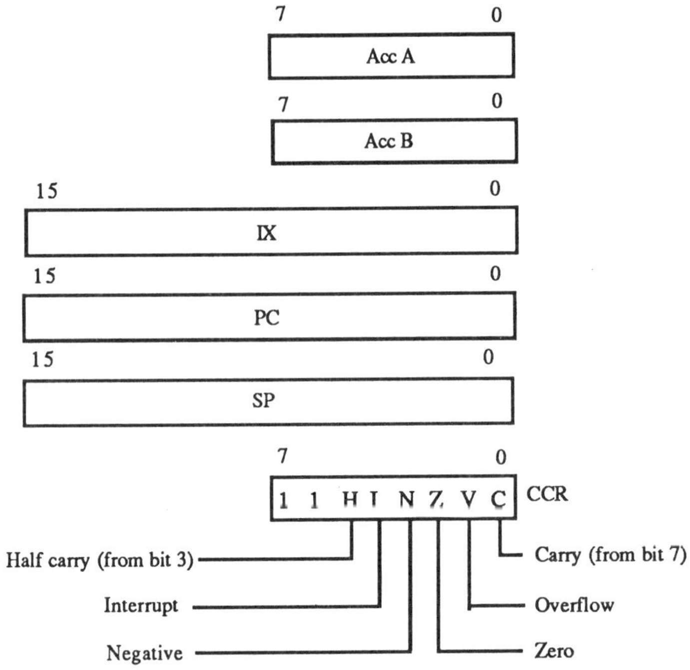

Figure 5.3 Basic internal registers of the M6802 microprocessor

The two 8-bit accumulators, A and B, are generally associated with data movement around the system. They frequently contain one of the operands and the result for a number of instructions. The *program counter* (PC) is 16 bits long, and it holds the address of the next op-code to be fetched and executed. The *index register* (IX) is 16 bits long, and it is used to generate an effective memory address. When the index register is used a two-byte *indexed addressing mode* instruction is fetched and executed; the first byte is the op-code, and the second byte is the number added to the current contents of the index register to form the memory address, which correspondingly gives access to the operand. For example, op-code $(EB)_{16}$, followed by $(0A)_{16}$, corresponding to ADDB $A, X in the assembly language, causes the microprocessor to add the operand value in memory location $(IX)_{16} + (0A)_{16}$ to the current contents of accumulator B, the result being placed in accumulator B.

The *condition code register* (CCR) consists of six ‘flags’ which provide status information about the last operation performed by the microprocessor. For example, the C bit will be set to '1' if there was a *carry* generated as the result of an addition operation, otherwise it will be cleared to '0'. The state of a particular

CCR flag may be usefully employed to determine the outcome of a *conditional branch* in a program. For example, if a zero-valued result has been produced, the condition code register Z bit will be set equal to 1, and we may want the microprocessor to execute a particular jump to subroutine instruction, otherwise we allow it to continue with fetching and executing the next instruction op-code (see Figure 5.4). To achieve this objective we may use the *branch if equal to zero* instruction, $(27)_{16}$, corresponding to BEQ in the assembly language, which is a *relative addressing mode* instruction.

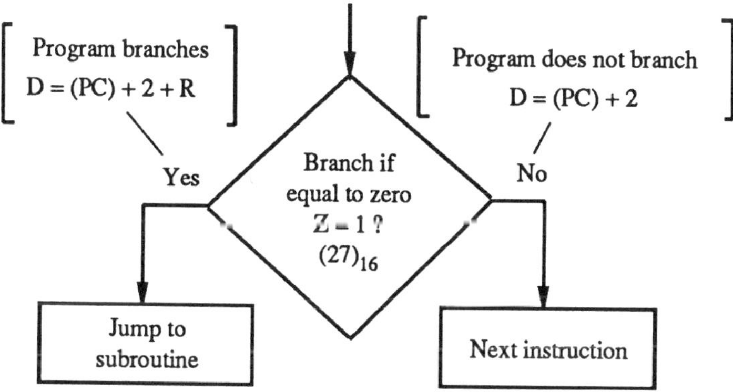

Figure 5.4 A typical branch operation

A relative addressing mode instruction is a two-byte instruction. The first byte is the op-code (conditional branch), and the second byte is a two's complement 8-bit binary number which is the branch *offset*, R. The relationship between the relative address and the absolute destination address of the branch instruction is

$$D = (PC) + 2 + R \tag{5.2}$$

where D is the absolute destination address, (PC) is the memory address of the branch instruction op-code, and R is the offset. If the program does not branch, then

$$D = (PC) + 2$$

In equation (5.2) the destination address must be within the range specified by

$$[((PC) + 2) + 127] \geq D \geq [((PC) + 2) - 128] \tag{5.3}$$

If the destination address is given a symbolic label in the assembly language program, the assembler automatically determines the offset value, provided that the range conditions specified by equation (5.3) are satisfied.

When it is desired to transfer control outside the range specified by equation (5.3) it is possible to branch to an *unconditional jump* instruction, which in turn will move program control to the desired instruction op-code.

A section of RAM is used by the microprocessor for last-in, first-out operations so that successive bytes of data may be 'stacked' one after the other. This part of memory is referred to as the *stack*. The 16-bit stack pointer (SP), shown in Figure 5.3, holds the memory address of the next vacant stack location. An accumulator byte may be stored on the stack using a *push* (PSH) instruction, and the last byte stored on the stack may be retrieved (brought back into the accumulator) using a *pull* (PUL) instruction. The stack is used for handling subroutines (see Figure 5.5) and interrupts.

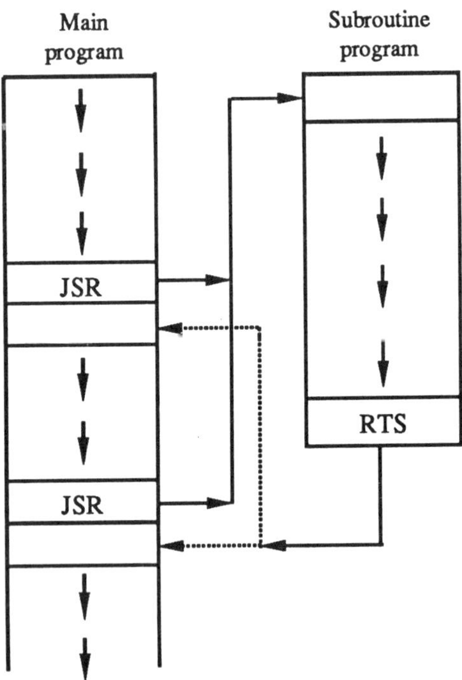

Figure 5.5 Subroutine call and return organisation

When a *jump to subroutine* (JSR) instruction is executed the *return address* is automatically saved on the stack. This return address points to the memory location containing the next instruction op-code immediately following the JSR instruction. A subroutine must be terminated by a return from subroutine (RTS) instruction, and after its execution the return address is pulled off the stack and placed in the program counter, thereby enabling the next instruction in the main program to be executed.

One of the main features of a microprocessor which make it suitable for digital signal processing applications is its ability to handle interrupts. The interrupt signal is often generated by a peripheral device, which commonly in a DSP system will be the A/D converter. On receipt of an *interrupt request* (signal generated when A/D conversion is complete) the microprocessor's *status* (contents of the microprocessor's internal registers) are stored on the stack, and they are restored to the microprocessor on completion of the *interrupt service routine* (ISR). The interrupt signal therefore causes the microprocessor to suspend execution of its main program and execute the interrupt service routine. At the end of this routine the return from interrupt (RTI) instruction is encountered and executed, thereby enabling resumption of the main program. Figure 5.6 shows the program organisation for handling an interrupt request upon encountering the *wait for interrupt* (WAI) instruction. The interrupt service routine could, for example, be used to evaluate the linear difference equation of a digital filter.

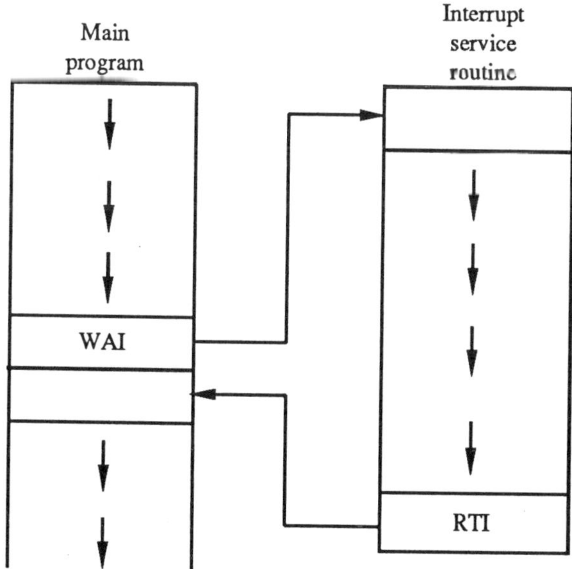

Figure 5.6 Program organisation for handling an interrupt request

5.2.2 Peripheral Interface Adapter (PIA)

Another important practical implementation consideration is the *interface* between the MPU and the A/D and D/A converters. The input/output of data between the MPU and the converters may be achieved under program control, through programmable interface adaptors (PIAs), see Figure 5.7.

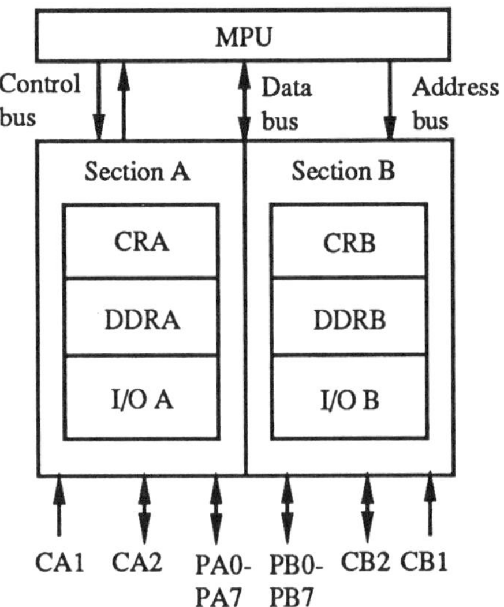

Figure 5.7 Block diagram of the MC6821 PIA

Referring to Figure 5.7 we see that the PIA is divided into two sections, i.e. A and B. Each section has three 8-bit registers: a control register (CRA or CRB), a data direction register (DDRA or DDRB), and an input/output register (I/O A or I/O B). The A section has eight data I/O lines, designated as PA0, PA1, PA2,..., PA7, and it has two control lines, designated as CA1 and CA2. Similarly the B section has eight data I/O lines, designated as PB0, PB1, PB2,..., PB7, and it has two control lines, designated as CB1 and CB2.

The PIA is a memory-mapped device, which means that its six internal registers are effectively treated as addressable RAM locations. However, only four addresses are required, as shown in the following example:

Address	*Register*
8008	Data direction register, DDRA (CRA, $b_2 = 0$) Input/output register, I/O A (CRA, $b_2 = 1$)
8009	Control register, CRA
800A	Data direction register, DDRB (CRB, $b_2 = 0$) Input/output register, I/O B (CRB, $b_2 = 1$)
800B	Control register, CRB

The function of each register will now be described.

The Control Register (CRA or CRB):
The control word format is shown in Figure 5.8.

b_7	b_6	b_5	b_4	b_3	b_2	b_1	b_0
IRQA(B)1 Flag	IRQA(B)2 Flag	CA2(CB2) Control			DDR Access	CA1(CB1) Control	

Figure 5.8 Control word format for MC6821 PIA

Bits b_0 and b_1 determine the CA1(CB1) operating mode. When $b_0 = 0$ this will prevent the CA1(CB1) line from interrupting the microprocessor, but when $b_0 = 1$ it allows the CA1 (CB1) line to interrupt the microprocessor. When $b_1 = 0$ the *interrupt flag* (IRQA(B)1, b_7) is set by a high-to-low transition on CA1(CB1), and alternatively, when $b_1 = 1$ the *interrupt flag* (IRQA(B)1, b_7) is set by a low-to-high transition on CA1(CB1).

Bit b_2 determines whether the data direction register or the I/O register is addressed. If $b_2 = 0$ the data direction register is selected, but if $b_2 = 1$ then the I/O register is selected.

Bits b_3, b_4 and b_5 determine the CA2(CB2) operating mode. When $b_5 = 0$ CA2 (CB2) is established as an input and b_3 and b_4 perform similarly to b_0 and b_1. That is, if in this case $b_3 = 0$ the CA2(CB2) interrupt line is disabled, but if $b_3 = 1$, then the CA2(CB2) interrupt line is enabled. Again taking the case when $b_5 = 0$, then if $b_4 = 0$ the interrupt flag (IRQA(B)2,b_6) is set by a high-to-low transition on CA2(CB2), but if in this case $b_4 = 1$, then the interrupt flag (IRQA(B)2,b_6) is set by a low-to-high transition on CA2(CB2). Let us now consider the case when $b_5 = 1$. In this case CA2(CB2) acts as an output, and it functions in one of three modes. However, we will only be concerned with the relatively simple set/reset mode. In this mode $b_5 = b_4 = 1$, and b_3 serves as a program-controlled output, such that CA2(CB2) is the set/reset output which follows the state of b_3 as it is changed by MPU *write to control register* operations.

Bit b_6 is the IRQA(B)2 interrupt flag which goes high on the active transition of CA2(CB2) if CA2(CB2) has been established as an input ($b_5 = 0$). This flag is reset to zero each time the MPU reads the corresponding I/O register, or it can be cleared by the hardware reset signal.

Bit b_7 is the IRQA(B)1 interrupt flag which goes high on the active transition of the CA1(CB1) input. This flag is reset to zero each time the MPU reads the corresponding I/O register, or it can be cleared by the hardware reset signal.

The Data Direction Register (DDRA or DDRB):
This register is used to establish each data I/O line as either an input or an output. This is achieved by having the MPU write 0s or 1s into the 8 bit positions of the DDR. Thus if $b_j = 1$, where $j = 0, 1, ..., 7$, in the DDR, then b_j in the I/O register will be established as an output, but if $b_j = 0$ in the DDR, then b_j in the I/O register will be established as an input.

The Input/Output Register (I/O A or I/O B):
When this register is addressed the data present on the established PIA inputs may be loaded into the MPU accumulator via a load accumulator (LDAA(B)) instruction. Alternatively data may be transferred from an MPU accumulator to the established PIA outputs via a store accumulator (STAA(B)) instruction.

The PIA's programmability makes it a rather complex device to set up and operate, but when considering a practical implementation of a DSP system only a small number of the large variety of available functions are needed to successfully interface the MPU to the A/D and D/A converters, and consequently the task of initialising the PIA to operate as the required interface is not too difficult. The following case study demonstrates how the M6802 microprocessor, associated devices and peripheral circuits may be used to implement a simple digital filter.

5.2.3 Case Study: M6802 Microprocessor-based Digital Filter

Aim:

The aim of this case study is to present sufficient information to enable the reader to understand the various practical considerations involved in producing a DSP system for real-time signal processing applications.

Using the given hardware and software details, the reader may gain hands-on experience by building, programming and testing the M6802-based digital filter described in this case study.

The Hardware:

A suitable M6802-based microprocessor system is shown in block diagram form in Figure 5.9.

Under program control the PIA generates the CA2-pulse (A/D convert command signal) to obtain the current sample value, $x(n)$, of the input signal. On completion of the A/D conversion process a status signal is generated by the A/D converter; this is a $1 \rightarrow 0$ transition which is accepted via the CA1 input to set the interrupt flag in the PIA control register. The resulting interrupt directs program control to the start of the interrupt routine. The interrupt routine is used to read $x(n)$ into the MPU via the designated PIA input lines (say PA0-PA7), and it is then used to evaluate $y(n)$, which is then output to the D/A converter via the designated PIA output lines (say PB0-PB7). The memory locations allocated for storing previous input and output sampled-data values used in evaluating the linear difference equation are updated and the microprocessor then returns from the interrupt routine. At the next sampling instant the process is repeated, see the flowchart shown in Figure 5.10.

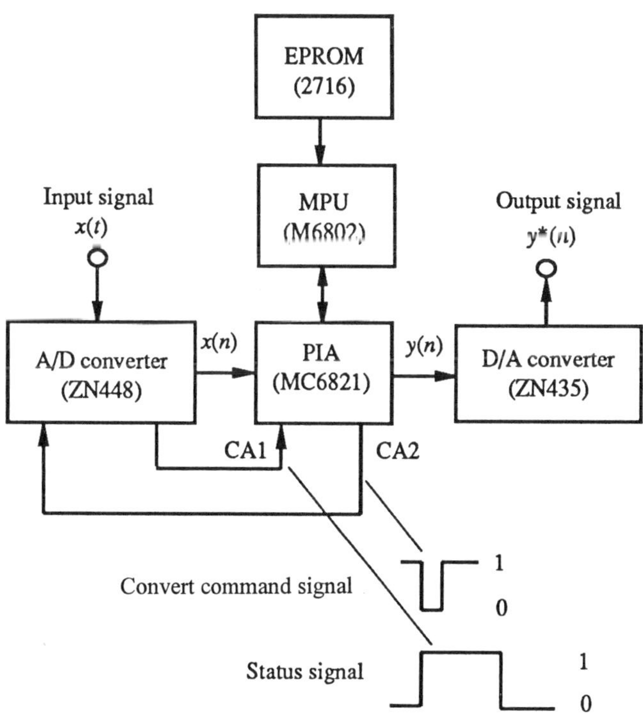

Figure 5.9 Block diagram of M6802-based DSP system

Figure 5.11 shows the integrated-circuits and component connections for the relatively inexpensive microprocessor system hardware, suitable for implementing digital signal processing operations. The memory map of this system is (all addresses being expressed as hexadecimal numbers):

M6802 RAM:	0000 - 007F	(scratch-pad memory)
MC6821 PIA:	8008 - 800B	(I/O interface)
2716 EPROM:	F800 - FFFF	(program/constants memory)

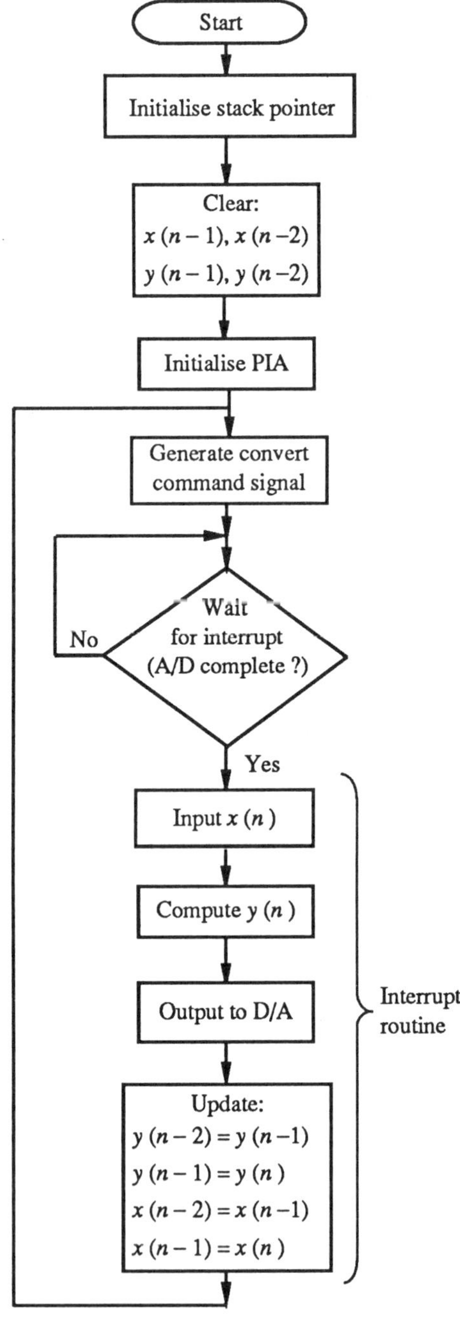

Figure 5.10 Flowchart for 2nd-order digital filter

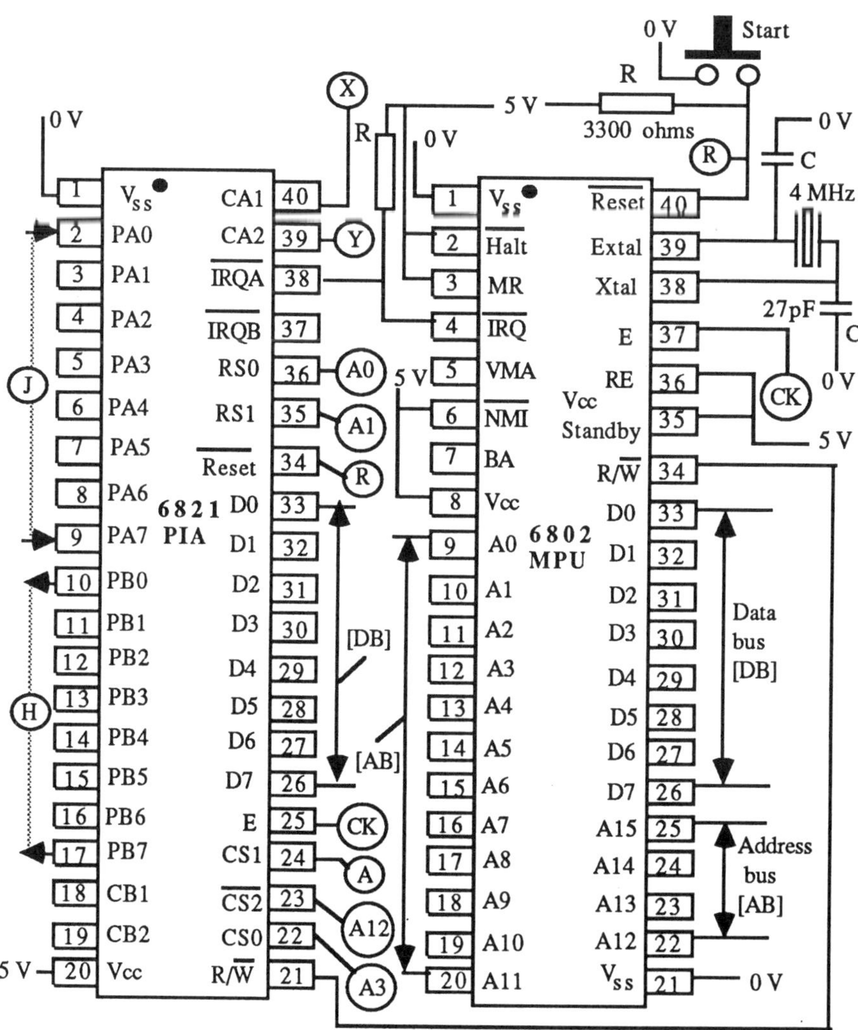

Figure 5.11 Hardware for microprocessor-based DSP system (Part 1)

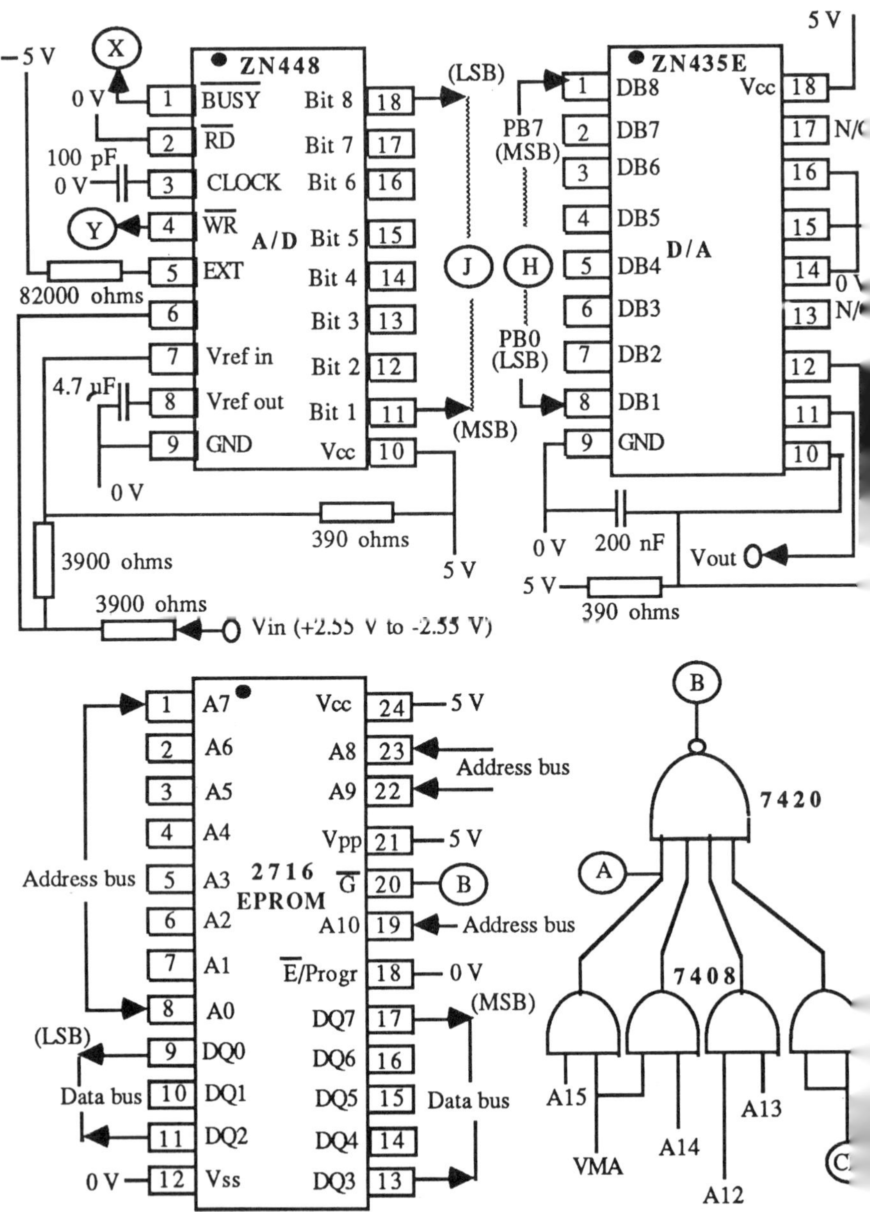

Figure 5.11 Hardware for microprocessor-based DSP system (Part 2)

The system hardware shown in Figure 5.11 does not include an anti-aliasing filter to bandlimit the input signal frequency range, consequently the highest frequency component in the input signal must not exceed the specified value of $f_s/2$ if aliasing is to be avoided. Also the hardware shown in Figure 5.11 does not include the required reconstruction filter. This may be kept simple by using a 1st-order *R-C* lowpass filter circuit to smooth the stepped-waveform produced at the D/A converter output.

Filter Example:

The digital filter design example described in WE2.26 (page 107) will be used to illustrate the implementation process. The specification for this filter is:

Lowpass filter characteristic with a cut-off frequency of 100 Hz.
Prototype is a 2nd-order Butterworth lowpass filter.
Bilinear z transform design method to be used.
Sampling frequency is 625 Hz.

The derived transfer function of this filter (page 108) is

$$G(z) = \frac{z^2 + 2z + 1}{6.88 z^2 - 4.62 z + 1.74}$$

and its corresponding linear difference equation is

$$\begin{aligned} y(n) = 0.145\, x(n) + 0.291\, x(n-1) + 0.145\, x(n-2) \\ + 0.671\, y[(n-1)] - 0.253\, y(n-2) \end{aligned} \tag{5.4}$$

Implementation of the Difference Equation:

Considering the need for computational efficiency, given that the M6802 microprocessor does not have a multiply instruction in its instruction set, it will be advantageous to implement equation (5.4) as

$$\begin{aligned} y(n) \cong 0.140625\, x(n) + 0.28125\, x(n-1) + 0.140625\, x(n-2) \\ + 0.671875\, y[(n-1)] - 0.25\, y(n-2) \end{aligned} \tag{5.5}$$

The coefficient values in equation (5.5) have been chosen to aid the required multiplication process by using shift-and-add operations to form the product. For example, the product 0.671875 $y(n-1)$ may be evaluated as

$$(0.5 + 0.125 + 0.03125 + 0.015625) \times y(n-1)$$

Suppose that $y(n-1)$ is a stored sampled-data value held in one of the two M6802 accumulators, or for increased precision in number representation, in the two accumulators with the integer part in accumulator A and the fractional part in accumulator B, then the product evaluation could be achieved as

original stored $y(n-1)$ value shifted one place right (= $0.5\,y(n-1)$)
added to

original stored $y(n-1)$ value shifted three places right (= $0.125\,y(n-1)$)
added to

original stored $y(n-1)$ value shifted five places right (= $0.03125\,y(n-1)$)
added to

original stored $y(n-1)$ value shifted six places right (= $0.015625\,y(n-1)$)

For example, if $y(n-1) = 20_{10}$, then the above operations produce:

Accumulator A								Binary point	Accumulator B							
0	0	0	1	0	1	0	0	•	0	0	0	0	0	0	0	0
0	0	0	0	1	0	1	0		0	0	0	0	0	0	0	0
0	0	0	0	0	0	1	0		1	0	0	0	0	0	0	0
0	0	0	0	0	0	0	0		1	0	1	0	0	0	0	0
0	0	0	0	0	0	0	0		0	1	0	1	0	0	0	0
0	0	0	0	1	1	0	1		0	1	1	1	0	0	0	0

Therefore we see that $1101.0111_2 = 13.4375_{10}$ (which is the correct result for 20 x 0.671875).

It may be noted that four of the coefficients in equation (5.5) involve a value of 0.140625 (0.28125 = 2 x 0.140625; 0.671875 = 0.140625 + 0.53125), consequently 0.140625 multiplied by a sampled-data value is a repetitive operation in the evaluation of $y(n)$, and this is best achieved using a subroutine.

The assembly language program listing for the implementation of the digital filter defined by equation (5.5) is given in Table 5.2. It contains comments to assist the reader in following the sequence of events outlined in the flowchart shown in Figure 5.10.

```
                      NAM    DIGFIL
       0000     X1    EQU    0       RAM LOCATION
       0001     X2    EQU    X1+1    RAM LOCATION
       0002     Y1    EQU    X2+1    RAM LOCATION
       0003     Y2    EQU    Y1+1    RAM LOCATION
       0004     ACK   EQU    Y2+1    RAM LOCATION
       0005     XN    EQU    ACK+1   RAM LOCATION
       0060     SP    EQU    $60     STACK POINTER
       8008     PIA1  EQU    $8008   PIA I/O A OR DDRA
       8009     PIA2  EQU    $8009   PIA CRA
       800A     PIA3  EQU    $800A   PIA I/O B OR DDRB
       800B     PIA4  EQU    $800B   PIA CRB
F800                  ORG    $F800
F800   8E 0060  START LDS    #SP     (SP) = 0060
F803   4F             CLR A
F804   97 00          STA A  X1      (X1) = 0
F806   97 01          STA A  X2      (X2) = 0
F808   97 02          STA A  Y1      (Y1) = 0
F80A   97 03          STA A  Y2      (Y2) = 0
F80C   97 04          STA A  ACK     (ACK) = 0
F80E   B7 8009        STA A  PIA2    (CRA) = 0
F811   B7 800B        STA A  PIA4    (CRB) = 0
F814   B7 8008        STA A  PIA1    (DDRA) = 0, A:IN
F817   43             COM A
F818   B7 800A        STA A  PIA3    (DDRB) = FF, B:OUT
F81B   86 3C          LDA A  #$3C
F81D   B7 8009        STA A  PIA2    (CRA) = 3C, CRA S/R
                *                    OUTPUT = 1
                *                    CA1 DISABLED
                *                    I/O A SELECTED
F820   B7 800B        STA A  PIA4    (CRB) = 3C
                *                    I/O B SELECTED
F823   86 34    LOOP  LDA A  #$34
F825   B7 8009        STA A  PIA2    CA2 OUTPUT = 0
F828   86 3D          LDA A  #$3D
F82A   B7 8009        STA A  PIA2    CA2 OUTPUT = 1
                *                    CA1 ENABLED
                *                    CONVERT STARTED
F82D   0E             CLI            CLEAR INTERRUPT
                *                    MASK
F82E   3E             WAI            WAIT FOR
                *                    INTERRUPT
F82F   0F             SEL            SET INTERRUPT
                *                    MASK
F830   7E F823        JMP    LOOP    REPEAT LOOP
F833   4F       COMP  CLR A          START
                *                    SUBROUTINE
F834   54             LSR B
F835   54             LSR B
F836   54             LSR B          (B)=0.125 B
F837   1B             ABA            (A)=0.125 B
F838   54             LSR B
```

```
F839   54                     LSR B
F83A   54                     LSR B              (B)=0.015625 B

F83B   1B                     ABA                (A)=0.140625 B
F83C   39                     RTS                RETURN FROM
                       *                         SUBROUTINE
F83D   F6  8008        INTR   LDA B    PIA1      START INTERRUPT
                       *                         ROUTINE
                       *                         (B)=XN
F840   D7  05                 STA B    XN        SAVE XN
F842   BD  F833               JSR      COMP
F845   97  04                 STA A    ACK       (ACK)=0.140625 XN
F847   25  43                 BCS      SAT       IF OVERFLOW
                       *                         SATURATE OUTPUT
F849   D6  00                 LDA B    X1        (B)=X1
F84B   BD  F833               JSR      COMP
F84E   48                     ASL A              (A)=2 (0.140625 X1)
F84F   9B  04                 ADD A    ACK       (A)=0.140625 XN +
                       *                             0.28125 X1
F851   97  04                 STA A    ACK       SAVE (A) IN ACK
F853   25  37                 BCS      SAT       IF OVERFLOW
                       *                         SATURATE OUTPUT
F855   D6  01                 LDA B    X2
F857   BD  F833               JSR      COMP
F85A   9B  04                 ADD A    ACK       (A)=0.140625 XN +
                       *                             0.28125 X1 +
                       *                             0.140625 X2
F85C   97  04                 STA A    ACK       SAVE (A) IN ACK
F85E   25  2C                 BCS      SAT       IF OVERFLOW
                       *                         SATURATE OUTPUT
F860   D6  02                 LDA B    Y1
F862   BD  F833               JSR      COMP
F85A   9B  04                 ADD A    ACK       (A)=0.140625 XN +
                       *                             0.28125 X1 +
                       *                             0.140625 X2 +
                       *                             0.140625 Y1
F867   D6  02                 LDA B    Y1        (B)=Y1
F869   54                     LSR B              (B)=0.5 Y1
F86A   1B                     ABA                (A)=0.140625 XN +
                       *                             0.28125 X1 +
                       *                             0.140625 X2 +
                       *                             0.640625 Y1
F86B   54                     LSR B              (B)=0.25 Y1
F86C   54                     LSR B              (B)=0.125 Y1
F86D   54                     LSR B              (B)=0.0625 Y1
F86E   54                     LSR B              (B)=0.03125 Y1
F86F   1B                     ABA                (A)=0.140625 XN +
                       *                             0.28125 X1 +
                       *                             0.140625 X2 +
                       *                             0.671875 Y1
F870   25  1A                 BCS      SAT       IF OVERFLOW
                       *                         SATURATE OUTPUT
```

```
F872  D6 03           LDA B   Y2      (B)=Y2
F874  54              LSR B           (B)=0.5 Y2
F875  54              LSR B           (B)=0.25 Y2
F876  50              NEG B           (B)=-0.25 Y2
F877  1B              ABA             (A)=0.140625 XN +
                *                        0.28125 X1 +
                *                        0.140625 X2 +
                *                        0.671875 Y1 -
                *                        0.25 Y2 = YN
F878  2B 18           BMI     ZERO    IF MINUS SET YN=0
F87A  B7 800A         STA A   PIA3    OUTPUT YN
F87D  D6 02           LDA B   Y1      (B)=Y1
F87F  D7 03           STA B   Y2      (Y2)=Y1  UPDATE
F881  97 02           STA A   Y1      (Y1)=YN  UPDATE
F883  D6 00           LDA B   X1      (B)=X1
F885  D7 01           STA B   X2      (X2)=X1  UPDATE
F887  D6 05           LDA B   XN      (B)=XN
F889  D7 00           STA B   X1      (X1)=XN  UPDATE
F88B                  RTI             RETURN FROM
                *                     INTERRUPT
F88C  86 FF     SAT   LDA A   #$FF    (A)=FF
F88E  B7 800A         STA A   PIA3    SATURATE OUTPUT
F891  3B              RTI             RETURN FROM
                *                     INTERRUPT
F892  4F        ZERO  CLR A           (A)=0
F893  B7 800A         STA A   PIA3    ZERO THE OUTPUT
F896  3B              RTI             RETURN FROM
                *                     INTERRUPT
                *
FFF8                  ORG     $FFF8
FFF8  F83D      IRQV  FDB     INTR    DEFINE INTERRUPT
                *                     VECTOR
FFFE                  ORG     $FFFE
FFFE  F800      RSTV  FDB     START   DEFINE RESET
                *                     VECTOR
                *
                      OPT     LS      PRINT ASM OUTPUT
                *                     AND SYMBOLS
                *
                      END
```

Table 5.2 Assembly language program for digital filter implementation

***Performance Evaluation*:**

The performance of the digital lowpass filter may be evaluated using a squarewave input test signal having a period T_p, and expressed by the following Fourier series representation:

$$x(t) = \frac{2}{\pi}\left[\sin \omega_1 t + \frac{1}{3}\sin 3\omega_1 t + \frac{1}{5}\sin 5\omega_1 t + \cdots\right]$$

where $\omega_1 = 2\pi/T_p$. The considerable attenuation of the high frequency nth odd harmonic components (of the form $(1/n)\sin n\omega_1 t$) in the input signal, resulting from the filtering process, produces an output signal $y(t)$ which is an acceptable approximation to a sinusoidal signal with a predominant fundamental frequency component, that is

$$x(t) \cong \frac{2}{\pi}\sin \omega_1 t$$

Figure 5.12 shows the output waveform $y(t)$ resulting from the implementation of the lowpass digital filter linear difference equation (equation 5.5), using the input signal defined above.

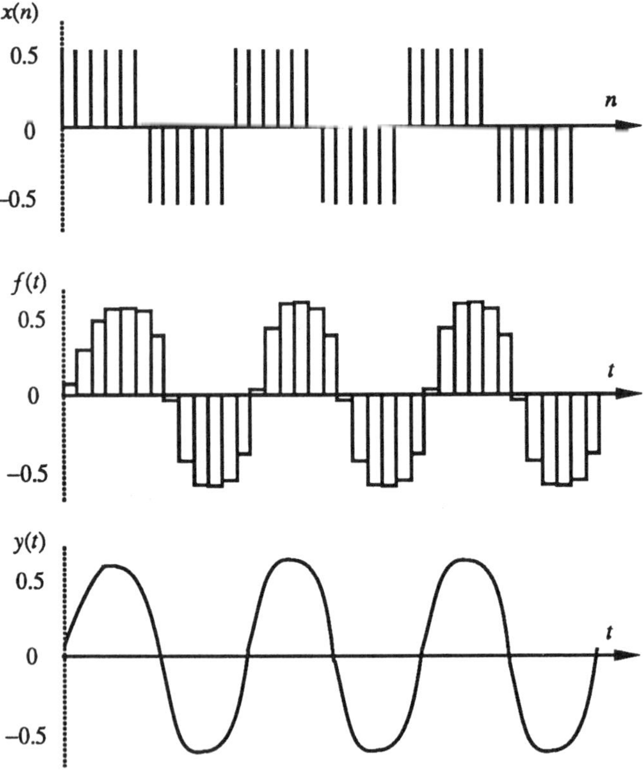

Figure 5.12 Waveforms obtained using DSP system.
Top: Input test signal, $x(n)$.
Centre: D/A converter output signal, $f(t)$.
Bottom: Reconstruction filter output signal, $y(t)$.

Figure 5.13 shows the magnitude/frequency spectra of the input test signal, $x(n)$, and of a sampled version of the reconstruction filter output signal, $y(n)$, computed via the FFT, with signals $x(n)$ and $y(n)$ obtained using a sampling frequency of 625 Hz. The attenuation ('reduction/removal') of the higher frequency components is clearly demonstrated by comparing the spectra.

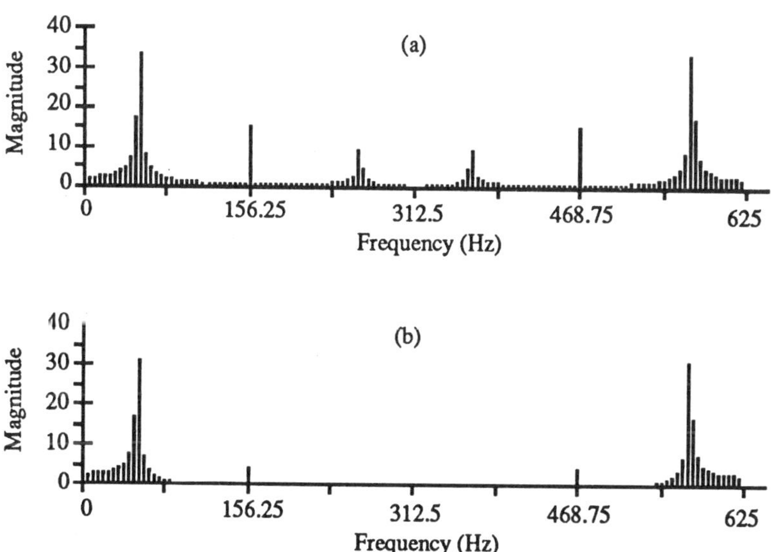

Figure 5.13 Magnitude/frequency spectra:
(a) Spectrum of signal, $x(n)$ (b) Spectrum of signal $y(n)$.

5.3 DSP Chips

DSP chips are special microprocessor devices having hardware architectures and instruction sets designed for high-speed digital signal processing applications. Texas Instruments is one of the world's leading suppliers of DSP chips and over many years they have had remarkable success with their TMS 320 family of integrated-circuits. There are other notable DSP chip manufacturers (e.g. Motorola) which play a major role in providing products for the DSP applications market. However, for this book, it is considered inappropriate to try to review and describe a wide range of chips available from a number of the leading suppliers. The authors feel that a suitable basic introduction to the main features of DSP chips and to associated implementation considerations can be achieved via a concise study of Texas Instruments' TMS320C26 DSP chip, which has been used in producing their relatively inexpensive TMS320C2x DSP Starter Kit (a PC peripheral-card containing a TMS320C26 chip and a TLC32040 analogue interface circuit).

5.3.1 TMS320C26 Digital Signal Processor

To illustrate the features of a typical DSP device we will consider the TMS320C26, but we will restrict our attention to only those details which will allow a simple practical digital filter implementation to be described. Comprehensive details of the TMS320C2x family of devices can be found in the 'TMS320C2x User's Guide', available from Texas Instruments.

A simplified block diagram of the TMS320C2x DSP chip is shown in Figure 5.14. It is based on a Harvard-type architecture having separate program and data memory spaces. Each memory space has its own address and data buses, thereby enabling instructions and data to be fetched from memory concurrently. This feature provides a significant processing speed improvement when compared with microprocessor devices based on the von Neumann-type architecture.

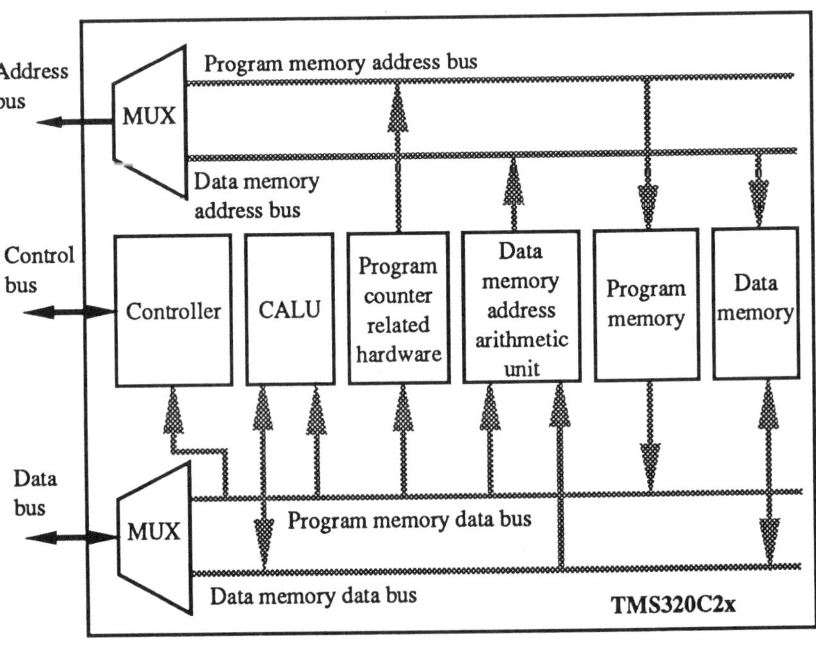

Figure 5.14 Simplified block diagram of the TMS320C2x DSP chip

The TMS320C26 provides three relatively large on-chip RAM blocks, configurable as separate program and data spaces, or as three continuous data blocks to allow increased flexibility in system design. Also an off-chip 64K-word directly addressable data memory space is included to facilitate implementation of DSP algorithms. The memory configuration flexibility can be demonstrated by considering the CONF instruction mode decoding table and the microprocessor/microcomputer mode select pin state. The CONF instruction mode decoding table is shown in Table 5.3.

CNF1	CNF0	B0	B1	B2	B3
0	0	Data	Data	Data	Data
0	1	Program	Data	Data	Data
1	0	Program	Program	Data	Data
1	1	Program	Program	Data	Program

Table 5.3 CONF mode decoding table

Figure 5.15 shows the TMS320C26 memory map after a CONF 1 instruction has been executed.

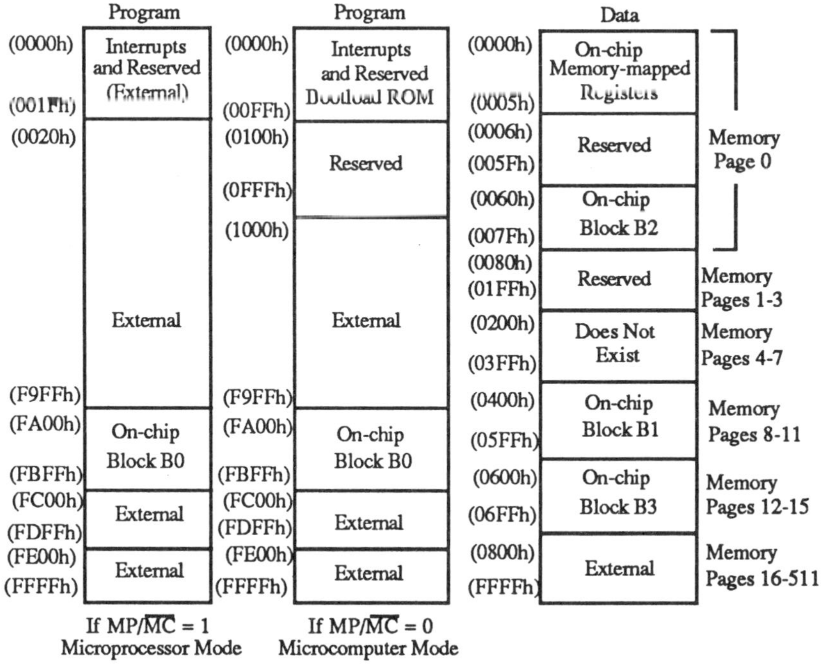

Figure 5.15 TMS320C26 memory-map after a CONF 1 instruction

The TMS320C26 can operates in one of two possible modes, namely the microprocessor mode or the microcomputer mode. On power-up, or when the TMS320C26 is reset, the program counter (PC) is set to zero. If the TMS320C26 is set to operate in the microprocessor mode (MP/ $\overline{\text{MC}}$ pin connected to +5V), the lower portion of the program memory is external as shown in Figure 5.15, and a branch instruction is required in program memory location zero to direct program control to the start of the user program. If the TMS320C26 is set to operate in the microcomputer mode (MP/ $\overline{\text{MC}}$ pin connected to 0V), a bootload (booting-up) program in the lower portion of the program memory (see Figure 5.15) is executed on power-up to load the user program into the internal memory before executing it.

Six memory-mapped registers are provided in the data memory space (see Figure 5.15) and are therefore accessed as normal data memory locations. These registers are listed in Table 5.4.

Register	Memory address	Definition
DDR (15-0)	0	Serial port data receive register
DXR (15-0)	1	Serial port data transmit register
TIM (15-0)	2	Timer register
PRD (15-0)	3	Period register
IMR (15-0)	4	Interrupt mask register
GREG (7-0)	5	Global memory allocation register

Table 5.4 Memory-mapped registers

The TMS320C2x internal hardware is briefly summarised below:

Accumulator (ACC):
A 32-bit register split in two halves: ACCH (accumulator high) and ACCL (accumulator low). Used for storage of ALU output.

Arithmetic Logic Unit (ALU):
A 32-bit two's-complement arithmetic logic unit for performing various arithmetic and logic operations. It has two 32-bit input ports and one 32-bit output port connected to the accumulator.

Auxiliary Register Arithmetic Unit (ARAU):
A 16-bit unsigned arithmetic unit used to perform operations on auxiliary register data. It is mainly used in generating data memory addresses.

Auxiliary Register File (AR0-AR7):
A register file containing eight 16-bit auxiliary registers (AR0-AR7), used for addressing data memory, temporary storage, or integer arithmetic processing through the ARAU.

Auxiliary Register File Bus (AFB):
A 16-bit bus that carries data from the AR pointed to by the ARP.

Auxiliary Register Pointer (ARP):
A 3-bit register used to select one of eight auxiliary registers.

Auxiliary Register Pointer Buffer (ARB):
A 3-bit register used to buffer the ARP.

Central Arithmetic Logic Unit (CALU):
The grouping of the ALU, multiplier, accumulator, and scaling shift register.

Data Bus (D):
A 16-bit bus used to route data to/from data memory.

Data Memory Address Bus (DAB):
A 16-bit bus that carries the data memory address.

Data Memory Page Pointer (DP):
A 9-bit register pointing to the address of the current page. Data pages are 128 words each, resulting in 512 pages of addressable data memory space (some locations are reserved).

Direct Data Memory Address Bus (DRB):
A 16-bit bus that carries the direct address for the data memory, which is the concatenation of the DP register with the seven least significant bits of the instruction.

Global Memory Allocation Register (GREG):
An 8-bit memory-mapped register for allocating the size of the data memory space to be globally accessible by other processors operating within a multiprocessor system.

Instruction Register (IR):
A 16-bit register used to store the currently executing instruction.

Interrupt Flag Register (IFR):
A 6-bit register used to flag (a) active-low inputs produced by external interrupts on pins, $\overline{\text{INT0}}$, $\overline{\text{INT1}}$, and $\overline{\text{INT2}}$, (b) the internal interrupts generated by the transmit and receive sections of the internal serial port, XINT/RINT, and (c) the internal timer interrupt, TINT. The IFR is not accessible through software.

Interrupt Mask Register (IMR):
A 6-bit memory-mapped register for masking external and internal interrupts.

Microcall Stack (MCS):
A single-word stack that temporarily stores the contents of the PFC while the PFC is being used to address data memory with the block move (BLKD/BLKP), multiply-accumulate(MAC/MACD), and table read/write (TBLR/TBLW) instructions.

Multiplier (MULT):
A 16 x 16-bit parallel multiplier.

Period Register (PRD):
A 16-bit memory-mapped register which holds the starting count value for the timer. It reloads the timer every time the timer decrements to zero.

Prefetch Counter (PFC):
A 16-bit counter used to prefetch program instructions. The PFC contains the address of the instruction currently being prefetched. To increase the processing speed, the TMS320C2x uses a three-level pipeline to enable three operations to be executed concurrently. During any instruction cycle, three different instructions can be active, each at a different stage of completion. For example, at the time when the N*th* instruction is being prefetched, the previous (N – 1)*th* instruction is being decoded, and the previous (N – 2)*th* instruction is being executed. Generally, the pipeline is transparent to the user, but in some cases the pipeline sequence is broken when, for example, conditional branch instructions are encountered. The PFC is updated when a new prefetch is initiated. The PFC is also used to address program memory when using the block move (BLKP), multiply-accumulate(MAC/MACD), and table read/write (TBLR/TBLW) instructions, and to address data memory using the block move (BLKD) instruction.

Product Register(PR):
A 32-bit product register used to hold the multiplier product. The PR can also be accessed as the most or least significant words by using the SPH/SPL (store P register high/low) instructions.

Program Bus (P):
A 16-bit bus used to route instructions from program memory (and data from data memory for the MAC and MACD instructions).

Program Counter (PC):
A 16-bit program counter used to address program memory. The PC always contains the address of the next instruction to be executed. The PC contents are updated following each instruction decode operation.

Program Memory Address Bus (PAB):
A 16-bit bus that carries the program memory address.

Queue Instruction Register (QIR):
A 16-bit register used to store prefetched instructions.

Random Access Memory (RAM, B0):
A RAM block with 256 locations each holding a 16-bit word. It can be configured as either data or program memory (512 locations for TMS320C26).

Random Access Memory (RAM, B1):
A data RAM block organised as 256 locations each holding a 16-bit word, (512 locations for TMS320C26 which can configured as program or data memory).

Random Access Memory (RAM, B2):
A data RAM block organised as 32 locations each holding a 16-bit word.

Random Access Memory (RAM, B3):
This RAM block exists in the TMS320C26 only. It consists of 512 locations each holding a 16-bit word, and it can be configured as either data or program memory.

Read Only Memory (ROM):
A ROM block organised as 4096 locations each holding a 16-bit word for the TMS320C25, or 256 locations for the TMS320C26, or 8192 locations for the TMS320C28.

Repeat Counter (RPTC):
An 8-bit counter to control the repeated execution of a single instruction. When it is loaded with an integer number, I, it causes the next single instruction to be executed (I + 1) times.

Serial Port Data Receive Register (DRR):
A 16-bit memory-mapped serial port data receive register holding the data received on the DR (data receive) input pin. Only the eight least significant bits are used in the byte mode.

Serial Port Data Transmit Register (DXR):
A 16-bit memory-mapped serial port data transmit register holding the data to be transmitted via the DX (data transmit) output pin. Only the eight least significant bits are used in the byte mode.

Serial Port Receive Shift Register (RSR):
A 16-bit register used to shift in serial port data from the RX pin. RSR contents are sent to the DRR after a serial transfer is completed. RSR is not directly accessible through software.

Serial Port Transmit Shift Register (XSR):
A 16-bit register used to shift out serial port data onto the DX pin. XSR contents are loaded from DXR at the beginning of a serial port transmit operation. XSR is not directly accessible through software.

Shifters:
Shifters are located at the ALU input, the accumulator output, and the product register output. Also an in-place shifter is located within the accumulator. Through program instructions, these shifters enable numerical scaling and normalisation to be carried out via right and left shifts of data values.

Stack:
A hardware stack, containing 8 locations each holding a 16-bit word, is used to store the PC during interrupts or calls. The ACCL and data memory values may also be pushed onto and popped from the stack.

Status Registers (ST0, ST1):
Two 16-bit status registers that contain status and control bits.

Temporary Register (TR):
A 16-bit register that holds either an operand for the multiplier or a shift code for the scaling shifter.

Timer (TIM):
A 16-bit memory-mapped register holding the current count of the on-chip timer which is continuously decremented. It can be used in timing control applications.

The TMS320C2x family of DSP chips provides three maskable user interrupts $\overline{\text{INT0}}$, $\overline{\text{INT1}}$, and $\overline{\text{INT2}}$ to enable external devices to interrupt the processor. Internal interrupts are generated by the serial port (RINT and XINT), by the timer (TINT), and by the software interrupt (TRAP) instruction. The interrupts are prioritised as defined in Table 5.5.

Interrupt source	Interrupt vector location	Priority level	Function
$\overline{\text{RS}}$	0h	1 (highest)	External reset signal
$\overline{\text{INT0}}$	2h	2	External user interrupt 0
$\overline{\text{INT1}}$	4h	3	External user interrupt 1
$\overline{\text{INT2}}$	6h	4	External user interrupt 2
TINT	18h	5	Internal timer interrupt
RINT	1Ah	6	Serial port receive interrupt
XINT	1Ch	7 (lowest)	Serial port transmit interrupt
TRAP	1Eh	N/A	TRAP instruction address

Table 5.5

The TRAP interrupt (used for software interrupts) is not prioritised, but it does have its own interrupt vector location. Each interrupt address is spaced apart by two memory locations so that branch instructions can be accommodated in the interrupt vector locations if required.

When an interrupt occurs it is stored in the 6-bit interrupt flag register (IFR). External interrupts $\overline{\text{INT0}}$, $\overline{\text{INT1}}$, and $\overline{\text{INT2}}$ and internal interrupts RINT, XINT and TINT are stored in the IFR until they are recognised; they are automatically cleared by the interrupt acknowledge $\overline{\text{IACK}}$ signal or by the reset $\overline{\text{RS}}$ signal. No instructions are provided for reading from/writing to the IFR.

The TMS320C2x has a memory-mapped interrupt mask register (IMR) for masking internal and external interrupts, see Figure 5.16.

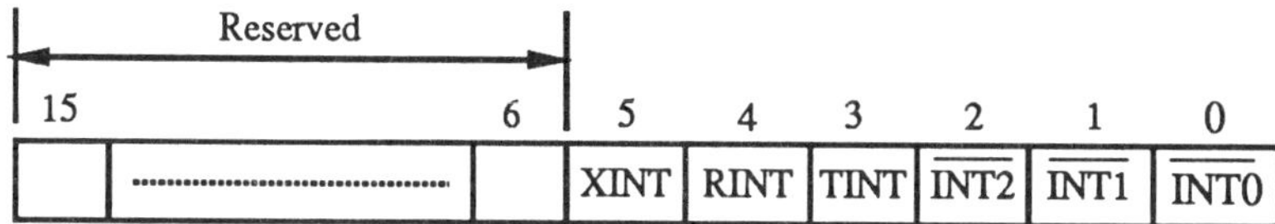

Figure 5.16 Interrupt mask register

A '1' in bit positions 0 through 5 of the IMR enables the corresponding interrupt, provided that the interrupt mode bit (INTM), which is bit 9 of status register ST0, is '0'. The IMR is accessible with memory read and write operations. When the IMR is read, the unused bits (6 through 15) are read as '1's. The lower six bits are used to read from or write to the IMR. The interrupt mode bit (INTM) is set to '1' by the interrupt acknowledge $\overline{\text{IACK}}$ signal, the DINT instruction, or by the reset signal. The interrupt mode bit (INTM) is reset to '0' by the EINT instruction.

To facilitate the computation of the sum of products of two data sequences, the TMS320C2x contains a dedicated central arithmetic logic unit (CALU) for performing high-speed multiply and accumulate operations. Figure 5.17 shows the CALU in block diagram form. The multiplier takes two inputs, one from the 16-bit temporary register (TR), the other from the multiplexer used to select the 16-bit word on the data memory data bus or the 16-bit word on the program memory data bus, and places the 32-bit result in the product register (PR). There are also two inputs to the arithmetic logic unit (ALU), one from the multiplexer which selects the numerically scaled version of the PR contents or the numerically scaled version of the data word existing on the data memory data bus, the other is the accumulator contents. The resulting ALU output value is held in the accumulator. A shifter is placed at the output of the accumulator to facilitate numerical scaling of the computed results.

The TMS320C2x supports three forms of memory addressing, namely, immediate addressing, direct addressing, and indirect addressing.

Immediate addressing:
For this addressing mode, the instruction consists of an op-code followed immediately by a data value. There are single-word short immediate instructions for 8-bit and 13-bit data values, and two-word long immediate instructions for 16-bit data values. For example, the assembly language instructions, ADDK 6Eh and ADLK 6E6Eh respectively cause the DSP chip to add $(6E)_{16}$ or $(6E6E)_{16}$ to the current contents of the accumulator.

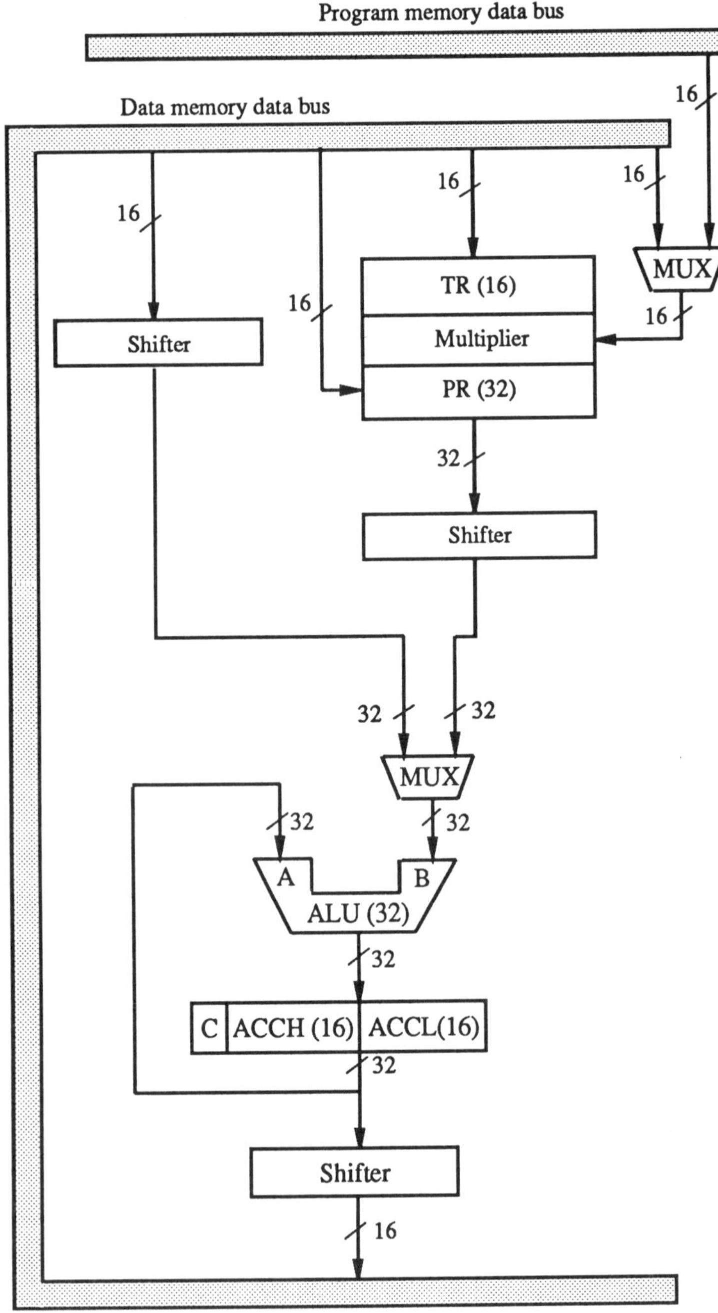

Figure 5.17 Central arithmetic logic unit block diagram

Direct addressing:
For this addressing mode, the instruction consists of an op-code followed by the least significant 7 bits of the data memory address, which is concatenated with the contents of the data memory page pointer (DP) to form the data memory address. For example, if DP = 8, the assembly language instruction ADD 1, 2 causes the contents of data memory location $(0401)_{16}$ to be left-shifted 2 bits (multiplied by 4) before being added to the current contents of the accumulator. The contents of the data memory location remain unchanged.

Indirect addressing:
For this addressing mode (denoted by * in the assembly language), the contents of the current auxiliary register, pointed to by the auxiliary register pointer (ARP), are used as the data memory address. After accessing the data, the contents of the current auxiliary register may be manipulated by the auxiliary register arithmetic unit (ARAU). The current auxiliary register can be incremented/decremented by one (denoted by *+ and *– respectively in the assembly language), or the contents of auxiliary register 0 (AR0) can be added to/subtracted from the current auxiliary register (denoted by *0+ and *0– respectively in the assembly language), or the contents of auxiliary register 0 (AR0) can be added to/subtracted from the current auxiliary register with reverse carry propagation (denoted by *BR0+ and *BR0– respectively in the assembly language). For example, if ARP = 1 and AR1 = $(0401)_{16}$, the assembly language instruction ADD *–,2 causes the contents of data memory location $(0401)_{16}$ to be left-shifted two places before being added to the accumulator, and the contents of AR1 are autodecremented by one to $(0400)_{16}$.

The TM320C2x DSP chip has a complex programmable processor architecture with a powerful instruction set that supports numeric-intensive signal processing operations and general purpose applications.

The TMS320C2x DSP Starter Kit uses a TLC32040 analogue interface circuit to enable the required A/D and D/A conversions to be performed. Using the starter kit it is possible to implement a digital filter using a small number of the available TMS320C26 instructions. We will therefore restrict our consideration to those instructions used in the following case study, and these are summarised (in alphabetical order) below.

APAC *Add P register to Accumulator*

The contents of the P register are shifted as defined by the product shift mode bits (PM) in the ST1 status register, and added to the contents of the accumulator. The result is left in the accumulator.

Note: If the two PM bits (bits 0 and 1 in Status Register ST1) are 00, the multiplier's 32-bit product is loaded into the ALU with no shift.

ANDK *AND Immediate With Accumulator With Shift*

The 16-bit immediate constant is left-shifted as specified and ANDed with the accumulator. The result is left in the accumulator. Low-order bits below and high-order bits above the shifted value are treated as zeros, clearing the corresponding bits in the accumulator.

Note: The accumulator's most-significant bit is always zeroed regardless of the shift-code value.

B *Branch Unconditionally*

The current auxiliary register (AR) and auxiliary register pointer (ARP) are modified as specified, and control passes to the designated program memory address (pma).

Note: No AR or ARP modification occurs if nothing is specified in those fields. The pma can be either a symbolic or numeric address.

EINT *Enable Interrupt*
The interrupt-mode flag (INTM) in the status register is cleared (set to '0'). Maskable interrupts are enabled after the instruction following EINT executes. This allows an interrupt service routine to re-enable interrupts and execute a RET instruction before any other pending interrupts are processed.

Note: The load status register (LST) instruction does not affect INTM.

IDLE *Idle Until Interrupt*
The IDLE instruction forces the program being executed to wait until an interrupt or reset occurs. The PC is incremented once only, and the device remains in an idle state until interrupted.

LAC *Load Accumulator With Shift*
The contents of the specified data memory address are left-shifted and loaded into the accumulator. During shifting, low-order bits are zero-filled. High-order bits are sign-extended if the status register ST1 sign-extension mode bit (SXM) = 1 and zeroed if SXM = 0.

LACK *Load Accumulator Immediate Short*
The 8-bit constant is loaded into the accumulator right-justified. The upper 24 bits of the accumulator are zeroed because sign extension is suppressed.

LALK *Load Accumulator Immediate Long Immediate With Shift*
The left-shifted 16-bit immediate constant is loaded into the accumulator.

LDPK *Load Data Memory Page Pointer Immediate*
The data memory page pointer register (DP) is loaded with a 9-bit constant. The DP and 7-bit memory address are concatenated to form 16-bit direct data memory addresses. DP ≥ 8 specifies external data memory. DP = 4 through 7 specifies on-chip RAM blocks B0 or B1. Block B2 is located in the upper 32 words of page 0. DP may also be loaded by the LST and LDP instructions.

LT *Load T Register*
The T register is loaded with the contents of the specified data memory address (dma). The LT instruction may be used to load the T register in preparation for multiplication.

LTA *Load T Register and Accumulate Previous Product*
The T register is loaded with the contents of the specified data memory address (dma). The contents of the product register (P), shifted as defined by the PM status bits, are added to the accumulator, with the result left in the accumulator. The function of the LTA instruction is included in the LTD instruction.

LTD *Load T Register, Accumulate Previous Product, and Move Data*
The T register is loaded with the contents of the specified data memory address (dma). The contents of the product register (P), shifted as defined by the PM status bits, are added to the accumulator, with the result left in the accumulator. The contents of the specified data memory address are also copied to the next higher data memory address.

The instruction is valid for blocks B1 and B2 and also valid for block B0 if block B0 is configured as data memory. The data move function is continuous across the boundary of blocks B0 and B1, but cannot be used with external data memory or memory-mapped registers.

Note: If used with external data memory, the function of LTD is identical to that of LTA.

MPY *Multiply*
The contents of the T register are multiplied by the contents of the addressed data memory location. The result is placed in the P register.

ORK *OR Immediate With Accumulator With Shift*
The left-shifted 16-bit immediate constant is ORed with the accumulator. The result is left in the accumulator. Low-order bits below and high-order bits above the shifted value are treated as zeros. The corresponding bits of the accumulator are unaffected.

Note: The most significant bit of the accumulator is not affected, regardless of the shift code value.

RET *Return From Subroutine*
The contents of the top stack register are copied into the program counter. The stack is then popped one level. RET is used with call subroutine instructions.

RPTK *Repeat Instruction as Specified by Immediate Value*
The 8-bit immediate value is loaded into the repeat counter (RPTC). This causes the following instruction to be executed one time more than the number loaded into the RPTC (provided that it is a repeatable instruction). Interrupts are masked out until the next instruction has been executed the specified number of times. The RPTC is cleared by the reset signal.

SACL *Store Low Accumulator With Shift*
The low-order bits of the accumulator are shifted 0 to 7 bits as specified by the shift code, and stored in data memory. The low-order bits are filled with zeros, and the high-order bits are lost. The accumulator itself is unaffected.

SFR *Shift Accumulator Right*
The SFR instruction shifts the accumulator right one bit.

If SXM = 1, the instruction produces an arithmetic shift right. The sign bit (most-significant bit) is unchanged and is also copied into bit 30. Bit 0 is shifted into the carry bit (C).

If SXM = 0, the instruction produces a logical shift right. All of the accumulator bits are shifted by one bit right. The least-significant bit is shifted into the carry bit, and the most-significant bit is set to zero.

ZAC *Zero Accumulator*
The contents of the accumulator are replaced with zero. The ZAC instruction is implemented as a special case of the LACK instruction.

Note: ZAC assembles as LACK0.

The following TMS320C26 assembler language program includes a number of assembler directives, which are briefly summarised below.

.ds [address]	This directive tells the assembler to begin assembling source code into data memory starting at the specified address.
.end	This directive tells the assembler that the end of the program has been reached.
.entry	This directive tells the assembler the address of the program counter when a file is loaded.
.ps [address]	This directive tells the assembler to begin assembling into program memory starting at the specified address.
.set value	This directive equates a constant value to a symbol.
.word value	This directive initialises a 16-bit integer.

5.3.2 Case Study: TMS320C26-based Digital Filter

Aim:

The aim of this case study is to present information to enable the reader to understand the main practical considerations involved in producing a digital filter implemented using the TMS320C26 DSP chip.

The Hardware:

A simplified block diagram of the TMS320C2x DSP Starter Kit (containing a TMS320C26 DSP chip and a TLC32040 analogue interface circuit (AIC)) is shown in Figure 5.18. It is normally connected to communication port 1 of a personal computer (PC COM PORT 1) via an RS232 serial link.

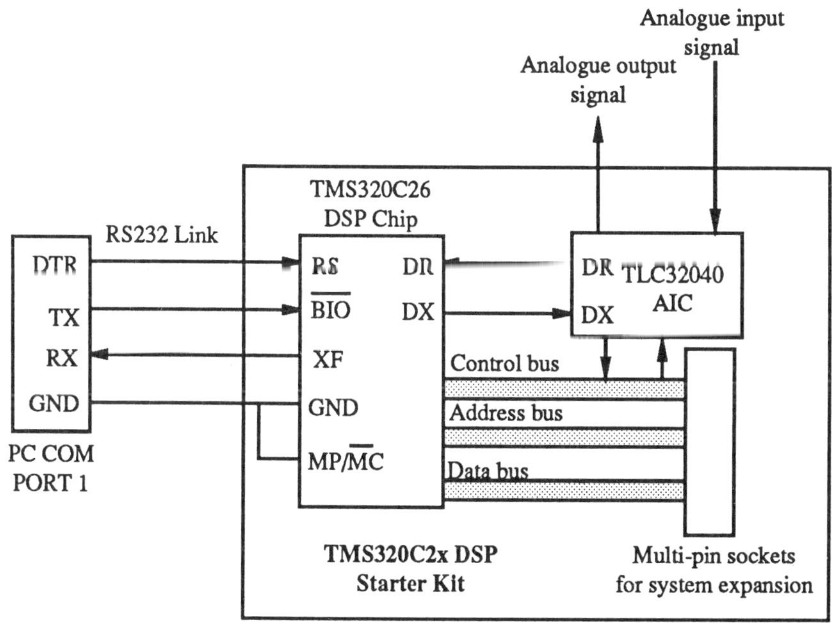

Figure 5.18 Simplified block diagram of TMS320C2x DSP Starter Kit

Basically, upon being reset by the PC (via the PC COM PORT DTR output), the TMS320C26 executes a bootloader program held in its internal ROM to download (via the $\overline{\text{BIO}}$ input pin) the user program from the PC to its internal program memory. The TMS320C26 returns status information to the PC via its XF output pin. On completion of the download operation the TMS320C26 executes the user program, and also communicates with the analogue interface circuit via its internal serial data port (the DR/DX link). In addition to the 14-bit A/D and D/A converters, the TLC32040 AIC chip contains an anti-aliasing filter, a reconstruction filter and a TMS320 DSP chip compatible serial data port interface circuit. The cutoff frequency of each filter and the clock frequency for the converters are programmable, and can therefore be initialised at the start of an assembly language program.

The data word bit pattern sent between the AIC and the TMS320C26 on the DR and DX lines is shown in Figure 5.19.

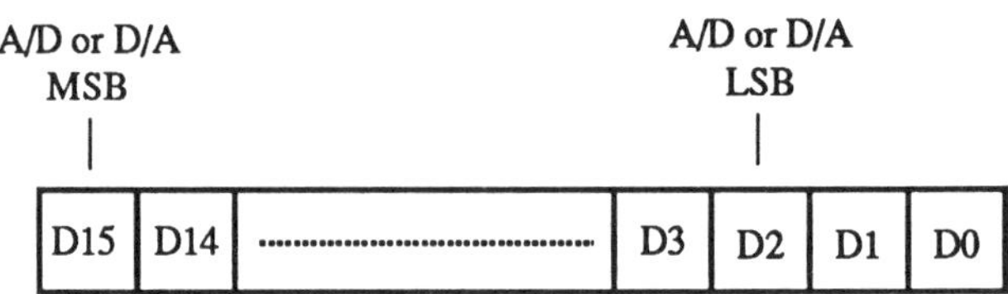

Figure 5.19 AIC DR or DX data word bit pattern

The AIC internal control register and frequency dividing counters can be accessed by setting the two least significant bits (D0 and D1) in the DX data word to '1' to activate secondary DX communication.

Filter Example:

The filter specification for this case study is:

Lowpass filter characteristic with a cut-off frequency of 5 kHz.
Prototype is a 2nd-order Butterworth lowpass filter.
Bilinear z-transform design method to be used.
Sampling frequency is 16 kHz.

The resulting digital filter linear difference equation is

$$y(n) = 0.4182\,x(n) + 0.8363\,x(n-1) + 0.4182\,x(n-2) - 0.4629\,y(n-1) - 0.2097\,y(n-2)$$

Implementation of the Difference Equation:

In implementing the linear difference equation, it is appropriate to scale-up the coefficient values which are fractional numbers, so that they can be conveniently stored in memory as integer numbers. However, there is a conflict in selecting a scaling factor, namely, a large scaling factor may cause an arithmetic overflow, whereas a small scaling factor may significantly increase quantisation noise. To achieve the scaling operation in a straightforward manner via left or right shifting instructions, the scaling factor is set equal to 2^m, where m is an integer. A scaling factor of $2^{13} = 8192$ is used in implementing the linear difference equation. Therefore, multiplying both sides of the linear difference equation by this scaling factor gives

$$8192\,y(n) = 3426\,x(n) + 6851\,x(n-1) + 3426\,x(n-2) - 3792\,y(n-1) - 1718\,y(n-2)$$

It is seen that the sum of products is computed using the scaled-up coefficients and equals a value of 8192 $y(n)$, which must then be scaled-down to $y(n)$ to obtain the correct output value. The required scaling-down operation in this case is achieved by right shifting 13 bit positions the sum of products value 8192 $y(n)$.

To implement this digital filter using the TMS320C2x DSP Starter Kit the assembly language program listed in Table 5.6 was developed.

```
***********************************
* Declaration of memory-mapped registers*
***********************************
DRR      .set    0       ;serial port data receive register
DXR      .set    1       ;serial port data transmit register
IMR      .set    4       ;interrupt mask register
**********************************************************
*Declaration of addresses for storing current/past input/output values*
**********************************************************
X        .set    400h    ;current input, x(n)
X-1      .set    401h    ;previous input, x(n-1)
X-2      .set    402h    ;previous input, x(n-2)
Y-1      .set    403h    ;previous output, y(n-1)
Y-2      .set    404h    ;previous output, y(n-2)
******************
*IIR filter coefficients*
*******************
         .ds     410h    ;start address of filter coefficient table
*                        ;scaling factor, SF = 8192
A0       .word   3426    ;A0 = 0.4182 * 8192
A1       .word   6851    ;A1 = 0.8363 * 8192
A2       .word   3426    ;A2 = A0
B1       .word   -3792   ;B1 = -0.4629 * 8192
B2       .word   -1718   ;B2 = -0.2097 * 8192
*************
*Interrupt vector*
*************
         .ps     0fa0ah  ;address of receive interrupt vector
         B       IIR     ;execute IIR filter routine
         .ps     0fa0ch  ;address of transmit interrupt vector
         B       TX      ;execute transmit interrupt  routine
*****************************************
*Clear locations reserved for past input/output values*
*****************************************
         .ps     0fb00h  ;start address of program section
         .entry          ;set program counter to start of program
         ZAC             ;clear ACC (accumulator)
```

```
          LDPK   8      ;point to page 8 (from 0400h to 047fh)
          SACL   X-1    ;clear past inputs
          SACL   X-2
          SACL   Y-1    ;clear past outputs
          SACL   Y-2
**************************************
*AIC (Analogue Interface Circuit) initialisation*
**************************************
          LDPK   0      ;point to page 0 (from 0000h to 007fh)
          LAC    IMR    ;ACC = (IMR)
          ORK    20h    ;enable transmit interrupt by
          SACL   IMR    ;setting XINT (bit 5 of IMR) to 1
          LACK   03h    ;ACC = 03
          IDLE          ;idle until interrupt
          SACL   DXR    ;initiate secondary communication
          LALK   4892h  ;ACC = 4892h
          IDLE          ;idle until interrupt
          SACL   DXR    ;TB/RB = 36/36 (sampling frequency = 16 kHz)
          IDLE          ;idle until interrupt
          LACK   03h    ;gain access to AIC internal register by
          SACL   DXR    ;initiating secondary communication protocol
          IDLE          ;idle until transmission interrupt
          LALK   0e3h   ;AIC control register:
          SACL   DXR    ;bit7 = bit6 =1, to set A/D gain = 1
*                       ;bit5 = 1, for synchronous transmit and receive
*                       ;mode
*                       ;bit4 =0, to disable the auxiliary analogue inputs
*                       ;bit3 = 0, to disable the loopback function
*                       ;bit2 = 0, to bypass the A/D bandpass filter
*                       ;bit1 = bit0 =1, to access AIC control register
          IDLE          ;idle until transmission interrupt
********************
*Get input sample value*
********************

          LAC    IMR    ;enable transmit interrupt by
          ORK    10h    ;setting RINT (bit 4 of IMR) to 1
          SACL   IMR    ;IMR = (ACC)
LOOP:     IDLE          ;wait for input sample from A/D
          B      LOOP
**************
*IIR filter routine*
**************
IRR:      LAC    DDR    ;get current input sample
          SFR
          SFR           ;shift LSB of A/D to bit0 position
          LDPK   8      ;point to page 8
```

```
        SACL  X      ;save current input sample
        ZAC          ;clear ACC
        LT    X-2    ;T reg. = x(n-2)
        MPY   A2     ;A2*x(n-2)
        LTD   X-1    ;T reg. = x(n-1), ACC = A2*x(n-2), and x(n-2) =
*                    ;x(n-1)
        MPY   A1     ;A1*x(n-1)
        LTD   X      ;T reg. = x, ACC = A1*x(n-1)+A2*x(n-2), and
*                    ;x(n-1) = x(n)
        MPY   A0     ;A0*x(n)
        LTA   Y-2    ;T reg. = y(n-2), ACC = A0*x(n)+A1*x(n-1)
*                    ;+ A2*x(n-2)
        MPY   B2     ;B2*y(n-2)
        LTD   Y-1    ;T reg. = y(n-1), ACC = A0*x(n)+A1*x(n-1)
*                    ;+ A2*x(n-2)+B2*y(n-2), and y(n-2) = y(n-1)
        MPY   B1     ;B1*y(n-1)
        APAC         ;ACC = A0*x(n)+A1*x(n-1)+A2*x(n-2)
*                    ;+B1*y(n-1)+B2*y(n-2)
        RPTK  12     ;ACC = (ACC)/SF = (ACC)/8192
        SFR
        SACL  Y-1    ;y(n-1) = y(n)
        LDPK  0      ;point to page 0
        SACL  DXR,2  ;output y(n) to D/A with LSB at bit2
        EINT         ;enable next interrupt from A/D
        RET          ;return from IIR filter routine
****************************
*Transmit interrupt service routine*
****************************
TX:     EINT         ;enable next interrupt from A/D or D/A
        RET          ;return from transmit interrupt service routine
        .end         ;end of program
```

Table 5.6 TMS320C26 Assembly language program for digital filter

This program was assembled and run using the TMS320C2x DSP Starter Kit. It performed the specified lowpass filtering process.

5.4 Concluding Remarks

In this chapter basic forms of microprocessor and DSP chip hardware and assembly language programming aspects of digital filter implementations have been introduced using two specific case studies. Both offer effective and inexpensive methods of producing practical forms of implementation, and both are suitable for students wishing to gain hands-on experience of real-time signal processing. This can be achieved via practical DSP laboratory/project assignment work involving designing, building, programming and testing the M6802 microprocessor-based digital filter, or by programming the TMS320C2x DSP Starter Kit.

Problems

P5.1

Convert the following memory addresses to their decimal equivalents:

(i) $(3E6C)_{16}$

(ii) $(A00FF3)_{16}$

(iii) $(111000101100010001101100)_2$

P5.2

Convert the following memory addresses to their hexadecimal equivalents:

(i) $(11010000111111000000000011010000)_2$

(ii) $(2002334)_{10}$

P5.3

With reference to the basic programming model of the M6802 microprocessor, draw a flowchart to represent the operations required to perform multiplication of two positive 8-bit binary numbers. For implementation, assume that the multiplier is held in memory location $(0000)_{16}$ and that the multiplicand is held in memory location $(0001)_{16}$. Also assume that a 'shift to the left' operation is used on the multiplicand, and that it will be necessary to have two memory locations available to hold the shifted multiplicand; memory location $(0001)_{16}$ can be used to hold the least significant (LS), byte and memory location $(0002)_{16}$ can be used to hold the most significant (MS) byte. The 16-bit result is to be held in Accumulator A (MS byte) and Accumulator B (LS byte).

P5.4

Determine the MC6821 PIA Control Register initialisation formats for the following two control line specifications:

	CA1	CB1	CA2	CB2
(a)	Enable interrupt input, set by a high-to-low transition	Disabled (not used)	Disabled (not used)	Enabled and used as a set/reset output
(b)	Enable interrupt input, set by a low-to-high transition	Enable interrupt input, set by a high-to-low transition	Enabled and used as set/reset output	Enabled and used as interrupt input set by a low-to-high transition

P5.5

With reference to the Case Study presented in Section 5.2.3 (page 268) suppose that the MC6821 PIA address range is to be changed to E480 - E483, what connection change to the CS0 PIA input (MC6821, pin 22) in Figure 5.11 is required? What corresponding changes have to be made to the assembler language program given in Table 5.2 (page 275)?

P5.6

With reference to the Case Study presented in Section 5.3.2 (page 292) what changes have to be made to the assembler language program given in Table 5.6 (page 295) to implement the digital filter implemented in the Case Study presented in Section 5.2.3? This digital filter is defined by equation (5.4) on page 273.

Answers to Problems

CHAPTER 1

P1.1 Minimum number of samples = 4000

P1.2 Key for following three graphs: a = 0.5 A; b = 0.05 A

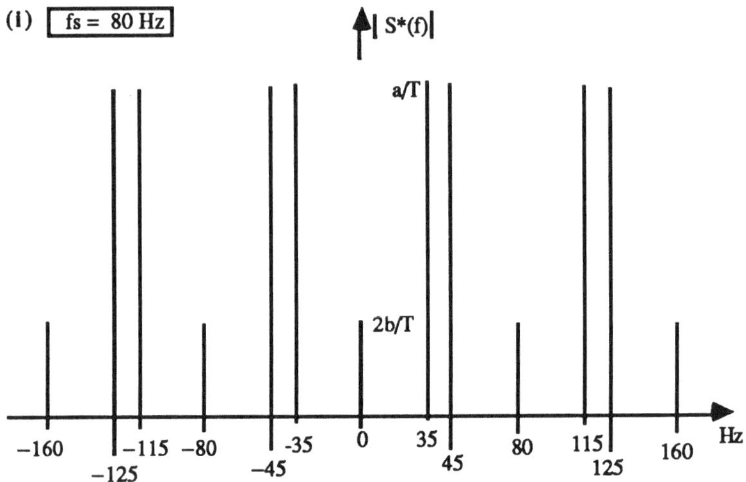

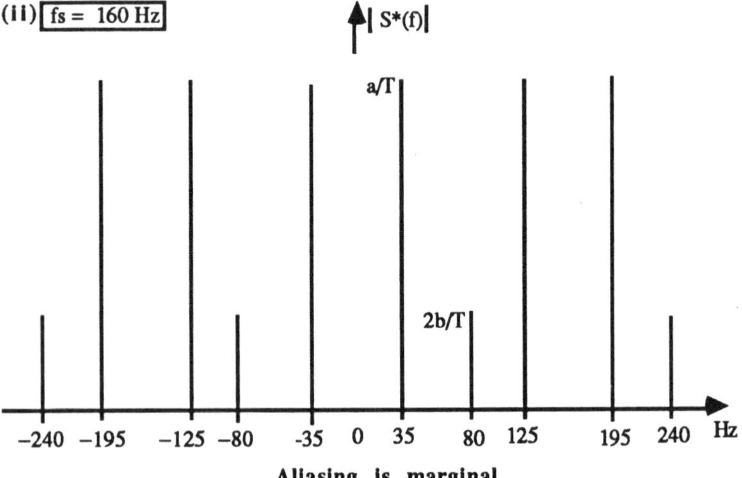

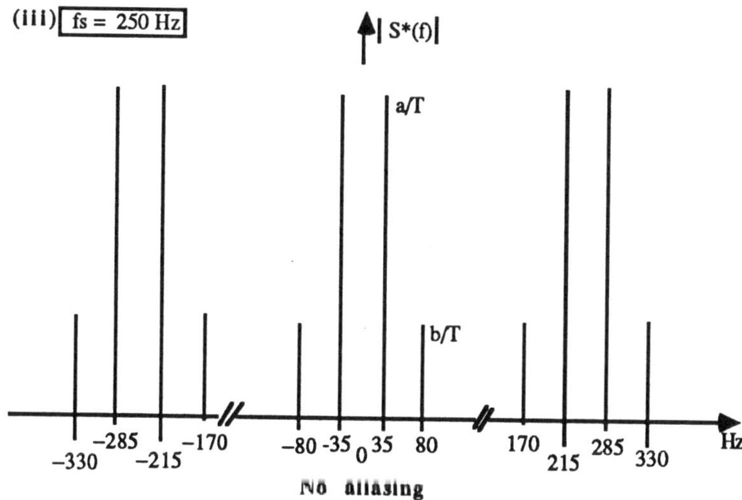

P1.3 Full-scale voltage range = 3 V

P1.4

(a) Offset binary:

(i) $V_i = (-1.400390625 \pm 0.0007326)$ V

(ii) $V_i = (0.9990234375 \pm 0.0007326)$ V

(b) Sign and magnitude:

(i) $V_i = (1.599609375 \pm 0.0007328)$ V

(ii) $V_i = (-0.9990234375 \pm 0.0007328)$ V

(c) One's complement:

(i) $V_i = (1.599609375 \pm 0.0007328)$ V

(ii) $V_i = (-1.99951171875 \pm 0.0007328)$ V

(d) Two's complement:

(i) $V_i = (1.599609375 \pm 0.0007326)$ V

(ii) $V_i = (-2.0009765625 \pm 0.0007326)$ V

P1.5 -0.912 dB

P1.6

(a) $$y(n) = 0.24\,x(n) + 0.48\,x(n-1) + 0.5\,x(n-2) + 0.9\,y(n-2)$$

(b) $y(0) = 0.24$
$y(1) = 0.48$
$y(2) = 0.716$
$y(3) = 0.432$
$y(4) = 0.6444$
$y(5) = 0.3888$
$y(6) = 0.57996$
$y(7) = 0.34992$
$y(8) = 0.521964$

(c) $$y(n) = 0.24\,x(n) + 0.48\,x(n-1) + 0.9\,y(n-2)$$

(d) $$y(n) = 0.24\,x(n) + 0.48\,x(n-1) + 0.5\,x(n-2)$$

$y(0) = 0.24$
$y(1) = 0.48$
$y(2) = 0.5$

All subsequent values of $y(n)$ are zero-valued (i.e. an FIR DSP system)

P1.7

$y(0) = -0.2$
$y(1) = 0.2$
$y(2) = 0.5$
$y(3) = -1.1$
$y(4) = 0.4$
$y(5) = 0.5$
$y(6) = -0.4$

All subsequent values of $y(n)$ are zero-valued (i.e. an FIR DSP system)

P1.8
Series connected:

$$y(n) = \{-0.096, -0.144, 0.232, 0.412, -0.308, -0.966, 0.48, 1.062, -0.21, -0.946, 0.084, 0.4\}$$

Parallel connected:

$$y(n) = \{0.08, 1.4, 2.64, -1.96, -2.66, 0.5, 1.5, 1.5, -1.7, -0.6, 0.8\}$$

P1.9

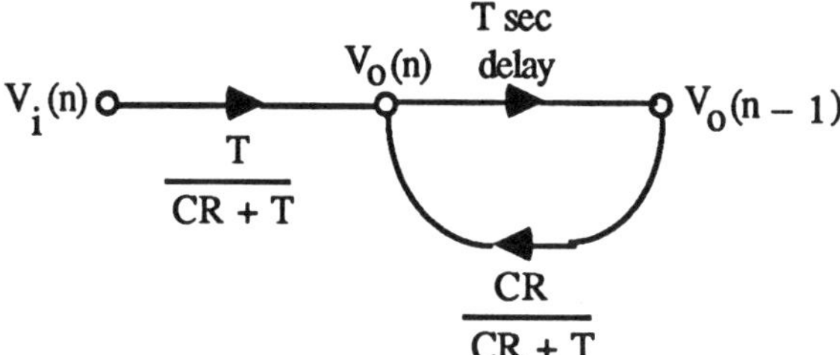

P1.10

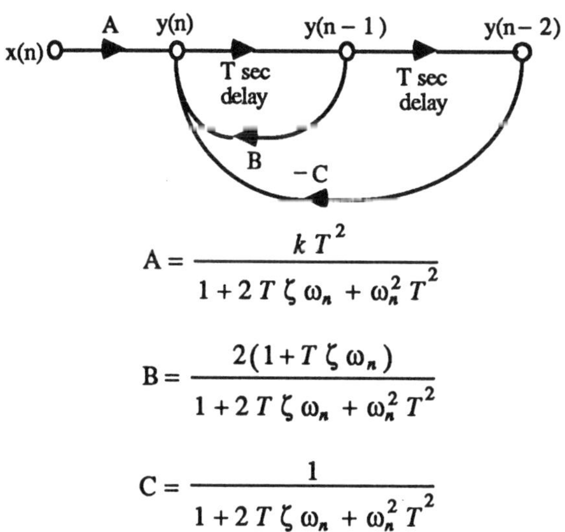

$$A = \frac{k\,T^2}{1 + 2\,T\,\zeta\,\omega_n + \omega_n^2\,T^2}$$

$$B = \frac{2(1 + T\,\zeta\,\omega_n)}{1 + 2\,T\,\zeta\,\omega_n + \omega_n^2\,T^2}$$

$$C = \frac{1}{1 + 2\,T\,\zeta\,\omega_n + \omega_n^2\,T^2}$$

CHAPTER 2

P2.1 $X(z) = 6 + 0.2\,z^{-1} - 11.4\,z^{-2} + 2.7\,z^{-4}$

P2.2

(a) $X(z) = \dfrac{z}{z - e^{-\alpha T}}$

(b) $X(z) = \dfrac{z\,T^2(z+1)}{(z-1)^3}$

(c) $X(z) = \dfrac{z\,T\,e^{-\alpha T}}{(z - e^{-\alpha T})^2}$

P2.3

(a) $$X(z) = \frac{z}{z - e^{-\alpha T}} - \frac{z}{z - e^{-\beta T}}$$

(b) $$X(z) = \frac{z^2 - z\cos\,\omega T}{z^2 - 2\,z\cos\,\omega T + 1}$$

(c) $$X(z) = \frac{z\sin\,\omega T}{z^2 - 2\,z\cos\,\omega T + 1}$$

P2.4 $$G(z) = \frac{2.5 \times z \times e^{-T} \times \sin\,2\,T}{z^2 - 2\,z\,e^{-T}\cos\,2\,T + e^{-2T}}$$

P2.5 $g(0) = 0 = g(t)$ when $t = 0$ s
$g(1) = 0.45 = g(t)$ when $t = 0.1$ s
$g(2) = 0.797 = g(t)$ when $t = 0.2$ s
$g(3) = 1.04 = g(t)$ when $t = 0.3$ s
(i.e. the DSP system is *impulse invariant*)

P2.6

(a) $$y(t) = k\left(1 - e^{\frac{-t}{CR}}\right)$$

(b) $$y(n) = \frac{k}{RC\left(1 - e^{-\frac{T}{RC}}\right)}\left[1 - e^{\frac{-(n+1)T}{RC}}\right]$$

(c) $y(0) = 2$
$y(1) = 3.96$
$y(2) = 5.88$
$y(3) = 7.77$

P2.7

(a) $$y(n) = 51.5\left[(0.980)^{n+1} - (0.961)^{n+1}\right]$$

(b) $y(0) = 1$
$y(1) = 1.941$
$y(2) = 2.826$
$y(3) = 3.657$

P2.8

(a) (i) $x(n) = 13(0.25)^n$

$x(0) = 13$ [see comment at end of answer for (a) (iii)]
$x(1) = 3.25$
$x(2) = 0.8125$
$x(3) = 0.203125$

(a) (ii) $x(n) = -12\,\delta(n) + 13(0.25)^n$

$x(0) = 1$
$x(1) = 3.25$
$x(2) = 0.8125$
$x(3) = 0.203125$

(a) (iii) $\dfrac{z+3}{z-0.25} = 1 + 3.25\,z^{-1} + 0.8125\,z^{-2} + 0.203125\,z^{-3} + \cdots$

$x(0) = 1$
$x(1) = 3.25$
$x(2) = 0.8125$
$x(3) = 0.203125$

Comparing the above sets of results it is seen that for (a) (i), when $n = 0$, the $x(0)$ value is incorrect, however, the other values for $n > 0$ are correct, i.e. only the initial value is incorrect. The correct initial value [$x(0) = 1$] can be obtained using the Initial Value Theorem.

(b) (i) $x(n) = 2 - (0.5)^n$

$x(0) = 1$
$x(1) = 1.5$
$x(2) = 1.75$
$x(3) = 1.875$

(b) (ii) $x(n) = 2(1)^n - (0.5)^n = 2 - (0.5)^n$

$x(0) = 1$
$x(1) = 1.5$
$x(2) = 1.75$
$x(3) = 1.875$

(b) (iii) $\dfrac{z^2}{z^2 - 1.5\,z + 0.5} = 1 + 1.5\,z^{-1} + 1.75\,z^{-2} + 1.875\,z^{-3} + \cdots$

$x(0) = 1$
$x(1) = 1.5$
$x(2) = 1.75$
$x(3) = 1.875$

(c) (i) $x(n) = 2(0.5)^n - 0.2(-0.1)^n$

$x(0) = 1.8$
$x(1) = 1.02$
$x(2) = 0.498$
$x(3) = 0.2502$

(c) (ii) $x(n) = 2(0.5)^n - 0.2(-0.1)^n$

$x(0) = 1.8$
$x(1) = 1.02$
$x(2) = 0.498$
$x(3) = 0.2502$

(c) (iii)

$$\frac{1.8z^2 + 0.3z}{z^2 - 0.4z - 0.05} = 1.8 + 1.02z^{-1} + 0.498z^{-2} + 0.2502z^{-3} + \cdots$$

$x(0) = 1.8$
$x(1) = 1.02$
$x(2) = 0.498$
$x(3) = 0.2502$

P2.9

(a) $y(n) = 1.2u(n) - 0.2(-0.25)^n$

$y(0) = 1$
$y(1) = 1.25$
$y(2) = 1.1875$
$y(3) = 1.203125$

(b) $g(n) = 2\delta(n) - (-0.25)^n$

P2.10

(a) Two zeros located at z = 0.5854 and z = – 0.0854.

Two poles located at z = – 0.5 and z = 0.4.

(b) Both poles are located inside the unit-circle in the z-plane, therefore the digital filter is stable.

(c) $g(n) = 0.25\delta(n) + (-0.5)^n - 0.25(0.4)^n$

(d) $$y(n) = x(n) - 0.5\,x(n-1) - 0.05\,x(n-2) - 0.1\,y(n-1) + 0.2\,y(n-2)$$

(e) $$G\left(e^{j\omega T}\right) = 2.07\angle 0^\circ$$

P2.11

$$G(z) = \frac{z^2 + 2z + 1}{3.4142\,z^2 + 0.5858}$$

(a) A double zero located at z = − 1.

A pair of complex conjugate poles located at z = ± j 0.4142.

(b) $$y(n) = 0.293\,x(n) + 0.586\,x(n-1) + 0.293\,x(n-2) - 0.1716\,y(n-2)$$

(c)

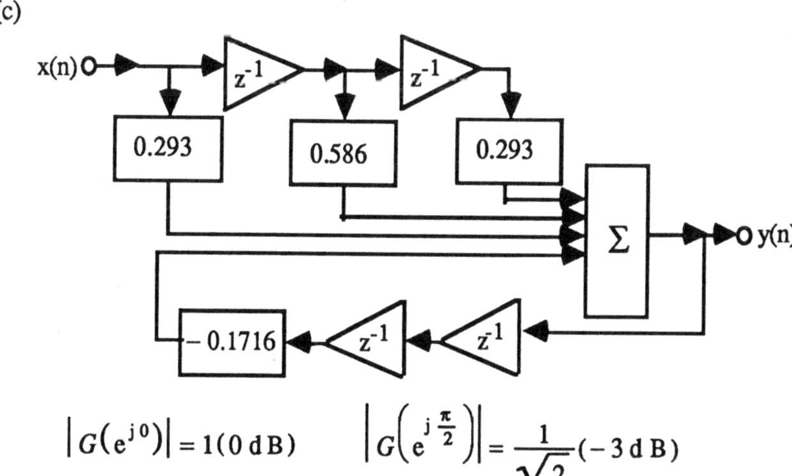

$$\left|G\left(e^{j0}\right)\right| = 1\,(0\,\mathrm{dB}) \qquad \left|G\left(e^{j\frac{\pi}{2}}\right)\right| = \frac{1}{\sqrt{2}}\,(-3\,\mathrm{dB})$$

P2.12

$$G(z) = \frac{z^2 - 2z + 1}{2.0797\,z^2 - 1.6978\,z + 0.5247}$$

(a) A double zero located at z = 1.

A pair of complex conjugate poles located at z = 0.4082 ± j 0.2927.

(b) $$y(n) = 0.4808\,x(n) - 0.9617\,x(n-1) + 0.4808\,x(n-2) + 0.8164\,y(n-1) - 0.2523\,y(n-2)$$

(c)

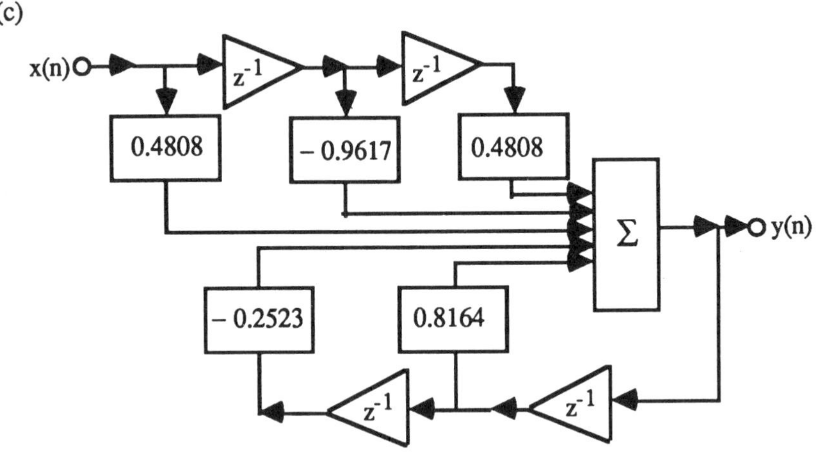

$$\left|G\left(e^{j0}\right)\right| = 0\,(\rightarrow \infty\,\mathrm{dB})$$

$$\left|G\left(e^{j0.32\pi}\right)\right| = 0.689\,(-3.236\,\mathrm{dB})$$

P2.13 $G(z) = \dfrac{z^2 + 0.36}{z^2 + 0.09}$

CHAPTER 3

P3.1
(a)

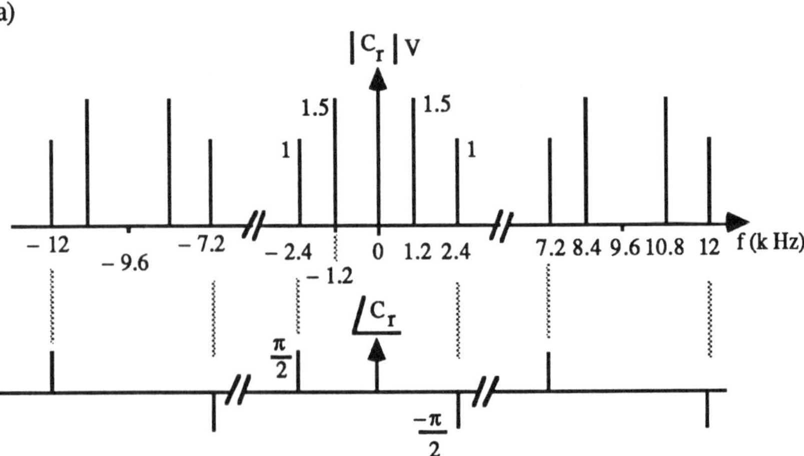

(b) $x(n) = \{3, 4.1213, 0, -4.1213, -3, -0.1213, 0, 0.1213\}$, which is a periodic sequence.

$$C_r = \frac{1}{8}\left[\sum_{n=0}^{7} x(n)\cos\left(\frac{n\pi r}{4}\right) - \mathrm{j}\sum_{n=0}^{7} x(n)\sin\left(\frac{n\pi r}{4}\right)\right] \mathrm{V}$$

r	0	1	2	3	4	5	6	7
C_r	0	1.5	$-\mathrm{j}$	0	0	0	$+\mathrm{j}$	1.5
$\lvert C_r \rvert$	0	1.5	1	0	0	0	1	1.5
$\angle C_r$	0	0	$-\pi/2$	0	0	0	$+\pi/2$	0

P3.2

(a) (i) $X(\mathrm{j}\,\omega) = 1$

(ii) $X(\mathrm{j}\,\omega) = \mathrm{e}^{-\mathrm{j}\,3\,\omega T}$

(b) Signal (a) (i):

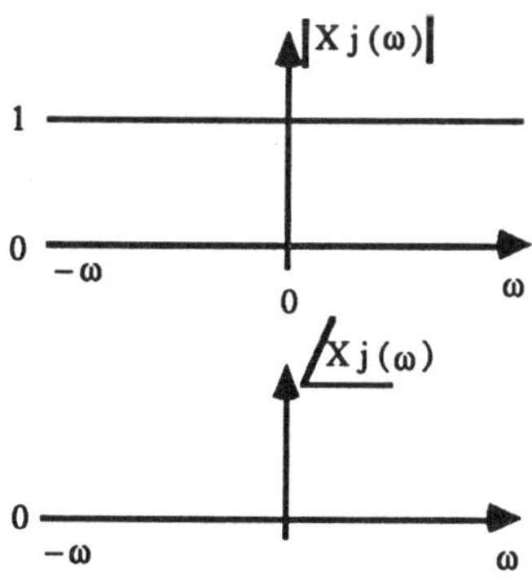

Signal (a) (ii):

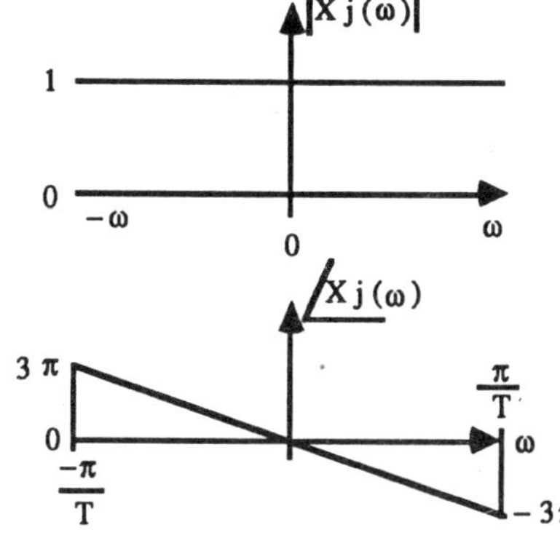

(c) (i)

$$x(n) = \frac{1}{2\pi} \int_{-\pi}^{\pi} X(\mathrm{j}\,\omega)\, \mathrm{e}^{\mathrm{j}\,n\,\omega T}\, \mathrm{d}(\omega T)$$

$$x(n) = \frac{1}{2\pi} \int_{-\pi}^{\pi} 1 \times \mathrm{e}^{\mathrm{j}\,n\,\omega T}\, \mathrm{d}(\omega T)$$

$$= \frac{\sin\, n\pi}{n\pi}$$

$n = 0$: $x(0) = 1 = \delta(n)$
n $\neq 0$: $x(n) = 0$

(ii)

$$x(n) = \frac{1}{2\pi} \int_{-\pi}^{\pi} X(\mathrm{j}\,\omega)\, \mathrm{e}^{\mathrm{j}\,n\,\omega T}\, \mathrm{d}(\omega T)$$

$$x(n) = \frac{1}{2\pi} \int_{-\pi}^{\pi} \mathrm{e}^{-\mathrm{j}\,3\,\omega T} \times \mathrm{e}^{\mathrm{j}\,n\,\omega T}\, \mathrm{d}(\omega T)$$

$$= \frac{\sin\,(n-3)\,\pi}{(n-3)\,\pi}$$

$n = 3$: $x(3) = 1 = \delta(n-3)$
$n \neq 3$: $x(n) = 0$

P3.3
(a)

$$x(n) = \begin{cases} \sin\left(\dfrac{2500\,\pi\,n}{5000}\right) & \text{for } 0 \leq n \leq 3 \\ 0 & \text{otherwise} \end{cases}$$

$$= \{0, 1, 0, -1\}$$

$$X_r = \sum_{n=0}^{3} x(n)\, \mathrm{e}^{-\frac{\mathrm{j}\,2\pi\,r\,n}{4}}$$

$$= \{0, -\mathrm{j}\,2, 0, +\mathrm{j}\,2\}$$

$$= \{0\angle 0^\circ,\ 2\angle -90^\circ,\ 0\angle 0^\circ,\ 2\angle 90^\circ\}$$

(b)

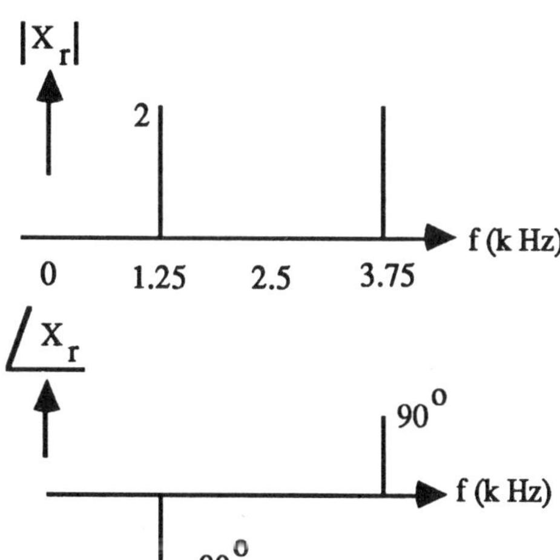

(c)

$$x(n) = \frac{1}{4}\sum_{r=0}^{3} X_r \, e^{\frac{j2\pi n r}{4}} = \{0, 1, 0, -1\}$$

P3.4
(a)

$$(i): \quad X(j\omega) = \frac{1}{1 - 0.6\,e^{-j\omega T}}$$

$$(ii): \quad X(j\omega) = \frac{1}{1 + 0.6\,e^{-j\omega T}}$$

(b) (i)

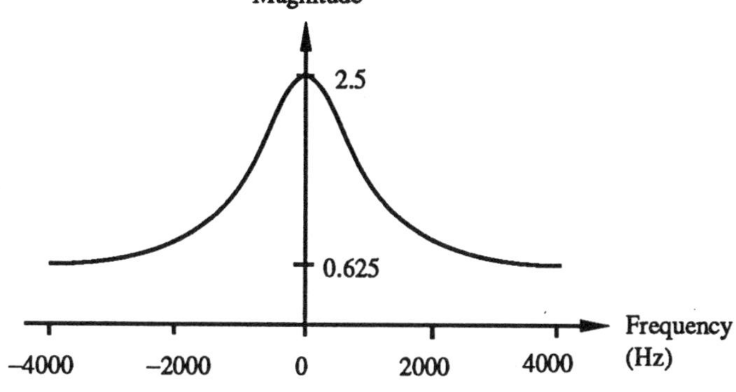

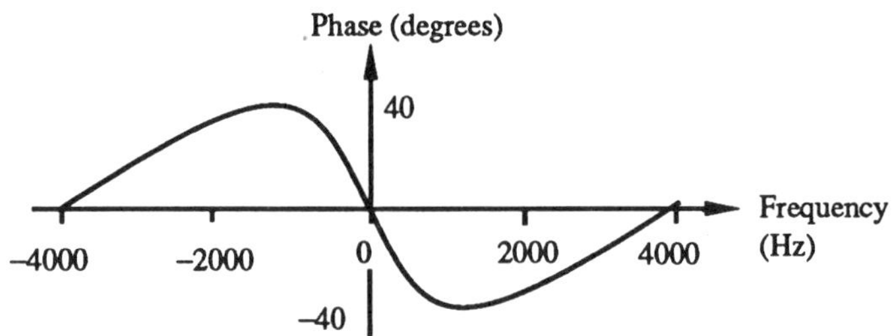

(ii)

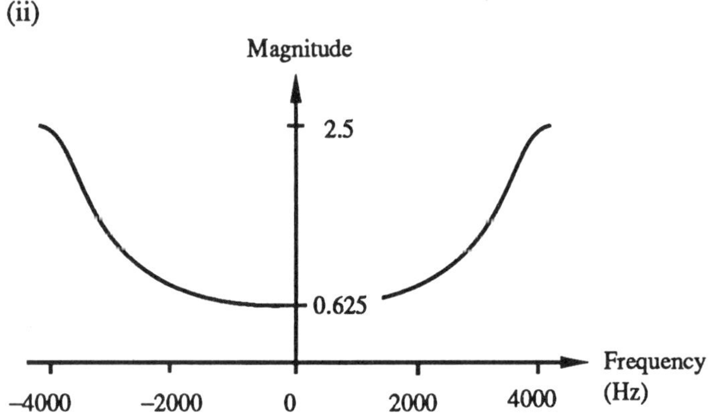

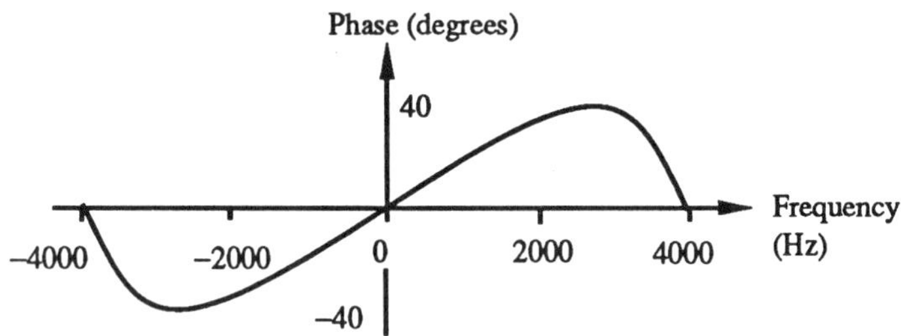

(c) (i) {2.4581, 1.1067 – j 0.8155, 0.7229 – j 0.4338, 0.6341 – j 0.1889, 0.6145, 0.6341 + j 0.1889, 0.7229 + j 0.4338, 1.1067 + j 0.8155}

(ii) {0.6145, 0.6341 + j 0.1889, 0.7229 + j 0.4338, 1.1067 + j 0.8155, 2.4581, 1.1067 – j 0.8155, 0.7229 – j 0.4338, 0.6341 – j 0.1889}

(d) (i)

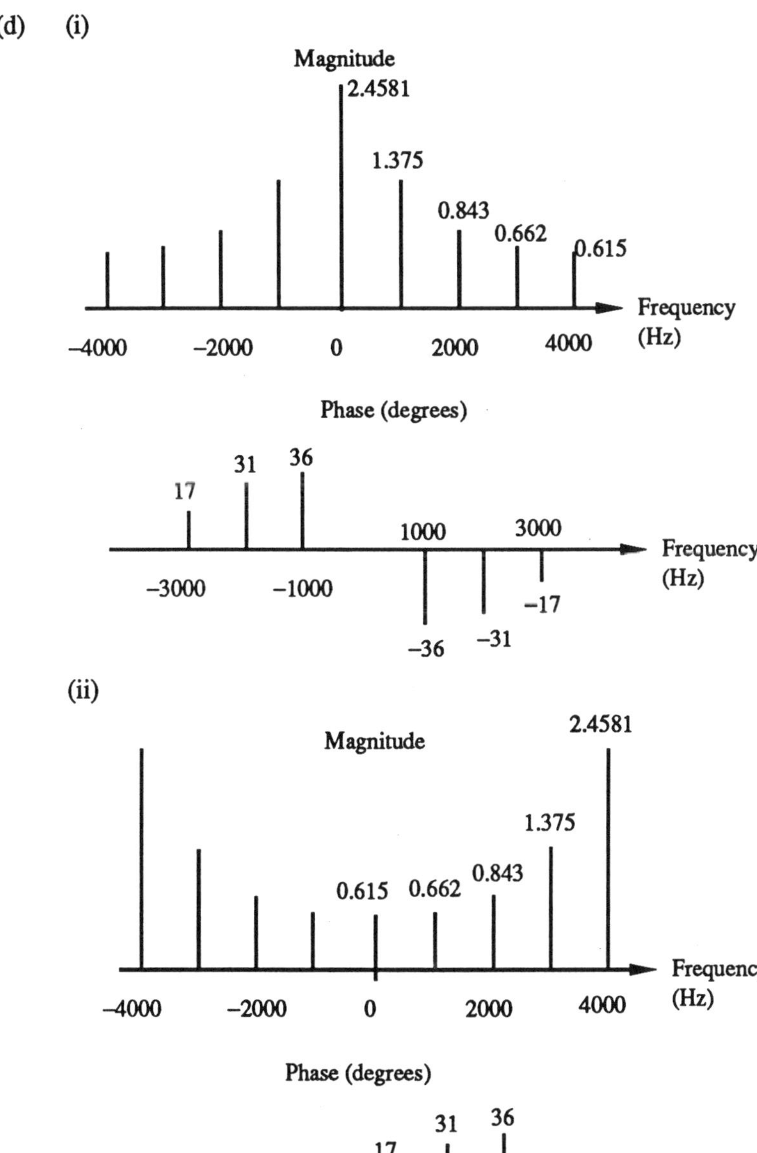

(e) The frequency spectra for (d) are basically sampled versions of the spectra shown in (b)

P3.5

(a) $X_5 = -0.4645 + j\,1.1213$

$X_6 = 1 - j$

$X_7 = -7.5355 + j\,3.1213$

(b) (i) {44, − 15.071 − j 6.2426, 2 + j 2, − 0.929 + j 2.2426, 0,
− 0.929 + j 2.2426, 2 − j 2, − 15.071 + j 6.2426}

(ii) {22, − 3.1213 + j 7.535, − 1 − j 1, 1.1213 − j 0.4645, 0,
1.1213 + j 0.4645, − 1 + j 1, − 3.1213 − j 7.535,}

(b) (iii) {66, − 18.1923 + j 1.2924, 1 + j 1, 0.1923 − j .2.7071, 0,
0.1923 + j 2.7071, 1 − j 1, − 18.1923 − j 1.2924,}

P3.6

(a) Butterfly diagram is shown on page 315

(b) Butterfly diagram is shown on page 316

P3.7

(a) {x(0), x(8), x(4), x(12), x(2), x(10), x(6), x(14),
x(1), x(9), x(5), x(13), x(3), x(11), x(7), x(15)}

(b) Number of computation stages = 4

(c)

Stage	Additions/Subtractions	Multiplications
1	8/8 (real)	0
2	4/4 (real) 4/4 (complex)	8 (complex)
3	2/2 (real) 6/6 (complex)	8 (complex)
4	1/1 (real) 7/7 (complex)	8 (complex)
Total	30 (real) 34(complex)	24 (complex)

(d) Reductions:

Additions/Subtractions	Multiplications
69.58 %	81.25 %

P3.8

(a), (b) and (c) y(n) = {10, 11, 7, 9, 14, 8, 5, 2}

P3.9

(a) and (b) y(n) = {5, 6.85, 7.55, 7.8, 7.8}

followed by the periodic sequence

{− 2.2, − 5.9, − 7.3, − 7.8, − 7.8, 2.2, 5.9, 7.3, 7.8, 7.8}

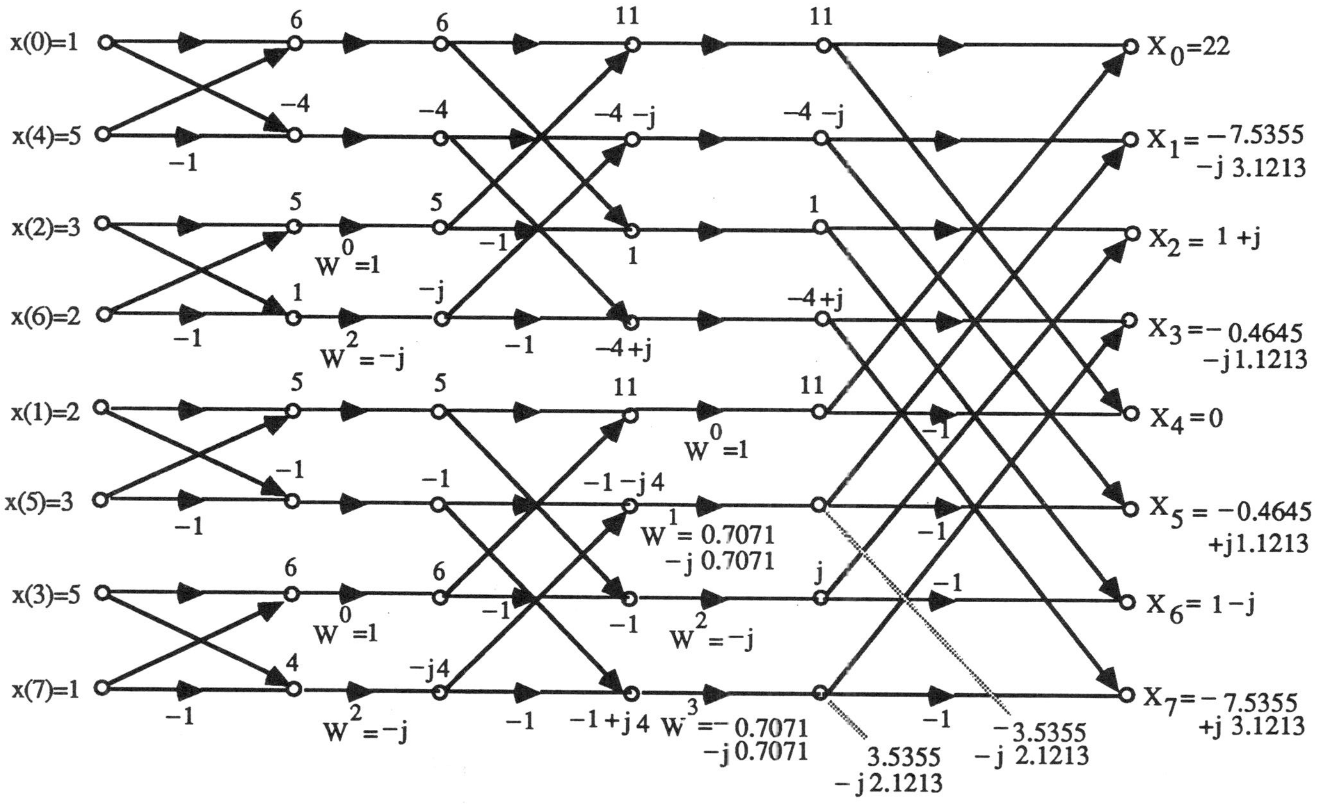
x(0)=1
x(4)=5
x(2)=3
x(6)=2
x(1)=2
x(5)=3
x(3)=5
x(7)=1
W^0=1
W^2=−j
W^0=1
W^2=−j
W^0=1
W^1 = 0.7071 −j 0.7071
W^2=−j
W^3=−0.7071 −j0.7071
−4 −j
−4+j
−1 −j4
−1+j4
3.5355 −j2.1213
−3.5355 −j 2.1213
X_0=22
X_1 = −7.5355 −j 3.1213
X_2 = 1 +j
X_3 = −0.4645 −j1.1213
X_4 = 0
X_5 = −0.4645 +j1.1213
X_6 = 1 −j
X_7 = −7.5355 +j 3.1213

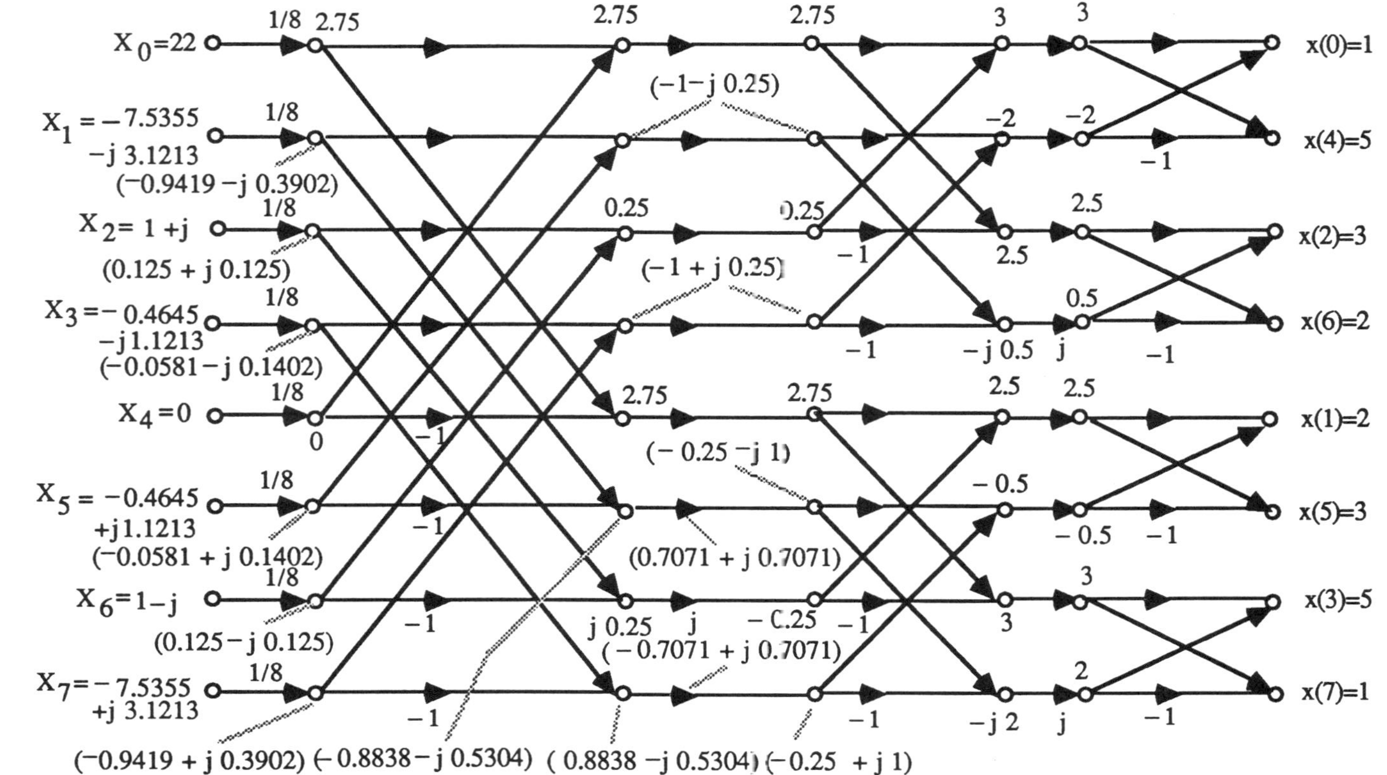
X0=22
X1=−7.5355 −j 3.1213
(−0.9419 −j 0.3902)
X2= 1 +j
(0.125 + j 0.125)
X3=−0.4645 −j1.1213
(−0.0581 −j 0.1402)
X4=0
X5=−0.4645 +j1.1213
(−0.0581 + j 0.1402)
X6=1−j
(0.125−j 0.125)
X7=−7.5355 +j 3.1213
(−0.9419 + j 0.3902) (−0.8838 −j 0.5304) (0.8838 −j 0.5304) (−0.25 + j 1)
(−1−j 0.25)
(−1 + j 0.25)
(− 0.25 −j 1)
(0.7071 + j 0.7071)
(−0.7071 + j 0.7071)
x(0)=1
x(4)=5
x(2)=3
x(6)=2
x(1)=2
x(5)=3
x(3)=5
x(7)=1

P3.10

(a), (b), and (c)

$$c_{xy}(p) = \{0, -0.1429, -0.2857, -0.2857, 0.1429, 0.4286, 0.1429\}$$

(d), (e), and (f)

$$c_{xx}(p) = \{0, -0.1429, 0, 0.2857, 0, -0.1429, 0\}$$

(g) $\rho_{xx}(p) = \{0, -0.1826, -0.3651, -0.3651, -0.1826, 0.5478, 0.1826\}$

(h) 180^0

P3.11

(a) (i) $\{0, -2, 8, -7, -2, -1, 8, -15, 8, 1, 4, -4, 8, -8, 4\}$

(ii) same as (i)

(b) $\{0, 2, 8, 7, 2, 1, 8, 15, 8, 1, 4, 4, 8, 8, 4, 1, -2, 1\}$

(c) Negative correlation occurs at $n = 7$, implying that the input sequence contains an inverted version of the pattern to be found

P3.12

(a) 10 kHz

(b) 2000

(c) 48

(d) 9.766 Hz

(e) Set sampling frequency to 20.48 kHz

P3.13

(a) 8-point Blackman window is

$$w(n) = 0.42 - 0.5\cos\left(\frac{2\pi n}{8-1}\right) + 0.08\cos\left(\frac{4\pi n}{8-1}\right)$$

$$= \{0, 0.0905, 0.4592, 0.9204, 0.9204, 0.4592, 0.0905, 0\}$$

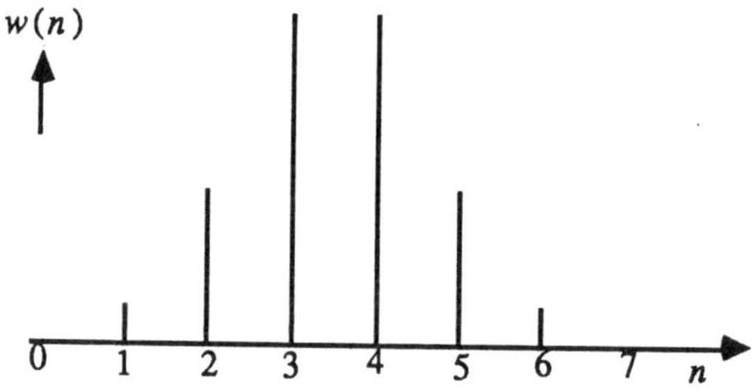

(b) $$|X_r| = \begin{Bmatrix} 0.7587, 1.2978, 0.9832, 0.2620, \\ 0.0213, 0.2620, 0.9832, 1.2978 \end{Bmatrix}$$

(c) $$|X_r| = \begin{Bmatrix} 0.6245, 1.3362, 1.2143, 0.4415, \\ 0.0747, 0.4415, 1.2143, 1.3362 \end{Bmatrix}$$

P3.14

(a) $E_{1000} = 4$ J
$P_{1000} = 0.5$ W

$E_{1300} = 3.64$ J
$P_{1300} = 0.455$ W

(b) $P_{1000}(r) = \{0, 2, 0, 0, 0, 0, 2, 0\}$

$P_{1300}(r) = \{0.0601, 1.2259, 0.4014, 0.1173, 0.0886, 0.1173, 0.4014, 1.2259\}$

(c) $P_{1000}(r) = \{0.0719, 0.2105, 0.1208, 0.0086\ 0, 0.0086, 0.1208, 0.2105\}$

$P_{1300}(r) = \{0.0488, 0.2232, 0.1843, 0.0244, 0.0007, 0.0244, 0.1843, 0.2232\}$

(d) Rectangular window:

$E_{1000} = 4$ J
$P_{1000} = 0.5$ W

$E_{1300} = 3.64$ J
$P_{1300} = 0.455$ W

Blackman window:

$E_{1000} = 0.752$ J
$P_{1000} = 0.094$ W

$E_{1300} = 0.913$ J
$P_{1300} = 0.114$ W

P3.15

f (kHz)	r	$\|X_r\|$			
7	7	2.2885	1.9185	0.9170	1.4056
6	6	0.9062	1.4668	2.2500	1.8767
5	5	0.0540	0.5133	0.9170	0.7803
4	4	0.0281	0.4051	0.0764	0.3568
3	3	0.0540	0.5133	0.9170	0.7803
2	2	0.9062	1.4668	2.2500	1.8767
1	1	2.2885	1.9185	0.9170	1.4056
0	0	0.7017	1.0949	0.0764	0.4696
	t (ms)	1	1.5	2	2.5

CHAPTER 4

P4.1 $$y(n) = \frac{1}{8}\begin{bmatrix} x(n) + x(n-1) + x(n-2) + x(n-3) \\ + x(n-4) + x(n-5) + x(n-6) + x(n-7) \end{bmatrix}$$

P4.2 $G(z) = 0.5 + 0.3018\, z^{-1} - 0.052\, z^{-3} - 0.052\, z^{-5} + 0.3018\, z^{-7}$

or for linear phase

$$G(z) = 0.3018 - 0.052\, z^{-2} - 0.052\, z^{-4} + 0.3018\, z^{-6} + 0.5 z^{-7} + 0.3018\, z^{-8} - 0.052\, z^{-10} - 0.052\, z^{-12} + 0.3018\, z^{-14}$$

P4.3 $G(z) = -0.0188 + 0.267\, z^{-2} + 0.5\, z^{-3} + 0.267\, z^{-4} - 0.0188\, z^{-6}$

P4.4

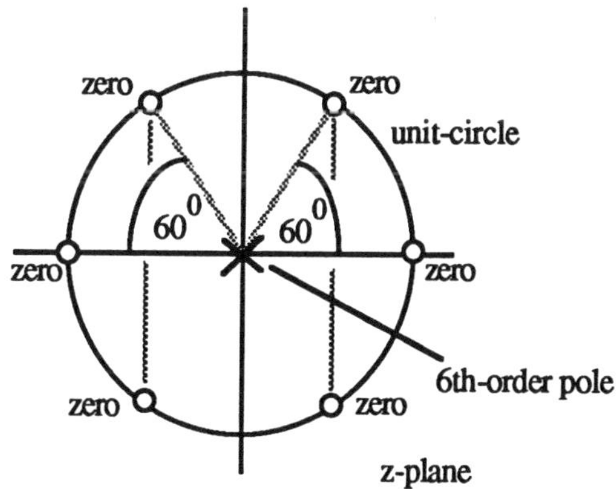

First peak occurs at 5/6 kHz

P4.5

(i) $$G(z) = \frac{0.2929 + 0.5858\, z^{-1} + 0.2929\, z^{-2}}{1 + 0.1716\, z^{-2}}$$

(ii) $$G(z) = \frac{0.2929 - 0.5858\, z^{-1} + 0.2929\, z^{-2}}{1 + 0.1716\, z^{-2}}$$

(iii) $$G(z) = \frac{0.0055 - 0.011\, z^{-3} + 0.0055\, z^{-4}}{1 + 1.7786\, z^{-2} + 0.8008\, z^{-4}}$$

(iv) $$G(z) = \frac{0.8949 + 1.7897\, z^{-3} + 0.8949\, z^{-4}}{1 + 1.7786\, z^{-2} + 0.8008\, z^{-4}}$$

(v) $$G(z) = \frac{0.4305 + 0.8610\ z^{-1} + 0.4305\ z^{-2}}{1 + 0.4537\ z^{-1} + 0.2683\ z^{-2}}$$

(vi) $$G(z) = \frac{0.4305 - 0.8610\ z^{-1} + 0.4305\ z^{-2}}{1 - 0.4537\ z^{-1} + 0.2683\ z^{-2}}$$

P4.6 Resulting correction filter output is
$C(n) = 0.51025\ T \sin(1000\ \pi\ n) + 0.10466\ T \sin(1500\ \pi\ n)$

P4.7 868 pW

P4.8 (i): $n = 4$ (rounding case) (ii): $n = 5$ (truncation case)

P4.9
For the deadband effect to exist: $-R \leq y(-1) \leq R$. But we must also consider the given $G(z)$ and note that $R = 0.5/(1 - 0.97) = 16.67$, clearly for the stated signal conditions the deadband effect will exist with a steady output value of 16.

CHAPTER 5

P5.1
(i) $(15980)_{10}$
(ii) $(10489843)_{10}$
(ii) $(14861420)_{10}$

P5.2
(i) $(1A1FC00D0)_{16}$
(ii) $(1E8D9E)_{16}$

P5.3 Flowchart is shown on page 321

P5.4 CRA = $(05)_{16}$ [set/reset output set to '0']
CRB = $(37)_{16}$ [set/reset output set to '0']

P5.5 Connect CS0 PIA input to M6802 address line A7 (or A10) instead of A3

Changes to be made to assembler language program are:

```
00009   E480   PIA1   EQU   $E480   PIA I/O A OR DDRA
00010   E481   PIA2   EQU   $E481   PIA CRA
00011   E482   PIA3   EQU   $E482   PIA I/O B OR DDRB
00012   E483   PIA4   EQU   $E483   PIA CRB
```

P5.6 Changes to be made to assembler language program are:

```
A0      .word   1188    ;A0 = 0.145 * 8192
A1      .word   2384    ;A1 = 0.291 * 8192
A2      .word   1188    ;A2 = A0
B1      .word   5497    ;B1 = 0.671* 8192
B2      .word   -1925   ;B2 = -0.235* 8192
```

Flowchart for P5.3:

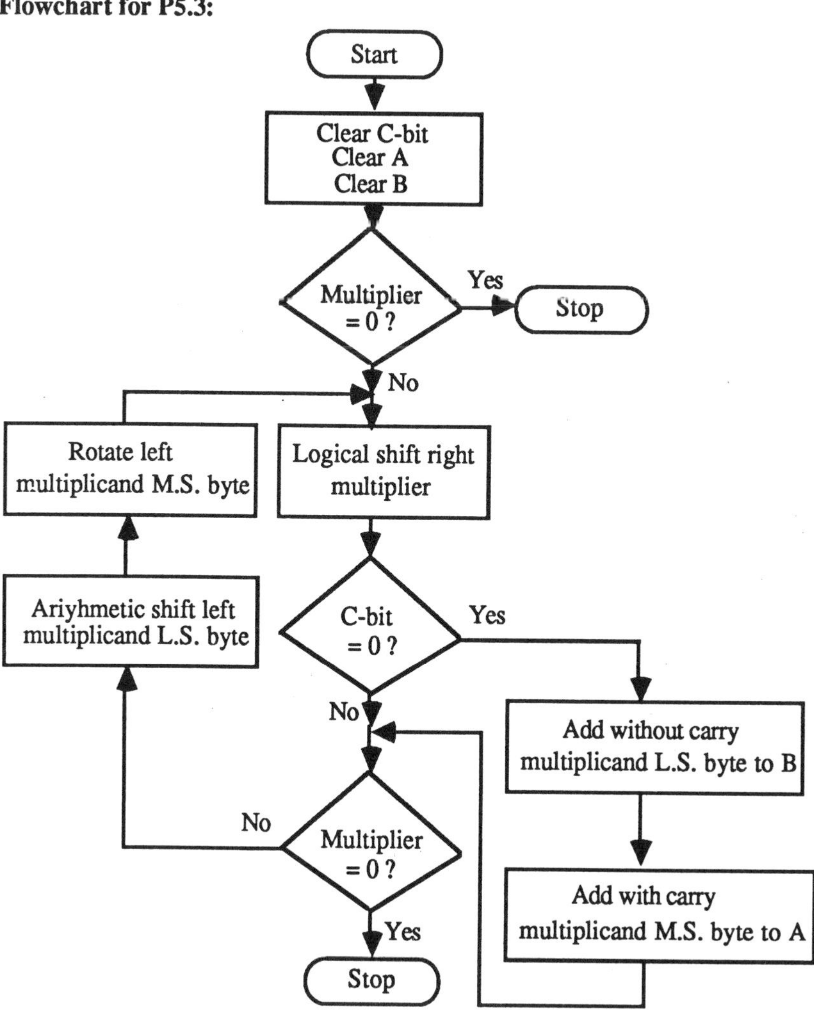

Bibliography

The authors have found the following books to be useful and informative sources of DSP reference material. Students wishing to extend their basic knowledge of DSP could start with one or more of these books when selected or assigned topics are to be studied further. The list is not intended to be a comprehensive catalogue of existing published DSP books; on the contrary, it is simply a limited selection which students can use to guide them in their further studies.

1. Cadzow, J. A., *Foundations of Digital Signal Processing and Data Analysis*, Collier Macmillan Publishers, London, 1987.

2. Cunningham, E. P., *Digital Filtering: An Introduction*, Houghton Mifflin Company, Boston, 1992.

3. Ifeachor, E. C. and Jervis, B. W., *Digital Signal Processing - A Practical Approach*, Addison-Wesley, Wokingham, England, 1993.

4. Kuc, R., *Introduction to Digital Signal Processing*, McGraw-Hill, New York, 1988.

5. Lynn, P. A., *Digital Signals, Processors and Noise*, Macmillan, Basingstoke, England, 1992.

6. Marvin, C. and Ewers, G. *A Simple Approach to Digital Signal Processing*, Texas Instruments, 1993.

7. *Military Linear Circuits Data Book*, Texas Instruments, 1992. (Contains Data Sheets on TLC32040 Analog(ue) Interface Circuit)

8. Proakis, J. G. and Manolakis, D. G., *Introduction to Digital Signal Processing*, Collier Macmillan Publishers, London, 1988.

9. Rorabaugh, C. B., *Digital Filter Designer's Handbook*, Tab Books, Division of McGraw-Hill Inc., Blue Ridge Summit, PA, 1993.

10. *TMS320C2*x *User's Guide - Revision C*, Texas Instruments, 1993.

11. *TMS320C2*x *DSP Starter Kit User's Guide*, Texas Instruments, 1993.

Index